SOME SUCCESSIVE APPROXIMATION METHODS IN CONTROL AND OSCILLATION THEORY

This is Volume 59 in
MATHEMATICS IN SCIENCE AND ENGINEERING
A series of monographs and textbooks
Edited by RICHARD BELLMAN, *University of Southern California*

A complete list of the books in this series appears at the end of this volume.

SOME SUCCESSIVE APPROXIMATION METHODS IN CONTROL AND OSCILLATION THEORY

Peter L. Falb

Division of Applied Mathematics
Brown University
Providence, Rhode Island

Jan L. de Jong

National Aerospace Laboratory NLR
Noordoostpolder, The Netherlands

1969
ACADEMIC PRESS
New York and London

ACADEMIC PRESS, INC.
111 Fifth Avenue, New York, New York 10003

United Kingdom Edition published by
ACADEMIC PRESS, INC. (LONDON) LTD.
Berkeley Square House, London W1X 6BA

LIBRARY OF CONGRESS CATALOG CARD NUMBER: 73-91420
AMS 1969 SUBJECT CLASSIFICATIONS 6562, 9301

PRINTED IN THE UNITED STATES OF AMERICA

PREFACE

Successive approximation methods have been used for the solution of two-point boundary value problems for a number of years. In this book, we examine several of these methods. Noting that two-point boundary value problems can be represented by operator equations, we adopt a functional analytic viewpoint and translate results on such operator theoretic iterative methods as Newton's method into the two-point boundary value problem context. Our emphasis is on results of potential practical applicability rather than on results of the greatest generality.

We owe a significant debt of gratitude to many of our colleagues for their invaluable assistance in the preparation of this book. In particular, we wish to thank Dr. W. E. Bosarge, Jr., of IBM, Professor Elmer Gilbert of the University of Michigan, and Professor Jack Hale of Brown University for their numerous helpful suggestions and comments. We also gratefully acknowledge the support that we have received from the United States Air Force under Grant No. AFOSR 693-67 and Grant No. AFOSR 814-66 and from the National Science Foundation under Grant No. GK-967 and Grant No. GK-2788. Finally, we should like to express our deep appreciation to Miss Kate Nolan for her excellent typing of the manuscript.

July 1969

PETER L. FALB
JAN L. DE JONG

CONTENTS

CHAPTER 4 APPLICATION TO CONTROL PROBLEMS

CHAPTER 5 APPLICATION TO OSCILLATION PROBLEMS

CHAPTER 6 SOME NUMERICAL EXAMPLES

SOME SUCCESSIVE APPROXIMATION METHODS IN CONTROL AND OSCILLATION THEORY

CHAPTER 1

INTRODUCTION

1.1. Introduction

The central theme of this book is the study of some iterative methods for the solution of two-point boundary value problems (TPBVP's) of the form

$$\dot{y} = F(y, t), \qquad g(y(0)) + h(y(1)) = c \tag{1.1}$$

or, of the form

$$y(n + 1) = F(y(n), y(n + 1), n), \qquad g(y(0)) + h(y(q)) = c \tag{1.2}$$

where F, g, and h are suitable vector valued functions and c is a constant vector. Such TPBVP's arise in control and oscillation problems.

The basic approach which we use is to represent the TPBVP by an operator equation and then apply functional analytic results on the iterative solution of operator equations. In other words, (1.1) or (1.2) is represented by an equivalent operator equation

$$y = T(y) \tag{1.3}$$

on a suitable Banach space and results relating to convergence of algorithms of the form $y_{n+1} = \varphi(y_n)$ for the solution of (1.3) are translated into convergence theorems for the iterative solution of (1.1) or (1.2). In particular, we examine the contraction mapping method, Newton's method and some multipoint methods. Our goal is to obtain convergence conditions and rates which depend upon the functions F, g, and h and other quantities known *a priori*.

1.2. Control Problems and Historical Notes

Optimal control theory has experienced an increasing growth of interest during the past two decades. Reasons for this growing interest include the stringent requirements of a rapidly developing space technology and the change in system design philosophy brought about by the high speed electronic computer. One area of control which receives considerable current attention is the numerical computation of optimal controls. This book is, in part, concerned with the theoretical and practical aspects of some closely related computational procedures for the numerical solution of certain classes of control problems.

An essential difference between optimal control problems and problems in conventional servomechanism theory is the explicit formulation of the control objective in optimal control problems. These control objectives are most frequently expressed as a functional defined on the set of admissible controls. This fact makes optimal control problems problems of the calculus of variations. The growing interest in optimal control therefore stimulated a renewed interest in the calculus of variations and variational techniques in general (see Berkovitz [B4] and Neustadt [N3]). One of the new variational techniques considered was based on a geometrical interpretation of optimal control problems. This led to an important contribution to control theory, namely the "maximum principle" of Pontryagin [P3]. At present, the Maximum Principle occupies an important position in control theory. Good surveys of other contributions to optimal control theory (as of 1965 and 1966) have been published by Paiewonski [P1] and Athans [A3].

Since optimal control problems often cannot be solved analytically, one has to resort to iterative numerical methods. A number of such methods for the computation of optimal controls have been and are being proposed. Loosely speaking, all these methods can be divided into two categories: namely, (1) direct and (2) indirect methods. Direct methods involve the generation of a sequence (or family) of control functions with the property that each successive control function results in a lower value of the cost functional. Indirect methods involve the determination of functions (extremals) which satisfy the necessary conditions for an optimum. Since the application of the Pontryagin principle (or the multiplier rule of the calculus of variations) results in necessary conditions for optimality in the form of a TPBVP, most indirect methods are essentially methods for the solution of these TPBVP's.

An example of a method which can be classified as a direct method is the well known gradient method. This method was first proposed for control problems by Bryson [B10] and Kelley [K5]. Since then, numerous applications and modifications of it have been reported in the literature. An example of an indirect method is the so-called "shooting method" (Breakwell [B8]). This method consists of the systematic variation of the initial values of solutions of the differential equation until the final values satisfy the terminal conditions. Since the solutions of optimal control problems are often very sensitive to changes in the initial conditions, the "shooting method" has often not been very successful in applications. A second indirect method, which is essentially an improvement of the "shooting method," is the method of the second variation (Breakwell *et al.* [B9] and Kelley *et al.* [K6]). This method is based on the use of linear perturbation equations for the evaluation of the corrections of the initial values. An indirect method which is basically different from the two methods mentioned is the generalized Newton-Raphson method (McGill and Kenneth [K7, M3]). This method, which is also known as the quasi-linearization method (Bellman and Kalaba [B3]), is based on the replacement of the nonlinear TPBVP by a sequence of linear problems whose solutions converge to the solution of the original nonlinear TPBVP. Another indirect method based on this general idea is Picard's method. The generalized Newton-Raphson method (which we call Newton's method) and Picard's method are two of the basic methods considered here.

These methods by no means exhaust the different types of computational procedures for the solution of optimal control problems. An important class of indirect methods which should be mentioned is the class of methods which make use of finite difference techniques (e.g., Van Dine *et al.* [V1]). Also, a number of computational procedures have been developed for optimal control problems with special properties (e.g., linearity in the state or in the control). Examples of these methods are the methods proposed by Neustadt [N2] and Barr and Gilbert [B1]. Another class of methods, which can be classified as both direct and indirect involves dynamic programming (Bellman [B2]). In this case the necessary condition for optimality is a special type of functional equation instead of a TPBVP. As a result of the large computer memory requirements, dynamic programming is not always effective in the solution of realistic optimal control problems.

The merits of various iterative procedures can be judged on the basis of such criteria as speed of convergence, sensitivity to numerical errors such as roundoff and truncation errors, computability of error bounds and existence of convergence conditions. These criteria, which are partly practical and partly theoretical in nature, are important in deciding which iterative method is to be used in a particular problem as well as for the comparison of different methods. Knowledge of the factors on which these criteria depend provides considerable insight into a computational procedure. This, in turn, may lead to a better practical utilization of the method.

Theoretical aspects of these criteria have been investigated by numerous applied mathematicians, among them the Russian Kantorovich. Kantorovich was one of the first to realize the power of functional analysis methods in the unification and development of a mathematical theory of iterative methods [K2]. As illustrated in his book [K3] as well as in the books by Collatz [C4] and Goldstein [G3] and in the article of Antosiewicz and Rheinboldt [A2], many practical iterative methods can be viewed as special applications in particular function spaces of such basic iterative methods as the method of contraction mappings, the method of conjugate gradients, and Newton's method. Using this point of view, various functional analytic results on the convergence of the basic iterative methods can be translated into practical convergence criteria for particular versions of these iterative methods. A number of examples of such translations for the application of iterative methods to a variety of problems are given in the references mentioned.

Practical convergence criteria are few for most of the iterative methods used in the solution of optimal control problems. For the iterative methods considered here, some general results have been published previously. To be specific, practical convergence criteria for the application of Picard's and Newton's method to TPBVP's have been presented by Collatz [C4]. These results, however, pertain primarily to higher order TPBVP's given by a single differential equation rather than a system of first order differential equations. Therefore, they must be adapted to the usual type of problem arising in optimal control theory (which involve systems of differential equations). The only comparable results in the optimal control literature are the convergence theorems for the application of Newton's method published by McGill and Kenneth [M2] and Bellman and Kalaba [B3]. These theorems hold only for TPBVP's which are either of second order with both (linear) boundary conditions relating to the same variable [B3] or which can be expressed as a system of such second order problems. They are, therefore, not generally applicable. Motivated by this apparent lack of general results, we have as our first objective the derivation of generally applicable convergence criteria for the applications of Picard's and Newton's methods to the solution of optimal control problems.

Of the two methods, only Newton's method has been applied on a wide scale to problems arising in optimal control theory. Picard's method, although very old (Picard applied the method already in the year 1890) and well known in the mathematical literature, has not yet been used for the solution of optimal control problems to any appreciable extent. A second objective is therefore the consideration of the feasibility and practicality of the application of Picard's method to the solution of optimal control problems.

Problems with boundary conditions of the form

$$y(0) - y(1) = 0 \tag{2.1}$$

frequently arise in the study of oscillation problems and are often amenable to the methods which we discuss. Considerable work has been done on oscillation problems from this point of view. Excellent summaries of this work are given by Hale [H1, H2].

1.3. Description of Contents

We begin the actual development with a discussion of operator theoretic iterative methods in Chapter 2. We examine the method of contraction mappings, the modified contraction mapping method, Newton's method, and some multipoint methods. Our treatment is based on the work of Kantorovich [K3] and is aimed at those results which are amenable to practical use.

We consider the problem of developing suitable representations for continuous and discrete TPBVP's in Chapter 3. Since these representations involve linear TPBVP's in a critical way, we devote

Sections 3.2 and 3.3 to linear TPBVP's, i.e., to problems of the form

$$\dot{y} = V(t)\,y + f(t), \qquad My(0) + Ny(1) = c \tag{3.1}$$

$$\begin{aligned} &y(j+1) - y(j) = A(j)\,y(j+1) + B(j)\,y(j) + f(j), \\ &My(0) + Ny(q) = c. \end{aligned} \tag{3.2}$$

If (3.1) or (3.2) always has a unique solution for all f and c, then we call the set of matrices $\{V(t), M, N\}$ or $\{A(j), B(j), M, N\}$ a "boundary-compatible set." This notion of boundary compatibility is crucial to us. For example, if $\{V(t), M, N\}$ is boundary compatible, then (under suitable assumptions) the TPBVP (1.1) has the equivalent representation

$$\begin{aligned} y(t) = {} & H^{VMN}(t)\{c - g(y(0)) - h(y(1)) + My(0) + Ny(1)\} \\ & + \int_0^1 G^{VMN}(t, s)\{F(y(s), s) - V(s)y(s)\}\, ds \end{aligned} \tag{3.3}$$

where $H^{VMN}(t)$ and $G^{VMN}(t, s)$ are the Green's matrices associated with (3.1). In other words, (1.1) is represented by an operator equation (3.3). We discuss these representations, treat some examples, compute and estimate certain operator derivatives, and prove some lemmas on equivalence in the remainder of Chapter 3.

In Chapter 4, we combine the results of Chapters 2 and 3 to obtain convergence theorems for the iterative solution of TPBVP's of the type that arise in control. We briefly discuss the way in which optimal control problems can be reduced to TPBVP's using the Pontryagin principle. We then proceed to the main work of the chapter, i.e., the translation and application of the results of Chapters 2 and 3 to these TPBVP's.

We apply the results of Chapters 2 and 3 to several classes of TPBVP's arising in the study of oscillation problems in the brief Chapter 5. In particular, we examine "almost linear problems" and problems with boundary conditions of the form $y(0) = y(1)$ (so-called "periodic" boundary conditions). We also treat some second order examples in detail.

Finally, in Chapter 6, we study the numerical solution of some simple problems in order to obtain a better appreciation for the practical aspects of the iterative methods discussed in Chapters 4 and 5. We consider two "standard" trajectory optimization problems involving a low-thrust Earth-to-Mars orbital transfer and an oscillation problem for a simple spring with a nonlinear restoring force.

CHAPTER 2

OPERATOR THEORETIC ITERATIVE METHODS

2.1. Introduction

A large variety of control and oscillation problems can be reduced to two point boundary value problems (TPBVP's). We shall show, in Chapter 3, that such boundary value problems can be represented by operator equations of the form

$$y = T(y) \tag{1.1}$$

or of the form

$$F(y) = 0 \tag{1.2}$$

where T and F are suitable operators. Since Eqs. (1.1) and (1.2) can frequently be solved using iterative methods, we review several of these methods here. In particular, we discuss the method of contraction mappings and Newton's method. Both of these methods are methods of successive approximation in that they are characterized by the fact that each new iterate is obtained by a single transformation of the previous iterate.

Our treatment is based on the work of Kantorovich [K3]. However, since our discussion is aimed at the application of the theory to the solution of TPBVP's, we pay more attention to those results which can be easily evaluated and verified than to those results which, though sharper, are not amenable to practical use.

2.2. The Method of Contraction Mappings

We prove two fundamental theorems on the method of contraction mappings. These theorems lie at the heart of our entire development. We begin with the following.

DEFINITION 2.1. Let Y be a topological space and let T map Y into itself. Let y_0 be an element of Y. The sequence $\{y_n\}$ generated by the algorithm

$$y_{n+1} = T(y_n), \qquad n = 0, 1, \ldots \tag{2.2}$$

is called a contraction mapping or CM sequence for T based on y_0.

DEFINITION 2.3. Let Y be a topological space and let T be a map of Y into Y. A subset Ω of Y is T invariant (or simply invariant) if $T(\Omega) \subset \Omega$.

THEOREM 2.4. Let Y be a complete metric space with metric ρ and let Ω be a closed subset of Y. If T maps Y into Y, if Ω is T invariant, and if T is a contraction, i.e., if there is an α with $0 \leqslant \alpha < 1$ such that

$$\rho(T(y), T(y')) \leqslant \alpha\rho(y, y') \tag{2.5}$$

for all y, y' in Ω, then (i) the CM sequence $\{y_n\}$ for T based on any y_0 in Ω converges to the unique fixed point y^* of T in Ω, and (ii) the rate of convergence of $\{y_n\}$ is given by

$$\rho(y^*, y_n) \leqslant \frac{\alpha}{1-\alpha}\rho(y_n, y_{n-1}) \leqslant \frac{\alpha^n}{1-\alpha}\rho(y_1, y_0) \tag{2.6}$$

for $n = 1, 2, \ldots$.

Proof. Since Ω is T invariant and $y_0 \in \Omega$, we have $y_n \in \Omega$ for all n. It then follows from (2.5) that

$$\rho(y_{n+1}, y_n) = \rho(T(y_n), T(y_{n-1})) \leqslant \alpha\rho(y_n, y_{n-1}) \tag{2.7}$$

and hence, that

$$\rho(y_{n+1}, y_n) \leqslant \alpha^n\rho(y_1, y_0)$$

for all n. For any integer $p \geqslant 1$, we have

(2.8)

$$\begin{aligned}\rho(y_{n+p}, y_n) &\leqslant \rho(y_{n+p}, y_{n+p-1}) + \rho(y_{n+p-1}, y_{n+p-2}) + \cdots + \rho(y_{n+1}, y_n)\\ &\leqslant (\alpha^{p-1} + \alpha^{p-2} + \cdots + 1)\,\rho(y_{n+1}, y_n)\end{aligned}$$

$$\leqslant \frac{1-\alpha^p}{1-\alpha}\rho(y_{n+1}, y_n)$$

$$\leqslant \frac{1}{1-\alpha}\rho(y_{n+1}, y_n)$$

$$\leqslant \frac{\alpha^n}{1-\alpha}\rho(y_1, y_0).$$

As $\alpha < 1$, the sequence $\{y_n\}$ is Cauchy. Since Ω is closed and Y is complete, $\{y_n\}$ converges to an element y^* of Ω. Now,

$$\rho(y_{n+1}, T(y^*)) = \rho(T(y_n), T(y^*)) \leqslant \alpha\rho(y_n, y^*)$$

and so $\{y_n\}$ also converges to $T(y^*)$. Thus, $y^* = T(y^*)$.

If y' is another fixed point of T in Ω, then

$$\rho(y', y^*) = \rho(T(y'), T(y^*)) \leqslant \alpha\rho(y', y^*).$$

Since $0 \leqslant \alpha < 1$, we have $y' = y^*$. The inequality (2.6) is an immediate consequence of (2.7) and (2.8). Thus, the proof is complete.

Theorem 2.4 is a fixed point theorem. Its form is quite simple. A more general fixed point theorem applies to contraction mappings in pseudometric spaces where the value of the metric is no longer an element of the real line, but rather an element of a partially ordered space (see Collatz [C4]). A completely different form of fixed point theorem is Schauder's theorem in which the operator T is no longer a contraction but rather is a continuous mapping of a compact, convex set into itself [K3]. For our purposes, the present theorem is adequate. In fact, since our applications involve Banach spaces, we use a slightly weaker result in the sequel (Corollary 2.10).

DEFINITION 2.9. Let Y be a Banach space with $\|\cdot\|$ as norm. Let Ω be a closed subset of Y and let T map Y into Y. The Lipschitz norm of T on Ω, in symbols: $\square\, T \,\square_\Omega$, is given by

$$\square\, T \,\square_\Omega = \sup_{u,v\in\Omega}\{\| T(u) - T(v) \| / \| u - v \|\}$$

(note that $\square\, T \,\square_\Omega$ may be infinite). If T is Frechet differentiable on Ω, then the derivative norm of T on Ω, in symbols: $\square\, T \,\square_\Omega'$ is given by

$$\square\, T \,\square_\Omega' = \sup_{y\in\Omega} \| T'_{(y)} \| .$$

We now have the following.

COROLLARY 2.10. Let Y be a Banach space and let $\bar{S} = \bar{S}(y_0, r)$ be the closed sphere in Y with center y_0 and radius r. Let T map Y into Y and suppose that (i) T is defined on $\bar{S}(y_0, r)$, and (ii) there are real numbers η and α with $\eta \geqslant 0$ and $0 \leqslant \alpha < 1$ such that

$$\| y_1 - y_0 \| \leqslant \eta$$

$$(2.11) \qquad \square\, T \square_{\bar{S}} \leqslant \alpha < 1 \qquad \text{or} \qquad \square\, T \square_{\bar{S}}' \leqslant \alpha < 1$$

and

$$\frac{1}{1-\alpha}\eta \leqslant r$$

where $y_1 = T(y_0)$. Then the CM sequence $\{y_n\}$ for T based on y_0 converges to the unique fixed point y^* of T in $\bar{S}$ and the rate of convergence is given by

$$\| y^* - y_n \| \leqslant \frac{\alpha}{1-\alpha} \| y_n - y_{n-1} \| \leqslant \frac{\alpha^n}{1-\alpha} \| y_1 - y_0 \| .$$

Proof. In view of the proof of the theorem, it will be enough to show that $y_n \in \bar{S}$ for all n. Now, $\| T(y_0) - y_0 \| = \| y_1 - y_0 \| \leqslant \eta \leqslant [1/(1-\alpha)]\eta \leqslant r$ so that $y_1 \in \bar{S}$. Assuming that $y_0, y_1, \ldots, y_n$ are in $\bar{S}$ and noting that $\| T(u) - T(v) \| \leqslant \alpha \| u - v \|$ for all u, v in $\bar{S}$ by virtue of (2.11), we deduce that

$$\begin{aligned} \| y_{n+1} - y_0 \| &\leqslant \| y_{n+1} - y_n \| + \| y_n - y_{n-1} \| + \cdots + \| y_1 - y_0 \| \\ &\leqslant \| T(y_n) - T(y_{n-1}) \| \\ &\qquad + \| T(y_{n-1}) - T(y_{n-2}) \| + \cdots + \| y_1 - y_0 \| \\ &\leqslant (\alpha^n + \alpha^{n-1} + \cdots + 1) \| y_1 - y_0 \| \\ &\leqslant \frac{1-\alpha^{n+1}}{1-\alpha} \| y_1 - y_0 \| \\ &\leqslant \frac{1}{1-\alpha}\eta \leqslant r \end{aligned}$$

so that $y_{n+1} \in \bar{S}$. Thus, $y_n \in \bar{S}$ for all n by induction and the corollary is established.

Corollary 2.10 suffers from the drawback of requiring a direct estimate of $\Box$ T $\Box_s$. Kantorovich [K2], using the idea of a "majorant," derived a more "practical" convergence theorem for the case where T has a *continuous* Frechet derivative. We give the definition of a majorant and state and prove this theorem. Following that, we discuss its "practical" consequences.

DEFINITION 2.12 (Kantorovich [K3]). A real-valued function $\phi(t)$ defined on the interval $[t_0, t']$ $(t' = t_0 + r)$ is a majorant for an operator T defined on the closed sphere $\bar{S} = \bar{S}(y_0, r)$ of the Banach space Y if

(i) $\| T(y_0) - y_0 \| \leqslant \phi(t_0) - t_0$,

(ii) $\| T'_{(y)} \| \leqslant \phi'(t)$,

for all y, t with $\| y - y_0 \| \leqslant t - t_0 \leqslant r$.

We then have the following.

THEOREM 2.13 (Kantorovich [K3, Theorems XVIII 1.1 and XVIII 1.2]). Let Y be a Banach space and suppose that

(i) T maps $\bar{S} = \bar{S}(y_0, r)$ into Y and is continuously (Frechet) differentiable on $\bar{S}$, and

(ii) $\phi(t)$ is a differentiable majorant for T on $\bar{S}$ which has a unique fixed point t^* in $[t_0, t']$ and which satisfies the inequality

$$\phi(t') \leqslant t', \qquad t' = t_0 + r.$$

Then the CM sequence $\{y_n\}$ for T based on y_0 converges to the unique fixed point y^* of T in $\bar{S}$ and the rate of convergence of the sequence $\{y_n\}$ is given by

$$\| y^* - y_n \| \leqslant t^* - t_n$$

where t_n is the nth element of the CM sequence $\{t_n\}$ for ϕ based on t_0.

The proof of this theorem requires the following basic lemma on majorants.

LEMMA 2.14 (Kantorovich [K3]). Let Y be a Banach space, and let T and $\phi(t)$ be the operator and majorant, respectively, given in Theorem 2.13. Let the segments $[\bar{y}, \bar{y} + \Delta y]$ and $[\bar{t}, \bar{t} + \Delta t]$ belong to $\bar{S}$ and $[t_0, t']$, respectively. If $\| \bar{y} - y_0 \| \leqslant \bar{t} - t_0$ and $\| \Delta y \| \leqslant \Delta t$, then $\| T(\bar{y} + \Delta y) - T(\bar{y}) \| \leqslant \phi(\bar{t} + \Delta t) - \phi(\bar{t})$.

Proof. Using the Riemann integral for Banach space valued functions, we have

$$\int_{\bar{y}}^{\bar{y}+\Delta y} T'_{(y)}\, dy = \int_0^1 T'_{(\bar{y}+s\Delta y)}\, \Delta y\, ds = \lim_{|\lambda| \to 0} \sum_{k=0}^{n-1} T'_{(\bar{y}+\sigma_k \Delta y)}\, \Delta y (s_{k+1} - s_k)$$

where $|\lambda| = \max |(s_{k+1} - s_k)|$ and $\sigma_k \in [s_k, s_{k+1})$. Since $T'_{(y)}$ is continuous on the segment $[\bar{y}, \bar{y} + \Delta y] \subset \bar{S}$, the integral exists. We next consider the norm

$$\left\| T(\bar{y} + \Delta y) - T(\bar{y}) - \sum_{k=0}^{n-1} T'_{(\bar{y}+\sigma_k \Delta y)}\, \Delta y (s_{k+1} - s_k) \right\|$$

or, equivalently,

$$\left\| \sum_{k=0}^{n-1} [T(\bar{y} + s_{k+1} \Delta y) - T(\bar{y} + s_k \Delta y) - T'_{(\bar{y}+\sigma_k \Delta y)}\, \Delta y (s_{k+1} - s_k)] \right\| .$$

In view of the mean value theorem for differentiable operators ([K3], of Dieudonné [D1]), we have

$$\left\| \sum_{k=0}^{n-1} [T(\bar{y} + s_{k+1} \Delta y) - T(\bar{y} + s_k \Delta y) - T'_{(\bar{y}+\sigma_k \Delta y)}\, \Delta y (s_{k+1} - s_k)] \right\|$$

$$\leqslant \sum_{k=0}^{n-1} [\sup_{0<\theta<1} \| T'_{(\bar{y}+s_k \Delta y + \theta(s_{k+1}-s_k)\Delta y)} - T'_{(\bar{y}+\sigma_k \Delta y)} \| \, \| \Delta y \| \, (s_{k+1} - s_k)].$$

Hence, since $T'_{(y)}$ is continuous on $[\bar{y}, \bar{y} + \Delta y] \subset \bar{S}(y_0, r)$, we find that

$$\int_{\bar{y}}^{\bar{y}+\Delta y} T'_{(y)}\, dy = T(\bar{y} + \Delta y) - T(\bar{y}). \tag{2.15}$$

It follows that

$$\| \bar{y} + \tau \Delta y - y_0 \| \leqslant \tau \| \Delta y \| + \| \bar{y} - y_0 \| \leqslant \bar{t} + \tau \Delta t - t_0$$

for $\tau \in [0, 1]$. Therefore, by property (ii) of Definition 2.12,

$$\| T'_{(\bar{y}+\tau \Delta y)} \| \leqslant \phi'(\bar{t} + \tau \Delta t).$$

Using this together with (2.15) and the properties of the integral, we obtain the inequality

$$\| T(\bar{y} + \Delta y) - T(\bar{y}) \| = \left\| \int_{\bar{y}}^{\bar{y}+\Delta y} T'_{(y)}\, dy \right\| = \left\| \int_0^1 T'_{(\bar{y}+\tau\Delta y)}\, d\tau \right\|$$

$$\int_0^1 \| T'_{(\bar{y}+\tau\Delta y)} \|\, d\tau \leqslant \int_0^1 \phi'(\bar{t} + \tau\Delta t)\, d\tau = \int_{\bar{t}}^{\bar{t}+\Delta t} \phi'(t)\, dt$$

$$= \phi(\bar{t} + \Delta t) - \phi(\bar{t}).$$

Thus, the proof of the lemma is complete.

We are now prepared to prove Theorem 2.13.

Proof of Theorem 2.13. We give the proof of the theorem in four steps. First, we show that the CM sequence $\{t_n\}$ for ϕ based on t_0 exists and converges to the unique fixed point t^* of ϕ. Next, we use Lemma 2.14 to show that the CM sequence for T based on y_0 exists and that the norms $\| y_n - y_0 \|$ are bounded from above by the difference $t^* - t_0$. This, in turn, implies that the sequence $\{y_n\}$ converges to a fixed point y^* of T. In the third step, we show that this fixed point y^* is unique. In the final step, we prove the desired rate of convergence inequality.

To prove the existence and convergence of the CM sequence $\{t_n\}$, we first note that $\phi'(t) \geqslant 0$ for t in $[t_0, t']$. This implies that $\phi(t)$ is monotonically nondecreasing on $[t_0, t']$. We use this to show that the CM sequence $\{t_n\}$ for ϕ based on t_0 is contained in $[t_0, t']$ and is also monotonically nondecreasing. In particular, we prove by induction that

$$t_0 \leqslant t_k \leqslant t_{k+1} \leqslant t^* \leqslant t', \qquad k = 0, 1, 2, \ldots \tag{2.16}$$

where the last inequality follows immediately from the assumption that $t^* \in [t_0, t']$. In view of (i) of Definition 2.12, we have $t_1 - t_0 = \phi(t_0) - t_0 \geqslant \| T(y_0) - y_0 \| \geqslant 0$ and by the monotonicity of $\phi(t)$, $t_1 = \phi(t_0) \leqslant \phi(t^*) = t^* \leqslant t'$. Hence, for $k = 0$, $t_0 \leqslant t_1 \leqslant t^* \leqslant t'$. Assuming that (2.16) has been proved for all $k < n$, the monotonicity of $\phi(t)$ implies that $t_0 \leqslant t_n = \phi(t_{n-1}) \leqslant \phi(t_n) = t_{n+1} \leqslant \phi(t^*) = t^* \leqslant t'$. By induction, it follows then that $\{t_n\}$ is indeed a monotonically nondecreasing sequence of real numbers which is bounded from above and hence that $\{t_n\}$ converges to its least upper bound. In view of the fact that $\phi(t)$ is continuous, the limit to which $\{t_n\}$ converges must be a solution of $t = \phi(t)$. Since t^* is the unique fixed point of ϕ in $[t_0, t']$, we have $\lim_{n\to\infty} t_n = t^*$.

In precisely the same way, we can show that, for the CM sequence $\{\tilde{t}_n\}$ for ϕ based on $\tilde{t}_0 = t'$, we have

$$t^* \leqslant \tilde{t}_{k+1} \leqslant \tilde{t}_k \leqslant t', \qquad k = 0, 1, 2, \ldots. \tag{2.17}$$

This is so because $\tilde{t}_1 = \phi(t') \leqslant t'$, and, by the monotonicity of $\phi(t)$, $t^* = \phi(t^*) \leqslant \phi(t') = \tilde{t}_1$. Hence, for $k = 0$, $t^* \leqslant \tilde{t}_1 \leqslant t'$. Assuming that (2.17) has been proved for all $k < n$, it follows from the monotonicity of $\phi(t)$, that

$$t^* = \phi(t^*) \leqslant \phi(\tilde{t}_n) = \tilde{t}_{n+1} \leqslant \phi(\tilde{t}_{n-1}) = \tilde{t}_n \leqslant t'.$$

Induction then yields, as before, that the CM sequence $\{\tilde{t}_n\}$ for ϕ based on t' exists as a monotonically nonincreasing sequence which is bounded from below. Hence, since $\phi(t)$ is continuous, we have $\lim_{n\to\infty} \tilde{t}_n = t^*$. We shall make use of the sequence $\{\tilde{t}_n\}$ for the proof of the uniqueness of the fixed point y^* of T in the third step.

For the proof of the existence and the convergence of the CM sequence $\{y_n\}$, we compare the partial sums

$$\bar{t}_n = \sum_{k=1}^{n} \| y_k - y_{k-1} \| \qquad \text{and} \qquad t_n = \sum_{k=1}^{n} (t_k - t_{k-1}).$$

In particular, we use Lemma 2.14 and induction to prove that

$$\| y_k - y_{k-1} \| \leqslant t_k - t_{k-1}, \qquad k = 1, 2, \ldots \tag{2.18}$$

and

$$\| y_k - y_0 \| \leqslant t_k - t_0, \qquad k = 1, 2, \ldots. \tag{2.19}$$

Since $t_k \leqslant t'$ by (2.16), (2.19) implies that $y_k \in \bar{S}$. Thus, $\{y_n\}$ is defined.

For $k = 1$, we have $\| y_1 - y_0 \| = \| T(y_0) - y_0 \| \leqslant \phi(t_0) - t_0 = t_1 - t_0$. Therefore, both (2.18) and (2.19) hold for $k = 1$. Assuming that (2.18) and (2.19) have been proved for all $k \leqslant n$, we have

$$\| y_n - y_0 \| \leqslant t_n - t_0$$

$$\| y_n - y_{n-1} \| \leqslant t_n - t_{n-1}.$$

Application of Lemma 2.14 then gives

$$\| T(y_n) - T(y_{n-1}) \| \leqslant \| y_{n+1} - y_n \| \leqslant \phi(t_n) - \phi(t_{n-1}) \leqslant t_{n+1} - t_n$$

and consequently

$$\begin{aligned} \| y_{n+1} - y_0 \| &\leqslant \| y_{n+1} - y_n \| + \| y_n - y_0 \| \\ &\leqslant t_{n+1} - t_n + t_n - t_0 = t_{n+1} - t_0 . \end{aligned}$$

By induction, (2.18) and (2.19) hold for any $k \geqslant 1$.

It follows that, for an arbitrary positive integer p,

$$\begin{aligned} \| y_{n+p} - y_n \| &\leqslant \| y_{n+p} - y_{n+p-1} \| + \| y_{n+p-1} - y_{n+p-2} \| \\ &\quad + \cdots + \| y_{n+1} - y_n \| \\ &\leqslant t_{n+p} - t_{n+p-1} + t_{n+p-1} - t_{n+p-2} + \cdots + t_{n+1} - t_n \\ &= t_{n+p} - t_n \end{aligned} \tag{2.20}$$

and hence that $\{y_n\}$ is a Cauchy sequence (as $\{t_n\}$ is). Since y_n is an element of $\bar{S}$ for each n, the sequence converges to an element y^* of $\bar{S}$. The continuity of T on $\bar{S}$ implies that y^* is a fixed point of T.

We prove the uniqueness of the fixed point y^* by showing that every CM sequence $\{\tilde{y}_n\}$ for T based on an element $\tilde{y}_0$ of $\bar{S}$ converges to the fixed point y^*. To do so, we prove (by induction) that

$$\| \tilde{y}_k - y_k \| \leqslant \tilde{t}_k - t_k , \qquad k = 0, 1, 2, \ldots \tag{2.21}$$

and

$$\| \tilde{y}_k - y_0 \| \leqslant \tilde{t}_k - t_0 , \qquad k = 0, 1, 2, \ldots \tag{2.22}$$

where the $\tilde{t}_n$ are the elements of the CM sequence for ϕ based on t'.

For $k = 0$, we have, $\| \tilde{y}_0 - y_0 \| \leqslant r = t' - t_0$ since $\tilde{y}_0 \in \bar{S}$. Assuming that both (2.21) and (2.22) are satisfied for all $k \leqslant n$, we deduce from (2.21) and (2.17) that $\tilde{y}_n \in \bar{S}$. In addition, we have

$$\| \tilde{y}_n - y_n \| \leqslant \tilde{t}_n - t_0$$

while by (2.19)

$$\| y_n - y_0 \| \leqslant t_n - t_0 .$$

Application of Lemma 2.14 then yields

$$\| \tilde{y}_{n+1} - y_{n+1} \| = \| T(\tilde{y}_n) - T(y_n) \|$$
$$\leqslant \| \phi(\tilde{t}_n) - \phi(t_n) \| = \tilde{t}_{n+1} - t_{n+1}$$

which, in turn, implies that

$$\| \tilde{y}_{n+1} - y_0 \| \leqslant \| \tilde{y}_{n+1} - y_{n+1} \| + \| y_{n+1} - y_0 \|$$
$$\leqslant \tilde{t}_{n+1} - t_{n+1} + t_{n+1} - t_0 = \tilde{t}_{n+1} - t_0 .$$

By induction, both (2.21) and (2.22) hold for all $k \geqslant 0$.

Since both $\{t_n\}$ and $\{\tilde{t}_n\}$ converge to the same limit, we have $\lim_{n\to\infty} \| \tilde{y}_n - y_n \| = \lim_{n\to\infty} | \tilde{t}_n - t_n | = 0$. Therefore, any CM sequence $\{\tilde{y}_n\}$ for T based on $\tilde{y}_0$ in $\bar{S}$ converges to y^*. The uniqueness of y^* follows by considering the CM sequence $\{\hat{y}\}$ where $\hat{y}$ is any fixed point of T in $\bar{S}$.

The desired rate of convergence inequality follows from (2.20). Thus, the theorem is established.

Theorem 2.13 is not yet in a useful form for our purposes. Before the theorem can be applied, a majorant $\phi(t)$ has to be determined. One approach to deriving practical convergence conditions from Theorem 2.13 is to assume a certain functional form for $\phi(t)$ and to investigate what conditions have to be satisfied in order that $\phi(t)$ be a majorant for the (given) operator T. Such conditions constitute the first part of the practical convergence conditions; the second part follows from the conditions relating ϕ and T given in the theorem. In principle, many choices for the functional form of $\phi(t)$ are possible; however, only a few of these result in simple and practical convergence conditions. We discuss two such simple choices.

As our first selection we let $\phi(t)$ be a linear function of t, i.e.,

$$\phi(t) = \eta + \alpha t. \tag{2.23}$$

In order that this $\phi(t)$ be a majorant for a differentiable operator T, both inequalities of Definition 2.12 must be satisfied. This leads to the conditions

$$\| T(y_0) - y_0 \| = \| y_1 - y_0 \| \leqslant \eta \tag{2.24}$$

$$\sup_{y \in \bar{S}} \| T'_{(y)} \| \leqslant \alpha. \tag{2.25}$$

Theorem (2.13) requires that $\phi(t)$ be differentiable, have a unique fixed point in $[t_0, t']$, and satisfy the inequality $\phi(t') \leqslant t' = t_0 + r = r$ (as $t_0 = 0$ here). Clearly, the differentiability of $\phi(t)$ is assured, and $\phi(t) = t$ will have a unique solution if $\alpha < 1$. The inequality $\phi(t') \leqslant t'$ will be satisfied in $r = t' \geqslant [1/(1-\alpha)]\eta$. If these conditions are satisfied, then Theorem 2.13 guarantees the convergence of the CM sequence $\{y_n\}$ for T based on y_0 to the fixed point y^*. The nth term of the CM sequence for ϕ based on t_0 is, in the present case,

$$t_n = \frac{1-\alpha^n}{1-\alpha}\,\eta,$$

and furthermore,

$$t^* = \frac{1}{1-\alpha}\,\eta.$$

In view of this,

$$\| y^* - y_n \| \leqslant \frac{\alpha^n}{1-\alpha}\,\eta \tag{2.26}$$

or, if we replace η by $\| y_1 - y_0 \|$,†

$$\| y^* - y_n \| \leqslant \frac{\alpha^n}{1-\alpha} \| y_1 - y_0 \| . \tag{2.27}$$

In summary, we have found that if there are numbers α, η with $\eta > 0$ and $0 \leqslant \alpha < 1$ such that (2.24) and (2.25) are satisfied and $(1-\alpha)r \geqslant \eta$, then the CM sequence for T based on y_0 converges to the unique fixed point y^* of T in $\bar{S} = \bar{S}(y_0, r)$. Evidently, this is precisely Corollary 2.10 for the case where T has a continuous Frechet derivative. Thus, our first choice for $\phi(t)$ (2.23) yields no new convergence conditions although it does show that Corollary 2.10 for a differentiable T is a consequence of Theorem 2.13.

A second choice for $\phi(t)$ is the quadratic function

$$\phi(t) = \eta + \delta t + \frac{K}{2} t^2. \tag{2.28}$$

† In view of the equality sign in (2.24), inequality (2.26) holds for $\eta = \| y_1 - y_0 \|$. It follows that an increase in η, and hence, an increase in r, cannot result in a decrease of α. Since the fraction in (2.26) is a monotone increasing function of α, we may, therefore, replace η by $\| y_1 - y_0 \|$ without having to make the same change everywhere in the derivation.

This function is a majorant for T if the conditions of Definition 2.12 are satisfied. This leads to the requirements

$$\| T(y_0) - y_0 \| = \| y_1 - y_0 \| \leqslant \eta \tag{2.29}$$

and

$$\| T'_{(y)} \| \leqslant \delta + Kt \tag{2.30}$$

for all y with $\| y - y_0 \| \leqslant t$. If $T'_{(y)}$ is differentiable, or equivalently if T is twice differentiable, the last condition can be simplified by invoking the mean value theorem for differentiable operators. This yields

$$\| T'_{(y)} \| \leqslant \| T'_{(y_0)} \| + \| T'_{(y)} - T'_{(y_0)} \|$$

$$\leqslant \| T'_{(y_0)} \| + \sup_{0<\theta<1} \{\| T''_{(y_0+\theta(y-y_0))} \|\} \| y_1 - y_0 \| .$$

From this we deduce that (2.30) may be replaced by the inequalities $\| T'_{(y_0)} \| \leqslant \delta$ and $\sup_{y\in \bar{S}} \| T''_{(y)} \| \leqslant K$. [These inequalities imply (2.30).]

Theorem 2.13 requires that $\phi(t)$ be differentiable, have a unique fixed point t^* in $[0, t']$, and satisfy the inequality $\phi(t') \leqslant t' = t_0 + r = r$ (as $t_0 = 0$). The differentiability of $\phi(t)$ is clear. Since the roots of the quadratic equation $t = \phi(t) = \eta + \delta t + (K/2)t^2$ are given by

$$t_{1,2} = \frac{1 - \delta \pm \sqrt{(1 - \delta)^2 - 2K\eta}}{K},$$

the unique fixed point requirement leads to the conditions

$$h = \frac{K\eta}{(1 - \delta)^2} \leqslant \tfrac{1}{2}, \qquad \delta < 1 \tag{2.31}$$

and

(2.32)

$$\frac{(1 - \delta) - \sqrt{(1 - \delta)^2 - 2K\eta}}{K} \leqslant t' = r < \frac{(1 - \delta) + \sqrt{(1 - \delta)^2 - 2K\eta}}{K}.$$

Satisfaction of the inequality $\phi(t') \leqslant t'$ is assured by (2.32).

If (2.29)–(2.32) hold, then Theorem 2.13 guarantees the convergence of the CM sequence $\{y_n\}$ (for T based on y_0) to the fixed point y^*. In addition, the convergence rate satisfies the desired inequality, $\| y^* - y_n \| \leqslant t^* - t_n$. We translate these inequalities in terms of η, K, and h.

For our choice of a quadratic $\phi(t)$, the evaluation of the sequence $\{t_n\}$ is rather complicated. Instead of evaluating the difference $(t^* - t_n)$ exactly, we give an estimate

$$
\begin{aligned}
t^* - t_n &= \eta + \delta t^* + \frac{K}{2} t^{*2} - \eta - \delta t_{n-1} - \frac{K}{2} t_{n-1}^2 \\
&= \delta(t^* - t_{n-1}) + \frac{K}{2} (t^* + t_{n-1})(t^* - t_{n-1}) \\
&\leqslant (\delta + Kt^*)(t^* - t_{n-1}).
\end{aligned}
\tag{2.33}
$$

Evidently, (2.33) holds for all $n \geqslant 1$. Since

$$t^* - t_0 = t^* = \frac{(1-\delta) - \sqrt{(1-\delta)^2 - 2K\eta}}{K} = \frac{1 - \sqrt{1-2h}}{h} \frac{\eta}{1-\delta},$$

we have

$$\delta + Kt^* = [1 - (1-\delta)\sqrt{1-2h}].$$

Repeated application of (2.33) leads to

$$
\begin{aligned}
t^* - t_n &\leqslant (\delta + Kt^*)^n (t^* - t_0) \\
&\leqslant [1 - (1-\delta)\sqrt{1-2h}]^n \left[\frac{1 - \sqrt{1-2h}}{h} \frac{\eta}{1-\delta}\right]
\end{aligned}
$$

so that

$$\| y^* - y_n \| \leqslant [1 - (1-\delta)\sqrt{1-2h}]^n \left[\frac{1 - \sqrt{1-2h}}{h} \frac{\eta}{1-\delta}\right]$$

or if we replace η by $\| y_1 - y_0 \|$

$$\| y^* - y_n \| \leqslant [1 - (1-\delta)\sqrt{1-2h}]^n \left[\frac{1 - \sqrt{1-2h}}{h(1-\delta)}\right] \| y_1 - y_0 \| .$$

The choice of a quadratic function for $\phi(t)$ thus leads to interesting convergence conditions; we summarize these in the following "practical" corollary of Theorem 2.13.

COROLLARY 2.34. Suppose that T is twice differentiable on $\bar{S} = \bar{S}(y_0, r)$ and that there are real numbers η, δ, and K with $\eta \geqslant 0$, $0 \leqslant \delta < 1$, and $K \geqslant 0$ such that

$$\| y_1 - y_0 \| \leqslant \eta, \qquad \| T'_{(y_0)} \| \leqslant \delta, \qquad \sup_{y \in \bar{S}} \{\| T''_{(y)} \|\} \leqslant K \tag{2.35}$$

and

$$\frac{1 - \sqrt{1 - 2h}}{h} \frac{\eta}{1 - \delta} \leqslant r < \frac{1 + \sqrt{1 - 2h}}{h} \frac{\eta}{1 - \delta} \tag{2.36}$$

where $h = K\eta/(1 - \delta)^2 \leqslant \frac{1}{2}$. Then the CM sequence $\{y_n\}$ for T based on y_0 converges to the unique fixed point y^* of T in $\bar{S}$ and the rate of convergence is given by

$$\| y^* - y_n \| \leqslant [1 - (1 - \delta) \sqrt{1 - 2h}]^n \left[\frac{1 - \sqrt{1 - 2h}}{h(1 - \delta)} \right] \| y_1 - y_0 \| . \tag{2.37}$$

Corollary 2.34 and Corollary 2.10 display several similarities. A direct comparison to determine which of these corollaries is preferable in practice is impossible because of the sensitivity of the convergence conditions to the operator T. Intuitively, we may view Corollary 2.10 as a linear contraction mapping theorem and Corollary 2.34 as a contraction mapping theorem for quadratic functions. It is to be expected that the conditions of either corollary will be best if the functional relationship between the norm of the operator T and the norms, $\| y_n - y_0 \|$, is of the same form as the corresponding majorant function. If the norm of the Frechet derivative of T is approximately constant over $\bar{S}$, then most likely Corollary 2.10 will yield the best convergence conditions. On the other hand, if the norm of $T'_{(y)}$ is almost zero for $y = y_0$ and increases with $\| y - y_0 \|$, then most likely Corollary 2.34 will yield the best convergence conditions. It may be remarked that we will encounter operators of the latter type later on in this chapter when we discuss convergence conditions for both the modified and pure Newton's method. For those cases, Corollary 2.34 yields the best convergence conditions.

2.3. The Modified Contraction Mapping Method

Direct application of the contraction mapping method often does not lead to a convergent sequence of approximations. Frequently, it is possible to modify T in such a way as to lead to a convergent sequence of approximations. With this objective in mind, we have the following.

LEMMA 3.1. Let T and V be maps of Y into Y. Suppose that $I - V$ is invertible and let P be the map of Y into itself given by

$$P(y) = [I - V]^{-1} [T(y) - V(y)].$$

Then y^* is a fixed point of T if and only if y^* is a fixed point of P.

Proof. If $y^* = T(y^*)$, then $y^* - V(y^*) = T(y^*) - V(y^*)$ and so $y^* = [I - V]^{-1}[T(y^*) - V(y^*)] = P(y^*)$. Conversely, if $y^* = P(y^*)$, then $[I - V](y^*) = T(y^*) - V(y^*)$ so that $y^* = T(y^*)$.

This simple lemma leads us to consider the application of the contraction mapping method to the modified equation

$$y - V(y) = T(y) - V(y)$$

where V is an operator with the property that $[I - V]$ is invertible. In other words, we consider the selection of an initial approximate solution y_0 and the generation of a sequence $\{y_n\}$ by one of the following three algorithms

(3.2) $$y_{n+1} - V(y_{n+1}) = T(y_n) - V(y_n)$$

(3.3) $$y_{n+1} = P(y_n) = [I - V]^{-1} [T(y_n) - V(y_n)]$$

(3.4) $$y_{n+1} = T(y_n) + V(y_{n+1} - y_n)$$

[where V is assumed linear in (3.4)]. We call any one of these algorithms a modified contraction mapping method and we call the sequence $\{y_n\}$ generated by such an algorithm, a *modified contraction mapping* (*or* MCM) *sequence for T based on y_0 and V*. We observe that the MCM sequence for T based on y_0 and V coincides with the CM sequence for P based on y_0. Thus, we can translate results of the previous section into the present context. In particular, we have the following.

PROPOSITION 3.5. Suppose that P is differentiable on $\bar{S} = \bar{S}(y_0, r)$ and that there are real numbers η, α with $\eta \geqslant 0$ and $0 \leqslant \alpha < 1$ such that

$$\|y_1 - y_0\| \leqslant \eta, \qquad \sup_{y \in \bar{S}}\{\|P'_{(y)}\|\} \leqslant \alpha, \qquad \frac{1}{1-\alpha}\eta \leqslant r. \tag{3.6}$$

Then the MCM sequence $\{y_n\}$ for T based on y_0 and V converges to the unique fixed point y^* of T in $\bar{S}$ and the rate of convergence is given by

$$\|y^* - y_n\| \leqslant \frac{\alpha}{1-\alpha}\|y_n - y_{n-1}\| \leqslant \frac{\alpha^n}{1-\alpha}\|y_1 - y_0\|. \tag{3.7}$$

COROLLARY 3.8. If V is a linear operator with $I - V$ invertible, if T is differentiable on $\bar{S}$, and if

$$\begin{aligned} &\|y_1 - y_0\| \leqslant \eta, \\ &\sup_{y \in \bar{S}}\{\|[I - V]^{-1}[T'_{(y)} - V]\|\} \leqslant \alpha, \qquad \frac{1}{1-\alpha}\eta \leqslant r, \end{aligned} \tag{3.9}$$

then the MCM sequence $\{y_n\}$ converges to the unique fixed point y^* of T in $\bar{S}$ and the rate of convergence is given by (3.7).

PROPOSITION 3.10. Suppose that P is twice differentiable on $\bar{S} = \bar{S}(y_0, r)$ and that there are real numbers η, δ, and K with $\eta \geqslant 0$, $0 \leqslant \delta < 1$, and $K \geqslant 0$ such that

$$\|y_1 - y_0\| \leqslant \eta, \qquad \|P'_{(y_0)}\| \leqslant \delta, \qquad \sup_{y \in \bar{S}}\{\|P''_{(y)}\|\} \leqslant K \tag{3.11}$$

and

$$\frac{1 - \sqrt{1-2h}}{h}\,\frac{\eta}{1-\delta} \leqslant r < \frac{1 + \sqrt{1-2h}}{h}\,\frac{\eta}{1-\delta} \tag{3.12}$$

where $h = (K\eta/(1-\delta)^2) \leqslant \frac{1}{2}$. Then the MCM sequence $\{y_n\}$ for T based on y_0 and V converges to the unique fixed point y^* of T in $\bar{S}$ and the rate of convergence is given by

$$\|y^* - y_n\| \leqslant [1 - (1-\delta)\sqrt{1-2h}]^n \left[\frac{1 - \sqrt{1-2h}}{h(1-\delta)}\right]\|y_1 - y_0\|. \tag{3.13}$$

COROLLARY 3.14. If V is a linear operator with $I - V$ invertible, if T is twice differentiable on $\bar{S}$, if

$$\| y_1 - y_0 \| \leqslant \eta, \tag{3.15}$$
$$\| [I - V]^{-1} [T'_{(y_0)} - V] \| \leqslant \delta, \qquad \sup_{y \in \bar{S}} \{ \| [I - V]^{-1} [T''_{(y)}] \| \} \leqslant K$$

and if (3.12) is satisfied, then the MCM sequence $\{y_n\}$ converges to the unique fixed point y^* of T in $\bar{S}$ and the rate of convergence is given by (3.13).

The significance of these propositions and corollaries lies in the fact that they extend the range of applicability of the contraction mapping method to fixed point problems for operators T that are not contraction mappings. The essence of the modified contraction mapping method is the application of the method of contraction mappings to an equivalent fixed point problem. In particular, it is possible to treat fixed point problems with operators T for which

$$\sup_{y \in \bar{S}} \| T'_{(y)} \| > 1.$$

The basic contraction mapping criterion

$$\sup_{y \in \bar{S}} \| T'_{(y)} \| \leqslant \alpha < 1$$

is, in this case, replaced by the condition that the Frechet derivative $P'_{(y)}$ be suitably small on $\bar{S}$. Alternatively, if

$$\sup_{y \in \bar{S}} \| [I - V]^{-1} [T'_{(y)} - V] \| \leqslant \alpha < 1$$

for some linear operator V with $I - V$ invertible, then we can anticipate convergence.

Corollaries (3.8) and (3.14) do not specify the linear operator V any further than requiring the norm

$$\sup_{y \in \bar{S}} \| [I - V]^{-1} [T'_{(y)} - V] \|$$

to be small. More information on the selection of V can be garnered from a consideration of the difference between two successive approximations.

We have

$$y_{n+1} - y_n = [I - V]^{-1}\,[T(y_n) - T(y_{n-1}) - V(y_n - y_{n-1})]$$

and, by the mean value theorem for differentiable operators,

$$\| y_{n+1} - y_n \| \leqslant \sup_{0<\theta<1} \{\| [I - V]^{-1}\,[T'_{(y_{n-1}+\theta(y_n-y_{n-1}))} - V] \|\} \, \| y_n - y_{n-1} \| \,.$$

The convergence of the MCM sequence $\{y_n\}$ will be most rapid if the linear operator V is chosen in such a way that the expressions

$$\text{(3.16)} \quad \sup_{0<\theta<1} \| [I - V]^{-1}\,[T'_{(y_{n-1}+\theta(y_n-y_{n-1}))} - V] \| \,, \qquad n = 1, 2, \ldots$$

are as small as possible. Evidently, a number of choice for V are possible. We discuss some of the more common selections.

From the expression (3.16) we can see that if we were allowed to select a different linear operator at each step of the iteration, then the choice

$$V_n = T'_{(y_n)}$$

would yield one of the best possible convergence rates. The iteration method based on this choice is known as *Newton's method.* This method is *not* a modified contraction mapping method because of the change in the linearization. We shall discuss Newton's method in the next section.

If we restrict ourselves to a fixed linear operator V and take into account the fact that the elements y_n are unknown beforehand, then an obvious choice for V is $V = T'_{(y_0)}$. The iteration method based on this selection of V is called the *modified Newton's method.* The modified Newton's method is the best known version of the modified contraction mapping method. Both corollaries apply to this method. In fact, a nice simplification arises in Corollary 3.14 in that we may take $\delta = 0$. We will not treat the modified Newton's method as a special method, but rather consider it a particular case of the modified contraction mapping method.

For one particular class of fixed point problems, a simple choice of V may lead to very simple computational procedures which may offset a possible loss in convergence rate. This particular class is the class of *almost linear fixed point problems*. These are given by equations of the form

$$y = T(y) = W(y) + \epsilon E(y)$$

where W is linear, E is a possibly nonlinear operator, and ϵ is a "small" number. The simple choice $V = W$ may be advantageous in such a problem. This choice for V makes the convergence conditions depend on ϵ. For example, the main convergence condition of the contraction mapping theorem becomes

$$\frac{1}{\epsilon} \sup_{y \in \bar{S}} \| T'_{(y)} \| \leqslant \sup_{y \in \bar{S}} \| [I - W]^{-1} E'_{(y_0)} \| \leqslant \frac{\alpha}{\epsilon} < \frac{1}{\epsilon}.$$

We discuss the application of these ideas to the iterative solution of almost linear two-point boundary value problems in Chapters 4 and 5.

As a final and trivial choice for V, we have $V = 0$. It is clear that this choice results in the original method of contraction mappings discussed in the previous section. The original method of contraction mappings can thus be considered a special case of the modified contraction mapping method.

We can also consider the modified contraction mapping method from another point of view. Suppose that we attempt to solve the equation $y = T(y)$ by improving successive iterates by corrections which are linear functions of the error. An algorithm for such a procedure is

$$y_{n+1} = y_n + \Lambda[T(y_n) - y_n]$$

where Λ is a nonsingular linear operator. An iterative procedure converges rapidly if the ratio of the norms of the differences between the successive iterates is small. We have

$$\| y_{n+1} - y_n \| \leqslant \sup_{0<\theta<1} \{\| I + \Lambda[T'_{(y_{n-1}+\theta(y_n - y_{n-1}))} - I] \|\} \| y_n - y_{n-1} \|$$

in the present case. It follows that the convergence will be improved if the expression $\sup_{y \in \bar{S}} \| I - \Lambda[I - T'_{(y)}] \|$ becomes smaller. In this light, we see that a good choice for the nonsingular operator Λ is given by $\Lambda = [I - V]^{-1}$ where V is a linear operator for which $\sup_{y \in \bar{S}} \| I - [I - V]^{-1}[I - T'_{(y)}] \| = \sup_{y \in \bar{S}} \| [I - V]^{-1}[T'_{(y)} - V] \|$ is small. Since this leads to an algorithm of the modified contraction mapping method, we have made our point.

2.4. Newton's Method

We noted in the preceding section that if we could choose a different V, say V_n, at each iteration, then we would obtain a more rapidly convergent algorithm. The particular choice, $V_n = T'_{(y_n)}$, leads to the iterative procedure

$$y_{n+1} - T'_{(y_n)} y_{n+1} = T(y_n) - T'_{(y_n)} y_n \tag{4.1}$$

which is called Newton's method.

We will first consider Newton's method as a special case of the method of contraction mappings and apply the contraction mapping theorem to it. Next, we show that the convergence conditions can be relaxed if the special relationship between successive elements of the iteration is taken into account. This leads to the theorem of Mysovskikh, which guarantees the convergence of the sequence of approximate solutions but not the uniqueness of the limiting solution. Finally, we prove the classic theorem of Kantorovich on the convergence of Newton's method for operator equations. The proof shows that by taking into account the special relationship between the successive elements of the sequence and by slightly narrowing the conditions of Mysovskikh's theorem, it is possible to let the convergence conditions for Newton's method depend almost exclusively on the initial approximate solution and to prove, in addition, the uniqueness of the limiting solution.

We now have the following.

DEFINITION 4.2. Let T map Y into itself and let y_0 be an element of Y. Let V_n be a sequence of elements of $\mathscr{L}(Y, Y)$. The sequence $\{y_n\}$ generated by any one of the following algorithms

$$y_{n+1} - V_n y_{n+1} = T(y_n) - V_n y_n \tag{4.3}$$

$$y_{n+1} = T(y_n) + V_n(y_{n+1} - y_n) \tag{4.4}$$

$$y_{n+1} = [I - V_n]^{-1} [T(y_n) - V_n(y_n)] = Q_n(y_n) \tag{4.5}$$

for $n = 0, 1, \ldots$, is called the Newton's method or NM sequence for T based on y_0 and $\{V_n\}$. If $V_n = T'_{(y_n)}$, then $\{y_n\}$ is called the Newton's method or NM sequence for T based on y_0.

We observe that if $V_n = T'_{(y_n)}$, then Q_n is independent of n in the sense that

$$Q_n(y_n) = [I - T'_{(y_n)}]\,[T(y_n) - T'_{(y_n)}y_n] = Q(y_n) \tag{4.6}$$

where Q is the map of Y into itself given by

$$Q(y) = [I - T'_{(y)}]^{-1}\,[T(y) - T'_{(y)}y] \tag{4.7}$$

(provided that the indicated derivatives and inverses exist). This observation allows us to view the application of Newton's method to the solution of $y = T(y)$ as equivalent to the application of the contraction mapping method to the solution of the equation $y = Q(y)$. More precisely, we have the following.

PROPOSITION 4.8 [K2]. Suppose that (i) T is twice continuously differentiable on $\bar{S} = \bar{S}(y_0, r)$, (ii) $[I - T'_{(y)}]^{-1}$ exists and is linear for y in $\bar{S}$, (iii) $[I - T'_{(y)}]^{-1}$ and $T''_{(y)}$ are (uniformly) bounded on $\bar{S}$ (i.e., $\sup_{y\in\bar{S}}\{\|[I - T'_{(y)}]^{-1}\|\} \leqslant D < \infty$ and $\sup_{y\in\bar{S}}\{\|T''_{(y)}\|\} \leqslant M < \infty$), and (iv) there are real numbers η and α with $\eta \geqslant 0$ and $0 \leqslant \alpha < 1$ such that

$$\|y_1 - y_0\| \leqslant \eta, \qquad \frac{1}{1-\alpha}\eta \leqslant r \tag{4.9}$$

and

$$\sup_{y\in\bar{S}}\{\|[I - T'_{(y)}]^{-1}[T''_{(y)}]\,(I - T'_{(y)})^{-1}(T(y) - y)\|\} \leqslant \alpha.^{\dagger} \tag{4.10}$$

Then the NM sequence $\{y_n\}$ for T based on y_0 converges to the unique fixed point y^* of T in $\bar{S}$ and the rate of convergence is given by

$$\|y^* - y_n\| \leqslant \frac{\alpha}{1-\alpha}\|y_n - y_{n-1}\| \leqslant \frac{\alpha^n}{1-\alpha}\|y_1 - y_0\|. \tag{4.11}$$

Proof. We first observe that, in view of Corollary 2.10 and the lemma following the proposition, $\{y_n\}$ converges to the unique fixed point y^* of Q in $\bar{S}$ and the rate of convergence is given by (4.11). However, since $[I - T'_{(y)}]^{-1}$ exists for all y in $\bar{S}$, it is clear that any fixed point of T in $\bar{S}$ is a fixed point of Q and conversely. Thus, the

† Note that $T''_{(y)} \in \mathscr{L}(Y, \mathscr{L}(Y, Y))$.

proposition will be established once we have verified the following lemma.

LEMMA 4.12. Let Q be the map of Y into itself given by (4.7) where T satisfies the conditions of the proposition. Then the Frechet derivative, $Q'_{(y)}$, of Q is given by

$$Q'_{(y)} = \{[I - T'_{(y)}]^{-1}[T(y) - T'_{(y)}y]\}' \tag{4.13}$$

$$= [I - T'_{(y)}]^{-1}[T''_{(y)}][I - T'_{(y)}]^{-1}[T(y) - y]$$

for y in $\bar{S}$.

Proof. We prove (4.13) by showing that

$$\lim_{\|\Delta y\| \to 0} \frac{1}{\|\Delta y\|} \|Q(y + \Delta y) - Q(y) - L\,\Delta y\| = 0 \tag{4.14}$$

where L is the linear operator given by

$$L = [I - T'_{(y)}]^{-1} T''_{(y)}[I - T'_{(y)}]^{-1}[T(y) - y].$$

The norm in (4.14) then becomes

$$\begin{aligned}(4.15)\quad &\|[I - T'_{(y+\Delta y)}]^{-1}[T(y + \Delta y) - T'_{(y+\Delta y)}(y + \Delta y)]\\ &- [I - T'_{(y)}]^{-1}[T(y) - T'_{(y)}y]\\ &- [I - T'_{(y)}]^{-1}[T''_{(y)}\,\Delta y][I - T'_{(y)}]^{-1}[T(y) - y]\|\\ &= \|[I - T'_{(y)} - (T'_{(y+\Delta y)} - T'_{(y)})]^{-1}[(T(y) - T'_{(y)}y)\\ &\quad - (T'_{(y+\Delta y)} - T'_{(y)})(y + \Delta y)\\ &\quad + (T(y + \Delta y) - T(y) - T'_{(y)}\,\Delta y)]\\ &\quad - [I - T'_{(y)}]^{-1}[T(y) - T'_{(y)}y]\\ &\quad - [I - T'_{(y)}]^{-1}[T''_{(y)}\,\Delta y][I - T'_{(y)}]^{-1}[T(y) - y]\| .\end{aligned}$$

Now

$$\begin{aligned}&[I - T'_{(y)} - (T'_{(y+\Delta y)} - T'_{(y)})]^{-1}\\ &\quad = \{[I - T'_{(y)}][I - [I - T'_{(y)}]^{-1}(T'_{(y+\Delta y)} - T'_{(y)})]\}^{-1}\end{aligned}$$

and so if we define a linear operator U by setting

$$U = [I - T'_{(y)}]^{-1}(T'_{(y+\Delta y)} - T'_{(y)}) \tag{4.16}$$

then

$$[I - T'_{(y)} - (T'_{(y+\Delta y)} - T'_{(y)})]^{-1} = [I - U]^{-1}[I - T'_{(y)}]^{-1}.$$

Letting D and M be positive real numbers as in (iii) of the proposition so that $\sup_{y\in\bar{S}}\{\|[I - T'_{(y)}]^{-1}\|\} \leqslant D$ and $\sup_{y\in\bar{S}}\{\| T''_{(y)}\|\} \leqslant M$, we have, in view of the mean value theorem for differentiable operators,

$$\begin{aligned} \| U \| &\leqslant \|[I - T'_{(y)}]^{-1}\| \, \| T'_{(y+\Delta y)} - T'_{(y)} \| \\ &\leqslant D \sup_{0<\theta<1} \| T''_{(y+\theta\Delta y)} \| \| \Delta y \| \leqslant DM \| \Delta y \| \end{aligned} \tag{4.17}$$

on the segment $[y, y + \Delta y]$. Choosing Δy so that

$$\| \Delta y \| \leqslant \frac{q}{DM} < \frac{1}{DM}, \qquad 0 \leqslant q < 1,$$

we get

$$\| U \| \leqslant q < 1.$$

It then follows that $[I - U]^{-1}$ exists and can be written in the form $[I - U]^{-1} = I + U + U^2 + \cdots$. Substitution of (4.16) into (4.15) yields

$$\begin{aligned} &\|[I + U + U^2 + \cdots][I - T'_{(y)}]^{-1}[(T(y) - T'_{(y)}y) \\ &\quad - (T'_{(y+\Delta y)} - T'_{(y)})(y + \Delta y) + (T(y + \Delta y) - T(y) - T'_{(y)}\Delta y)] \\ &\quad - [I - T'_{(y)}]^{-1}[T(y) - T'_{(y)}y] \\ &\quad - [I - T'_{(y)}]^{-1}[T''_{(y)}\Delta y][I - T'_{(y)}]^{-1}[T(y) - y]\| \\ &\qquad = \| - [I - T'_{(y)}]^{-1}[T'_{(y+\Delta y)} - T'_{(y)}](y + \Delta y) \\ &\qquad\quad + [I - T'_{(y)}]^{-1}[T(y + \Delta y) - T(y) - T'_{(y)}\Delta y] \\ &\qquad\quad - [I - T'_{(y)}]^{-1}[T''_{(y)}\Delta y][I - T'_{(y)}]^{-1}[T(y) - y] \end{aligned} \tag{4.18}$$

$$
\begin{aligned}
&+ U[I - T'_{(y)}]^{-1} [T(y) - T_{(y)} y] \\
&- U[I - T'_{(y)}]^{-1} [T'_{(y+\Delta y)} - T'_{(y)}](y + \Delta y) \\
&+ U[I - T'_{(y)}]^{-1} [T(y + \Delta y) - T(y) - T'_{(y)} \Delta y] \\
&+ U^2[I + U + U^2 + \cdots][I - T'_{(y)}]^{-1} [T(y) - T'_{(y)} y \\
&- (T'_{(y+\Delta y)} - T'_{(y)})(y + \Delta y) + T(y + \Delta y) \\
&- T(y) - T'_{(y)} \Delta y]\| .
\end{aligned}
$$

Noting that

$$
\begin{aligned}
(4.19) \quad & - [I - T'_{(y)}]^{-1} [T'_{(y+\Delta y)} - T'_{(y)}](y + \Delta y) \\
& + U(I - T'_{(y)}]^{-1} [T(y) - T'_{(y)} y] \\
& \quad = - U[I - T'_{(y)}]^{-1} [y - T'_{(y)} y] \\
& \quad \quad - U \Delta y + U[I - T'_{(y)}]^{-1} [T(y) - T'_{(y)} y] \\
& \quad = [I - T'_{(y)}]^{-1} [T'_{(y+\Delta y)} - T'_{(y)}][I - T'_{(y)}]^{-1} [T(y) - y] - U \Delta y
\end{aligned}
$$

we find that

$$
\begin{aligned}
(4.20) \quad & \|[I - T'_{(y)}]^{-1} [T'_{(y+\Delta y)} - T'_{(y)} - T''_{(y)} \Delta y][I - T'_{(y)}]^{-1} [T(y) - y] \\
& - U \Delta y + [I + U][I - T'_{(y)}]^{-1} [T(y + \Delta y) - T(y) - T'_{(y)} \Delta y] \\
& - U^2(y + \Delta y) + U^2[I + U + U^2 + \cdots][I - T'_{(y)}]^{-1} \\
& \times [T(y) - T'_{(y)} y - (T'_{(y+\Delta y)} - T'_{(y)})(y + \Delta y) + T(y + \Delta y) \\
& - T(y) - T'_{(y)} \Delta y]\| \\
& \quad \leqslant \|[I - T'_{(y)}]^{-1} \| \, \| T'_{(y+\Delta y)} - T'_{(y)} - T''_{(y)} \Delta y \| \\
& \quad \quad \times \|[I - T'_{(y)}]^{-1} \| \, \| T(y) - y \| + \| U \| \, \| \Delta y \| \\
& \quad \quad + \|[I + U]\| \, \|[I - T'_{(y)}]^{-1} \| \\
& \quad \quad \times \| T(y + \Delta y) - T(y) - T'_{(y)} \Delta y \| + \| U \|^2 \| y + \Delta y\| \\
& \quad \quad + \| U \|^2 \| I + U + U^2 + \cdots \| \\
& \quad \quad \times \{\|[I - T'_{(y)}]^{-1} \| \, \| T(y) - T'_{(y)} y \| + \| U \| \, \| y + \Delta y \| \\
& \quad \quad + \|[I - T'_{(y)}]^{-1} \| \, \| T(y + \Delta y) - T(y) - T'_{(y)} \Delta y \|\}.
\end{aligned}
$$

The existence of the Frechet derivatives $T'_{(y)}$ and $T''_{(y)}$ implies that

$$\lim_{\|\Delta y\|\to 0} \{\| T(y + \Delta y) - T(y) - T'_{(y)} \Delta y \|/\| \Delta y \|\} = 0$$

$$\lim_{\|\Delta y\|\to 0} \{\| T'_{(y+\Delta y)} - T'_{(y)} - T''_{(y)} \Delta y \|/\| \Delta y \|\} = 0.$$

Denoting the bound on the norm (4.15) given by (4.20) by $A(\Delta y)$ we see that

$$\lim_{\|\Delta y\|\to 0} \{\| Q(y + \Delta y) - Q(y) - L \Delta y \|/\| \Delta y \|\} \leqslant \lim_{\|\Delta y\|\to 0} \{A(\Delta y)/\| \Delta y \|\} = 0 \tag{4.21}$$

which proves the lemma.

It is of interest to note that the convergence conditions of Proposition 4.8 have a special property that is not shared by the other results discussed in this section, namely, the conditions of Proposition 4.8 guarantee not only the convergence of the NM sequence based on y_0 but also the convergence of the NM sequence based on $\tilde{y}_0$ for any element $\tilde{y}_0$ of $\bar{S}$ for which $\| \tilde{y}_0 - y_0 \| \leqslant [1/(1 - \alpha)]\eta$. More precisely, we have the following.

COROLLARY 4.22. Suppose that the conditions of Proposition 4.8 are satisfied and that $\tilde{y}_0$ is an element of $\bar{S} = \bar{S}(y_0, r)$ for which $\| \tilde{y}_0 - y_0 \| \leqslant r_0 = \eta/(1 - \alpha)$. Then the NM sequence $\{\tilde{y}_n\}$ for T based on $\tilde{y}_0$ converges to y^*, the unique fixed point of T in $\bar{S}$.

Proof. The conditions of Proposition 4.8 guarantee that Q is a contraction on $\bar{S}$. We shall show that Q maps $\bar{S}_0 = \bar{S}(y_0, r_0)$ into $\bar{S}_0$ and that $\lim_{n\to\infty} \| \tilde{y}_n - y^* \| = 0$. To begin with, if $y^+ \in \bar{S}_0$, then $\| y^+ - y_0 \| \leqslant r_0 = \eta/(1 - \alpha)$ and

$$\begin{aligned} \| Q(y^+) - y_0 \| &\leqslant \| Q(y^+) - Q(y_0) \| + \| Q(y_0) - y_0 \| \\ &\leqslant \alpha \| y^+ - y_0 \| + \| y_1 - y_0 \| \\ &\leqslant \frac{\alpha}{1 - \alpha}\eta + \eta = \frac{\eta}{1 - \alpha} = r_0 \end{aligned} \tag{4.23}$$

as $y_1 = Q(y_0)$. Since $\tilde{y}_0$ is in $\bar{S}_0$, it follows from (4.23) that $\tilde{y}_n \in \bar{S}_0$ for all n by an induction argument.

We claim that

$$\| \tilde{y}_k - y^* \| \leqslant \alpha^k \| \tilde{y}_0 - y^* \| \tag{4.24}$$

for all $k \geqslant 1$. To see this, we simply note that $\| \tilde{y}_{n+1} - y^* \| = \| Q(\tilde{y}_n) - Q(y^*)\| \leqslant \alpha \| \tilde{y}_n - y^* \|$ and then use induction. Since $\alpha < 1$, it follows that $\lim_{n\to\infty} \| \tilde{y}_n - y^* \| = 0$ and so, the corollary is proved.

We now present two additional theorems on the convergence of Newton's method in the case where $V_n = T'_{(y_n)}$ and defer our consideration of the general case until later on. The proofs of these two theorems are based on an important relationship involving the norms of the differences between successive iterates. We derive this relationship in the following.

LEMMA 4.25. Suppose that T is twice continuously differentiable and that $\{y_n\}$ is an NM sequence for T based on y_0. Then

$$\| y_{n+1} - y_n \| \leqslant \tfrac{1}{2} \sup_{0<\theta<1} \{\|[I - T'_{(y_n)}]^{-1} [T''_{(y_{n-1}+\theta[y_n - y_{n-1}])}]\|\} \| y_n - y_{n-1} \|^2 \tag{4.26}$$

for $n = 1, 2, \ldots$.

Proof. First observe that

$$\begin{aligned} y_{n+1} - y_n &= [I - T'_{(y_n)}]^{-1} [T(y_n) - T'_{(y_n)} y_n] - y_n \\ &= [I - T'_{(y_n)}]^{-1} [T(y_n) - y_n] \\ &= [I - T'_{(y_n)}]^{-1} [T(y_n) - T(y_{n-1}) - T'_{(y_{n-1})}(y_n - y_{n-1})] \end{aligned}$$

and then note that

$$\| y_{n+1} - y_n \| \leqslant \tfrac{1}{2} \sup_{0<\theta<1} \{\|[I - T'_{(y_n)}]^{-1} [T''_{(y_{n-1}+\theta(y_n - y_{n-1}))}]\|\} \| y_n - y_{n-1} \|^2$$

by virtue of the properties of twice differentiable maps (see Kantorovich and Akilov [K3]).

Newton's method is often said to exhibit "quadratic convergence" in reference to the inequality (4.26). In other words, the norm of the difference between successive iterates is smaller than a number which is proportional to the square of the preceding difference.

Our first theorem based on Lemma 4.25 is that of Mysovskikh. This theorem involves convergence conditions which are considerably weaker than those of Proposition 4.8. However, the theorem does not guarantee uniqueness of the fixed point. We have the following.

THEOREM 4.27 (Mysovskikh [K3]). Suppose that (i) T is twice differentiable on $\bar{S} = \bar{S}(y_0, r)$, (ii) $[I - T'_{(y)}]^{-1}$ exists and is linear for all y in $\bar{S}$, (iii) there is an $M > 0$ such that $\| T(y) - T(y') - T'_{(y')}(y - y')\| \leqslant \frac{1}{2}M. \| y - y' \|^2$ for y, y' in $\bar{S}$,[†] and (iv) there are real numbers η, K, and h with $\eta \geqslant 0$, $K \geqslant 0$, and $h = K\eta < 2$ such that

$$\| [I - T'_{(y_0)}]^{-1} [T(y_0) - y_0] \| = \| y_1 - y_0 \| \leqslant \eta \tag{4.28}$$

$$\sup_{\tilde{y}, y \in \bar{S}} \{\|[I - T'_{(\tilde{y})}]^{-1} T''_{(y)} \|\} \leqslant K \tag{4.29}$$

and

$$\sum_{k=0}^{\infty} \left(\frac{h}{2}\right)^{2^k - 1} \eta < r. \tag{4.30}$$

Then the NM sequence $\{y_n\}$ for T based on y_0 converges to a fixed point y^* of T in $\bar{S}$ and the rate of convergence is given by

$$\| y^* - y_n \| \leqslant \frac{(h/2)^{2^n - 1}}{1 - (h/2)^{2^n}} \| y_1 - y_0 \| \tag{4.31}$$

for $n = 0, 1, \ldots.$

Proof. We give the proof in three steps. We first prove that $y_n \in \bar{S}$ for all n. Next we show that $\{y_n\}$ is a Cauchy sequence and hence converges. Finally, we use the inequalities derived during the course of the proof to establish (4.31).

Let η_n and h_n be given by

$$\eta_0 = \eta, \qquad \eta_n = \left(\frac{h_{n-1}}{2}\right)\eta_{n-1} \tag{4.32}$$

$$h_0 = h = K\eta, \qquad \frac{h_n}{2} = \frac{K\eta_n}{2} = \left(\frac{h_{n-1}}{2}\right)^2 \tag{4.33}$$

[†] Note that (iii) is satisfied if $T''_{(y)}$ is uniformly bounded on $\bar{S}$. In that case, we may take $M = \sup_{y \in \bar{S}} \{\| T''_{(y)} \|\}$.

for $n = 0, 1, \ldots$. We now show by induction that

$$\| y_{k+1} - y_k \| \leqslant \eta_k \quad \text{and} \quad \| y_{k+1} - y_0 \| \leqslant r \tag{4.34}$$

for $k = 0, 1, \ldots$. For $k = 0$, (4.34) is a direct consequence of the hypotheses. Now, assuming that (4.34) holds for $k \leqslant n - 1$, we have

$$\| y_{n+1} - y_n \| \leqslant \tfrac{1}{2} \sup_{0<\theta<1} \{\|[I - T'_{(y_n)}]^{-1} [T''_{(y_{n-1}+\theta(y_n-y_{n-1}))}]\|\} \| y_n - y_{n-1} \|^2$$

$$\leqslant \tfrac{1}{2} K \eta_{n-1}^2 = \frac{h_{n-1}}{2} \eta_{n-1} = \eta_n$$

for $k = n$. Moreover, it follows from the definitions (4.32) and (4.33) of η_n and h_n that

$$\eta_n = \left(\frac{h_0}{2}\right)^{2^{n-1}+2^{n-2}+\cdots+1} \eta_0 = \left(\frac{h_0}{2}\right)^{2^n-1} \eta_0 \tag{4.35}$$

for all n. Using (4.35), we find that

$$\| y_{n+1} - y_0 \| \leqslant \| y_{n+1} - y_n \| + \| y_n - y_{n-1} \| + \cdots + \| y_1 - y_0 \| \tag{4.36}$$

$$\leqslant \eta_n + \eta_{n-1} + \cdots + \eta_0 = \sum_0^n \left(\frac{h_0}{2}\right)^{2^k-1} \eta_0$$

$$\leqslant \sum_0^\infty \left(\frac{h}{2}\right)^{2^k-1} \eta_0 \leqslant r$$

and so the induction argument is complete. Thus, $y_n \in \bar{S}$ for all n.

Letting m be a positive integer, we have

$$\| y_{n+m} - y_n \| \leqslant \sum_{i=0}^{m-1} \eta_{n+i} = \sum_{i=0}^{m-1} \left(\frac{h_n}{2}\right)^{2^i-1} \eta_n \tag{4.37}$$

$$= \left[\sum_{i=0}^{m-1} \left(\frac{h_n}{2}\right)^{2^i-1}\right] \left(\frac{h_0}{2}\right)^{2^n-1} \eta_0 .$$

Since $h = h_0 < 2$, we deduce that $\lim_{n\to\infty} \| y_{n+m} - y_n \| = 0$. The sequence $\{y_n\}$ is thus a Cauchy sequence in the closed sphere $\bar{S}$ of the Banach space Y and hence converges to an element y^* of $\bar{S}$. We claim that y^* is a fixed point of T. To see this, we observe that

$$\| T(y_n) - y_n \| = \| T(y_n) - T(y_{n-1}) - T'_{(y_{n-1})}(y_n - y_{n-1})\|$$
$$\leqslant \tfrac{1}{2} M \| y_n - y_{n-1} \|^2$$

by virtue of (iii). Since T is continuous and $\{y_n\}$ converges to y^*, we deduce that

$$\lim_{n\to\infty} \| T(y_n) - y_n \| = \| T(y^*) - y^* \| \leqslant \tfrac{1}{2} M \lim_{n\to\infty} \| y_n - y_{n-1} \|^2 = 0$$

and so our claim is valid.

The rate of convergence inequality (4.31) follows from (4.37) by letting m approach infinity and noting that the development remains valid for $\eta_0 = \| y_1 - y_0 \|$. Thus, the theorem is established.

The next theorem to be presented here is the well-known theorem of Kantorovich on the convergence of Newton's method. This theorem does not require the verification of the existence of the inverse of $[I - T'_{(y)}]$ for all y in $\bar{S}$. Instead, the inverse need only exist for the initial approximate solution. This constitutes a practical improvement which is made possible by placing additional restrictions on the remaining conditions. The second main difference lies in the fact that the theorem of Kantorovich guarantees the uniqueness of the limiting solution. To prove this uniqueness, Corollary 2.34 on the convergence of the modified Newton's method (i.e., the modified contraction mapping method for $\delta = 0$) is used. This is possible because the convergence conditions for the NM sequence are identical to those of the MCM sequence. Except for these differences, both theorems are closely related and both proofs are based on an examination of a particular sequence rather than on contraction properties of the operator.

THEOREM 4.38 (Kantorovich [K3]). Suppose that (i) T is twice continuously differentiable on $\bar{S} = \bar{S}(y_0, r)$, (ii) $[I - T'_{(y_0)}]^{-1}$ exists and is linear, and (iii) there are real numbers η, K, and h with $\eta \geqslant 0$, $K \geqslant 0$, and $h = K\eta \leqslant \frac{1}{2}$ such that

$$\|[I - T'_{(y_0)}]^{-1} [T(y_0) - y_0]\| = \| y_1 - y_0 \| \leqslant \eta \tag{4.39}$$

$$\sup_{y\in\bar{S}}\{\|[I - T'_{(y_0)}]^{-1} T''_{(y)} \|\} \leqslant K \tag{4.40}$$

and

$$\frac{1-\sqrt{1-2h}}{h}\eta \leqslant r < \frac{1+\sqrt{1-2h}}{h}\eta. \tag{4.41}$$

Then, the NM sequence $\{y_n\}$ for T based on y_0 converges to the unique fixed point y^* of T in $\bar{S}$, the rate of convergence is given by

$$\| y^* - y_n \| \leqslant \frac{1}{2^{n-1}}(2h)^{2^n-1}\| y_1 - y_0 \| \leqslant \frac{1}{2^{n-1}}\| y_1 - y_0 \| \tag{4.42}$$

and an error bound for y_1 is given by

$$\| y^* - y_1 \| \leqslant \frac{1-h-\sqrt{1-2h}}{h}\| y_1 - y_0 \| \leqslant \frac{h}{1-h}\| y_1 - y_0 \|. \tag{4.43}$$

Proof (Antosiewicz [A1]). We give the proof in several stages as in Theorem 4.27. We first prove that $[I - T'_{(y_n)}]^{-1}$ exists and that $y_n \in \bar{S}$ for every n. Next we show that $\{y_n\}$ is a Cauchy sequence and so converges to an element y^* of $\bar{S}$. We then establish that $y^* = T(y^*)$ and that the fixed point is unique. Finally, we prove (4.42) and (4.43).

Let η_n, K_n, h_n, and r_n be given by

$$\begin{aligned} &\eta_0 = \eta, && \eta_n = \frac{h_{n-1}}{2(1-h_{n-1})}\eta_{n-1} \\ &K_0 = K, && K_n = \frac{K_{n-1}}{1-h_{n-1}} \\ &h_0 = K_0\eta_0 = h, && h_n = K_n\eta_n = \frac{h_{n-1}^2}{2(1-h_{n-1})^2} \\ &r_0 = \frac{1-\sqrt{1-2h_0}}{h_0}\eta_0, && r_n = \frac{1-\sqrt{1-2h_n}}{h_n}\eta_n \end{aligned} \tag{4.44}$$

for $n = 0, 1, \ldots$. Since $h_0 \leqslant \frac{1}{2}$, we have $h_n \leqslant \frac{1}{2}$ for $n = 0, 1, 2, \ldots$. Moreover, in view of (4.44) we also have

$$\begin{aligned} r_n &= \frac{1-\sqrt{1-2h_n}}{h_n}\eta_n \\ &= \frac{1-\sqrt{1-[h_{n-1}^2/(1-h_{n-1})^2]}}{h_{n-1}^2/2(1-h_{n-1})^2}\cdot\left[\frac{h_{n-1}}{2(1-h_{n-1})}\right]\eta_{n-1} \end{aligned} \tag{4.45}$$

$$= \frac{1 - h_{n-1} - \sqrt{1 - 2h_{n-1}}}{h_{n-1}} \eta_{n-1}$$

$$= r_{n-1} - \eta_{n-1} .$$

We prove by induction that

$$[I - T'_{(y_k)}]^{-1} \quad \text{exists and is linear} \tag{4.46}$$

$$\sup_{y \in \bar{S}} \| [I - T'_{(y_k)}]^{-1} T''_{(y)} \| \leqslant K_k \tag{4.47}$$

$$\| y_{k+1} - y_k \| \leqslant \eta_k \tag{4.48}$$

$$\| y_p - y_q \| \leqslant r_q - r_p , \qquad k + 1 \geqslant p > q \geqslant 0 \tag{4.49}$$

where (4.49) implies that ($p = k + 1, q = 0$)

$$\| y_{k+1} - y_0 \| \leqslant r_0 - r_{k+1} \leqslant r_0 \tag{4.50}$$

for $k = 0, 1, 2, \ldots$. For $k = 0$, (4.46)–(4.49) are direct consequences of the hypotheses. Now assume that (4.46)–(4.49) hold for all $k \leqslant n - 1$. Then, for $k = n$, we have

$$\begin{aligned}
[I - T'_{(y_n)}]^{-1} &= [I - T'_{(y_{n-1})} + T'_{(y_{n-1})} - T'_{(y_n)}]^{-1} \\
&= \{[I - T'_{(y_{n-1})}][I - [I - T'_{(y_{n-1})}]^{-1} \\
&\quad \times [T'_{(y_n)} - T'_{(y_{n-1})}]]\}^{-1}
\end{aligned} \tag{4.51}$$

and

$$\begin{aligned}
&\| [I - T'_{(y_{n-1})}]^{-1} [T'_{(y_n)} - T'_{(y_{n-1})}] \| \\
&\leqslant \sup_{0<\theta<1} \{ \| [I - T'_{(y_{n-1})}] T''_{(y_{n-1}+\theta(y_n - y_{n-1}))} \| \} \| y_n - y_{n-1} \| \\
&\leqslant K_{n-1} \eta_{n-1} = h_{n-1} \leqslant \tfrac{1}{2} .
\end{aligned} \tag{4.52}$$

Hence, by the well-known theorem of Banach on the inverse of the sum of the identity and a small operator, the inverse of the operator $I - [I - T'_{(y_{n-1})}]^{-1}[T'_{(y_n)} - T'_{(y_{n-1})}]$ exists, is linear, and is, in view of (4.52), bounded by

$$\| \{ I - [I - T'_{(y_{n-1})}]^{-1} [T'_{(y_n)} - T'_{(y_{n-1})}] \}^{-1} \| \leqslant \frac{1}{1 - h_{n-1}} . \tag{4.53}$$

It follows from (4.51) and the induction hypothesis that $[I - T'_{(y_n)}]^{-1}$ exists and is given by

$$[I - T'_{(y_n)}]^{-1} = \{I - [I - T'_{(y_{n-1})}]^{-1}[T'_{(y_n)} - T'_{(y_{n-1})}]\}^{-1} \times [I - T'_{(y_{n-1})}]^{-1}. \tag{4.54}$$

We then deduce that

(4.55)

$$\begin{aligned}
&\sup_{y \in \bar{S}} \{\|[I - T'_{(y_n)}]^{-1} T''_{(y)}\|\} \\
&= \sup_{y \in \bar{S}} \{\|\{I - [I - T'_{(y_{n-1})}]^{-1}[T'_{(y_n)} - T'_{(y_{n-1})}]\}^{-1}[I - T'_{(y_{n-1})}]^{-1} T''_{(y)}\|\} \\
&\leqslant \|\{I - [I - T'_{(y_{n-1})}]^{-1}[T'_{(y_n)} - T'_{(y_{n-1})}]\}^{-1}\| \sup_{y \in \bar{S}} \{\|[I - T'_{(y_{n-1})}]^{-1} T''_{(y)}\|\} \\
&\leqslant \frac{K_{n-1}}{1 - h_{n-1}} = K_n .
\end{aligned}$$

Using Lemma 4.25, we immediately obtain the inequality

$$\begin{aligned}
\| y_{n+1} - y_n \| &\leqslant \tfrac{1}{2} \sup_{0<\theta<1} \{\|[I - T'_{(y_n)}]^{-1}[T''_{(y_{n-1}+\theta(y_n-y_{n-1}))}]\|\} \| y_n - y_{n-1} \|^2 \\
&\leqslant \tfrac{1}{2} \frac{K_{n-1}}{1 - h_{n-1}} \eta_{n-1}^2 \\
&= \frac{h_{n-1}}{2(1 - h_{n-1})} \eta_{n-1} = \eta_n .
\end{aligned} \tag{4.56}$$

But (4.56) and (4.45) imply that

$$\| y_p - y_q \| \leqslant \sum_{i=q}^{p-1} \| y_{i+1} - y_i \| \leqslant \sum_{i=q}^{p-1} \eta_i = \sum_{i=q}^{p-1} (r_i - r_{i+1}) = r_q - r_p \tag{4.57}$$

for $n + 1 \geqslant p > q \geqslant 0$. This proves (4.46)–(4.49) for $k = n$. By induction, these relations hold for all k. In view of (4.50) we have also shown that all the y_n are contained in $\bar{S}$.

Since $h_{n-1} \leqslant h_0 \leqslant \frac{1}{2}$, we can replace (4.44) in part by the inequalities

$$\eta_n = \frac{h_{n-1}}{2(1-h_{n-1})}\eta_{n-1} \leqslant h_{n-1}\eta_{n-1}$$

$$2h_n = \frac{h_{n-1}^2}{(1-h_{n-1})^2} \leqslant (2h_{n-1})^2$$

for $n = 0, 1, \ldots$. Repeated use of these inequalities yields

$$\begin{aligned}\eta_p &\leqslant h_{p-1}\eta_{p-1} \leqslant h_{p-1}h_{p-2}\eta_{p-2} \leqslant \cdots \leqslant h_{p-1}h_{p-2}\cdots h_q\eta_q \\ &\leqslant \frac{1}{2^{(p-q)}}[2h_q]^{2^0+2^1+\cdots+2^{p-q-1}}\eta_q \\ &= \frac{1}{2^{(p-q)}}[2h_q]^{2^{p-q}-1}\eta_q\end{aligned}$$

for $p > q$ and hence

$$\begin{aligned}\|y_{n+m}-y_n\| &\leqslant \sum_{i=0}^{m-1}\|y_{n+1+i}-y_{n+i}\| \leqslant \sum_{i=0}^{m-1}\eta_{n+i} \\ &\leqslant \sum_{i=0}^{m-1}\frac{1}{2^i}[2h_n]^{2^i-1}\eta_n \\ &\leqslant \left[\sum_{i=0}^{m-1}\frac{1}{2^i}[2h_n]^{2^i-1}\right]\frac{1}{2^n}[2h_0]^{2^n-1}\eta_0\end{aligned} \tag{4.58}$$

for any m. Letting n increase indefinitely, we find that

$$\lim_{n\to\infty}\|y_{n+m}-y_n\| = 0$$

and hence that $\{y_n\}$ is a Cauchy sequence. Thus, $\{y_n\}$ converges to an element y^* of $\bar{S}$. We claim that y^* is a fixed point of T. To see this, we observe that

$$\begin{aligned}\|T(y_n)-y_n\| &= \|T(y_n)-T(y_{n-1})-T'_{(y_{n-1})}(y_n-y_{n-1})\| \\ &\leqslant \tfrac{1}{2}M\|y_n-y_{n-1}\|^2\end{aligned}$$

where $M \geqslant K/\|[I - T'_{(y_0)}]^{-1}\|$. Since T is continuous and $\{y_n\}$ converges to y^*, we deduce that

$$\lim_{n\to\infty} \| T(y_n) - y_n \| = \| T(y^*) - y^* \| \leqslant \tfrac{1}{2} M \lim_{n\to\infty} \| y_n - y_{n-1} \|^2 = 0$$

and so, our claim is valid.

Now comparison of the hypotheses of the theorem and those of Corollary 2.34 shows that these conditions are identical for the case $\delta = 0$. Thus, we can generate an MCM sequence for T based on y_0 and $T'_{(y_0)}$ which will converge to the *unique* fixed point of T in $\bar{S}$. As y^* is a fixed point of T in $\bar{S}$, it must (*a fortiori*) be unique.

Letting m approach infinity in (4.58), we find that

$$\begin{aligned} \|y^* - y_n\| &\leqslant \sum_{i=0}^{\infty} \frac{1}{2^i} [2h_n]^i \frac{1}{2^n} [2h_0]^{2^n-1} \eta_0 \\ &\leqslant \sum_{i=0}^{\infty} \frac{1}{2^n} [2h_0]^{2^n-1} \eta_0 \\ &\leqslant \frac{1}{1-h_n} \frac{1}{2^n} [2h_0]^{2^n-1} \eta_0 \\ &\leqslant \frac{1}{2^{n-1}} [2h_0]^{2^n-1} \eta_0 . \end{aligned} \tag{4.59}$$

Since this inequality and our development remain valid for $\eta_0 = \| y_1 - y_0 \|$, we deduce that the rate of convergence inequality (4.42) is satisfied.

As for (4.43), we note that

$$\| y_n - y_1 \| \leqslant r_1 - r_n = r_1 - \left(\frac{1 - \sqrt{1 - 2h_n}}{h_n} \right) \eta_n \tag{4.60}$$

and hence, that

$$\begin{aligned} \| y^* - y_1 \| &\leqslant r_1 - \lim_{n\to\infty} \left(\frac{1 - \sqrt{1 - 2h_n}}{h_n} \right) \eta_n \\ &\leqslant r_1 = r_0 - \eta_0 = \frac{1 - h_0 - \sqrt{1 - 2h_0}}{h_0} \eta_0 \end{aligned} \tag{4.61}$$

by letting n approach infinity. Since we may replace η_0 by $\| y_1 - y_0 \|$ in (4.61), (4.43) is established and the proof of the theorem is complete.

We note, at this point, that the convergence factor h in Theorem 4.27 was allowed to have a value as great as 2 while the convergence factor h in Theorem 4.38 could only have a value as great as $\frac{1}{2}$. Thus, the "price" paid for the convenience of having convergence conditions determined almost exclusively by the initial approximation and for being certain of uniqueness, may amount to a worsening of the convergence conditions by a factor of 4. However, we shall see, in the sequel, that the practical advantages of Theorem 4.38 are usually sufficient to insure that it is preferable to Theorem 4.27.

We now turn our attention to a consideration of Newton's method for T based on y_0 and $\{V_n\}$. We prove two theorems. The first theorem essentially involves a modification of the contraction mapping method while the second theorem may be viewed as a generalization of the modified Newton's method. We have the following.

THEOREM 4.62. Suppose that (i) T is continuous on $\bar{S} = \bar{S}(y_0, r)$, (ii) $\{V_n\}$ is a sequence of elements of $\mathscr{L}(Y, Y)$ such that $I - V_n$ is invertible and $\| V_n \| \leqslant M$ for every n, (iii) $Q_n = [I - V_n]^{-1} [T - V_n]$ maps $\bar{S}$ into itself, and (iv) there are sequences $\{\alpha_n\}$ and $\{\beta_n\}$ with $\alpha_n \geqslant 0$ and $\beta_n \geqslant 0$ such that

$$\| Q_n(x) - Q_n(y) \| \leqslant \alpha_n \| x - y \| \tag{4.63}$$

$$\| Q_n(x) - Q_{n-1}(x) \| \leqslant \beta_n \| x \| \tag{4.64}$$

for x, y in $\bar{S}$ and

$$\sum_{k=1}^{\infty} \left(\prod_{i=1}^{k} \alpha_i \right) < \infty \tag{4.65}$$

$$\sum_{k=1}^{\infty} \delta_k < \infty \tag{4.66}$$

where δ_k is given by

$$\delta_k = \sum_{j=2}^{k} \left(\prod_{i=j}^{k} \alpha_i \right) \beta_{j-1} + \beta_k \tag{4.67}$$

for $k = 2, 3, \ldots$ and $\delta_1 = \beta_1$. Then the NM sequence for T based on y_0 and $\{V_n\}$ converges to a fixed point y^* of T in $\bar{S}$ and the rate of convergence is given by

$$\| y^* - y_n \| \leqslant \left\{ \sum_{k=n}^{\infty} \left(\prod_{i=1}^{k} \alpha_i \right) \right\} \| y_1 - y_0 \| + \left\{ \sum_{k=n}^{\infty} \delta_k \right\} (r + \| y_0 \|). \tag{4.68}$$

Proof. We observe that

$$\begin{aligned} \| y_{n+1} - y_n \| &= \| Q_n(y_n) - Q_{n-1}(y_{n-1}) \| \\ &\leqslant \| Q_n(y_n) - Q_n(y_{n-1}) \| + \| Q_n(y_{n-1}) - Q_{n-1}(y_{n-1}) \| \\ &\leqslant \alpha_n \| y_n - y_{n-1} \| + \beta_n \| y_{n-1} \| \\ &\leqslant \alpha_n \| y_n - y_{n-1} \| + \beta_n (r + \| y_0 \|) \end{aligned} \tag{4.69}$$

and hence, that

$$\begin{aligned} \| y_{n+p} - y_n \| &\leqslant \| y_{n+p} - y_{n+p-1} \| + \cdots + \| y_{n+1} - y_n \| \\ &\leqslant \left\{ \sum_{j=1}^{p} \left(\prod_{i=1}^{n+p-j} \alpha_i \right) \right\} \| y_1 - y_0 \| \\ &\quad + \left\{ \sum_{j=1}^{p} \delta_{n+p-j} \right\} (r + \| y_0 \|) \end{aligned} \tag{4.70}$$

for $p = 1, 2, \ldots$. It follows, in view of (4.65) and (4.66), that $\{y_n\}$ is a Cauchy sequence in $\bar{S}$ and so converges to an element y^* of $\bar{S}$. Since $y_{n+1} - T(y_n) = V_n(y_{n+1} - y_n)$ and T is continuous, we have

$$\begin{aligned} \lim_{n\to\infty} \| y_{n+1} - T(y_n) \| = \| y^* - T(y^*) \| &\leqslant \lim_{n\to\infty} \| V_n \| \cdot \| y_{n+1} - y_n \| \\ &\leqslant \lim_{n\to\infty} M \cdot \| y_{n+1} - y_n \| = 0 \end{aligned}$$

which shows that y^* is a fixed point of T. The rate of convergence inequality (4.68) follows from (4.70) by letting p approach infinity. Thus, the theorem is established.

THEOREM 4.71 (cf. Antosiewicz [A1]). Suppose that (i) T is continuously differentiable on $\bar{S} = \bar{S}(y_0, r)$, (ii) $\{V_n\}$ is a sequence of elements of $\mathscr{L}(Y, Y)$ such that $I - V_n$ is invertible for every n, (iii) $(I - T'_{y_0})^{-1}$ exists and is bounded, and (iv) there are real numbers η, α, β with $\eta \geqslant 0, 0 \leqslant \alpha < 1, 0 \leqslant \beta < 1$, $[(\alpha + \beta)/(1 - \alpha)] < 1$, and $\eta \leqslant r(1 - 2\alpha - \beta)$ such that

$$\|[I - T'_{y_0}]^{-1} [T(y_0) - y_0]\| \leqslant \eta \tag{4.72}$$

$$\sup_{y \in \bar{S}}\{\| T_y' - T'_{y_0} \|\} \leqslant \beta / \|[I - T'_{y_0}]^{-1} \| \tag{4.73}$$

$$\|[I - T'_{y_0}]^{-1} \| \| T'_{y_0} - V_n \| \leqslant \alpha \tag{4.74}$$

for all n. Then the NM sequence for T based on y_0 and $\{V_n\}$ converges to the unique fixed point y^* of T in $\bar{S}$ and the rate of convergence is given by

$$\| y^* - y_n \| \leqslant \left\{ \sum_{j=n}^{\infty} \left(\frac{\alpha + \beta}{1 - \alpha} \right)^j \right\} \| y_1 - y_0 \| \tag{4.75}$$

for $n = 1, 2, \ldots$.

Proof. We first observe that (4.74) implies that

$$\|\{I - [I - V_n]^{-1} [T'_{y_0} - V_n]\}\| = \|[I - V_n]^{-1} [I - T'_{y_0}]\| \leqslant 1/(1 - \alpha)$$

since

$$\|[I - T'_{y_0}]^{-1} [I - V_n] - I \| = \|[I - T'_{y_0}]^{-1} [T'_{y_0} - V_n]\| \leqslant \alpha < 1.$$

We then note that

$$\begin{aligned} \| y_1 - y_0 \| &= \|[I - V_0]^{-1} [T - I] y_0 \| \\ &= \|\{I - [I - V_0]^{-1} (T'_{y_0} - V_0)\}\{I - T'_{y_0}\}^{-1} \{T - I\} y_0 \| \\ &\leqslant \|[I - V_0]^{-1} [I - T'_{y_0}]\| \cdot \|[I - T'_{y_0}]^{-1} [T - I] y_0 \| \\ &\leqslant \frac{\eta}{1 - \alpha} \leqslant \frac{\eta}{1 - 2\alpha - \beta} \leqslant r^{\dagger} \end{aligned} \tag{4.76}$$

† Note that $1 - \alpha \geqslant 1 - 2\alpha - \beta$ as $0 \geqslant -(\alpha + \beta)$.

so that $y_1 \in \bar{S}$. Let us suppose that $y_1, \ldots, y_n$ are in $\bar{S}$. Then

$$\begin{aligned}(4.77)\qquad \| y_{n+1} - y_n \| &= \|[I - V_n]^{-1}[T - I]y_n\| \\ &\leqslant \|[I - V_n]^{-1}[I - T'_{y_0}]\| \cdot \|[I - T'_{y_0}]^{-1}[T - I]y_n\| \\ &\leqslant \frac{\alpha + \beta}{1 - \alpha}\| y_n - y_{n-1} \|\end{aligned}$$

since

$$\begin{aligned}(4.78)\quad [T - I]y_n &= [T - I](y_n) - [T - I](y_{n-1}) + [I - V_{n-1}](y_n - y_{n-1}) \\ &= T(y_n) - T(y_{n-1}) - T'_{y_0}(y_n - y_{n-1}) \\ &\quad + (T'_{y_0} - V_{n-1})(y_n - y_{n-1})\end{aligned}$$

so that

$$(4.79)\qquad \|[T - I]y_n\| \leqslant \frac{\beta \| y_n - y_{n-1} \|}{\|[I - T'_{y_0}]^{-1}\|} + \frac{\alpha \| y_n - y_{n-1} \|}{\|[I - T'_{y_0}]^{-1}\|}$$

by virtue of (4.73) and (4.74). It follows that

$$(4.80)\qquad \| y_{n+1} - y_n \| \leqslant \left(\frac{\alpha + \beta}{1 - \alpha}\right)^n \| y_1 - y_0 \|$$

and hence

$$\begin{aligned}(4.81)\quad \| y_{n+1} - y_0 \| &\leqslant \sum_0^n \left(\frac{\alpha + \beta}{1 - \alpha}\right)^j \| y_1 - y_0 \| \\ &\leqslant \frac{\eta}{1 - \alpha} \frac{1}{\left\{1 - \left(\frac{\alpha + \beta}{1 - \alpha}\right)\right\}} = \frac{\eta}{1 - 2\alpha - \beta} \leqslant r\end{aligned}$$

so that $y_{n+1} \in \bar{S}$. By induction, we have y_n in $\bar{S}$ for every n. Now, we deduce from (4.80) that

$$(4.82)\qquad \| y_{n+p} - y_n \| \leqslant \left\{\sum_{j=n}^{n+p} \left(\frac{\alpha + \beta}{1 - \alpha}\right)^j\right\} \| y_1 - y_0 \|$$

for $p = 1, 2, \ldots$. Since $(\alpha + \beta)/(1 - \alpha) < 1$, it follows that $\{y_n\}$ is a Cauchy sequence in $\bar{S}$ and therefore converges to an element y^* of $\bar{S}$. Moreover, letting p approach infinity, we see that (4.75) is valid.

To show that $T(y^*) = y^*$, we need only let n approach infinity in (4.79) as T is continuous. Finally, for the uniqueness, we simply note that if $T(\tilde{y}) = \tilde{y}$, then

$$\|\tilde{y} - y^*\| = \|\{I - T'_{y_0}\}^{-1}\{(I - T)\tilde{y} - (I - T)y^* - (I - T'_{y_0})(\tilde{y} - y^*)\}\|$$

$$\leqslant \beta \|\tilde{y} - y^*\| \qquad \text{and} \qquad \beta < 1.$$

Thus, the theorem is established.

A particularly useful choice of α, β, and η is given by $\eta = r(1 - \delta)$, $\alpha = \delta/3$, and $\beta = \delta/3$ where $0 < \delta < 1$ [A2].

2.5. Multipoint Methods†

In this section, we consider the class of multipoint methods given by

$$y_{n+1} = y_n - \phi_\alpha(y_n) = \psi_\alpha(y_n) \tag{5.1}$$

for integers $\alpha \geqslant 1$ where

$$\phi_\alpha(y) = \sum_{j=1}^{\alpha} (F_y')^{-1} F(\psi_{j-1}(y)) \tag{5.2}$$

and $\psi_0(y) = y$. We prove several convergence theorems for the entire class. The first theorem involves the order of convergence of the algorithms. In the second theorem, we give conditions under which the iterations (5.1) converge to a unique zero of F. The final theorem consists of practical convergence conditions analogous to Kantorovich's theorem on Newton's method [K3] and represents a natural generalization of Theorem 4.38.

We note that fixed point problems are also covered in our development. More precisely, if T maps Y into itself and if we let $F = I - T$, then the equations

$$F(y) = 0 \tag{5.3}$$

and

$$y = T(y) \tag{5.4}$$

† This section was written with the cooperation of W. E. Bosarge, Jr. and is based on Bosarge and Falb [B7].

are equivalent. The formulations (5.3) and (5.4) are used interchangeably in the sequel. For example, in the case of (5.4), we have

$$\psi_\alpha(y) = [(I - T_y')^{-1} (T - T_y')]^\alpha (y) \tag{5.5}$$

for integers $\alpha \geqslant 1$ as is easily proved by induction. If the mapping $Q(\cdot, \cdot)$ of $Y \times Y$ into Y is given by

$$Q(x, y) = [(I - T_x')^{-1} (T - T_x')] (y) \tag{5.6}$$

then (5.5) may be written in the form

$$\psi_\alpha(y) = Q(y, \psi_{\alpha-1}(y)) \tag{5.7}$$

for $\alpha \geqslant 1$ and (5.1) becomes

$$y_{n+1} = \psi_\alpha(y_n) = Q(y_n, \psi_{\alpha-1}(y_n)) \tag{5.8}$$

for $\alpha \geqslant 1$. We now have the following.

DEFINITION 5.9. Let y_0 be an element of Y. The sequence $\{y_n\}$ generated by the algorithm (5.1) is called a multipoint or M sequence for F based on y_0.

DEFINITION 5.10. Let $\psi(\cdot)$ map Y into itself and suppose that the algorithm $y_{n+1} = \psi(y_n)$ converges to a fixed point y^* of T. Then the convergence is of order $p \geqslant 1$ if

$$\lim_{n\to\infty} \frac{\| \psi(y_n) - y^* \|}{\| \psi(y_{n-1}) - y^* \|^p} = C \tag{5.11}$$

where C is a constant.

A basic result on order of convergence is the following.

THEOREM 5.12. Suppose that (i) T is twice continuously differentiable on $\bar{S} = \bar{S}(y^*, r)$ where y^* is a fixed point of T; (ii) $[I - T_y']^{-1}$ exists and is uniformly bounded on $\bar{S}$ with

$$\sup_{y\in\bar{S}}\{\|(I - T_y')^{-1}\|\} \leqslant B; \tag{5.13}$$

(iii) T''_y is uniformly bounded on $\bar{S}$ with

$$\sup_{y \in \bar{S}} \{\| T''_y \|\} \leqslant K; \tag{5.14}$$

and (iv) the constants r, B, and K satisfy the inequalities

$$r < 1 \quad \text{and} \quad BK \leqslant \tfrac{2}{3}. \tag{5.15}$$

Then, for an initial guess y_0 in $\bar{S}$, the M sequence $\{\psi_\alpha(y_n)\}$ lies in $\bar{S}$ and converges to y^* with order at least $\alpha + 1$. Moreover, the rate of convergence is given by

$$\begin{aligned} \| \psi_\alpha(y_n) - y^* \| &\leqslant c_\alpha \| \psi_\alpha(y_{n-1}) - y^* \|^{\alpha+1} \\ &\leqslant c_\alpha^{n+1} \| y_0 - y^* \|^{(\alpha+1)^{n+1}} \end{aligned} \tag{5.16}$$

where

$$\begin{aligned} c_1 &= \frac{BK}{2} \\ c_\alpha &= \left(1 + \frac{c_{\alpha-1} r^{\alpha-1}}{2}\right) BK c_{\alpha-1} \end{aligned} \tag{5.17}$$

for $\alpha \geqslant 2$.

Proof. The proof is by induction on α. First consider the case $\alpha = 1$. Since $y_0 \in \bar{S}$,

$$\begin{aligned} y^* - \psi_1(y_0) &= y^* - (I - T'_{y_0})^{-1} (T - T'_{y_0}) y_0 \\ &= -(I - T'_{y_0})^{-1} [(I - T) y^* - (I - T) y_0 \\ &\qquad - (I - T'_{y_0})(y^* - y_0)] \end{aligned} \tag{5.18}$$

and so, in view of (i), (ii), and (iii),

$$\| y^* - \psi_1(y_0) \| \leqslant \frac{BK}{2} \| y^* - y_0 \|^2 = c_1 \| y^* - y_0 \|^2 \leqslant \frac{r^2}{3}. \tag{5.19}$$

Since $r < 1$, $\psi_1(y_0) \in \bar{S}$. Now assume that $y_n = \psi_1(y_{n-1}) \in \bar{S}$. By an identical argument, we deduce that

$$\| y^* - y_{n+1} \| = \| y^* - \psi_1(y_n) \| \leqslant c_1 \| y^* - y_n \|^2 \leqslant \frac{r^2}{3} \tag{5.20}$$

and hence, that $y_{n+1} \in \bar{S}$. Thus, $\psi_1(y_n) \in \bar{S}$ for all $n \geqslant 0$. Repeated application of (5.20) shows that $\| y^* - y_{n+1} \| \leqslant c_1^{n+1} \| y^* - y_0 \|^{2^{n+1}} \leqslant r^{2^{n+1}}$ and so, $\lim_{n\to\infty} \| y^* - y_n \| = 0$. Thus, the theorem is true for $\alpha = 1$.

Suppose that the theorem holds for all $m \leqslant \alpha$. We shall show that it then holds for $\alpha + 1$. Since $y_0 \in \bar{S}$ and $\psi_\alpha(y_0) \in \bar{S}$,

$$(5.21)\quad \psi_{\alpha+1}(y_0) - y^* = (I - T'_{y_0})^{-1} [(T'_{y^*} - T'_{y_0})(\psi_\alpha(y_0) - y^*) - (I - T)(\psi_\alpha(y_0) - y^*) + (I - T'_{y^*})(\psi_\alpha(y_0) - y^*)]$$

and

$$(5.22)\quad \begin{aligned} \| \psi_{\alpha+1}(y_0) - y^* \| &\leqslant B[K \| y^* - y_0 \| \| \psi_\alpha(y_0) - y^* \| + \frac{K}{2} \| \psi_\alpha(y_0) - y^* \|^2] \\ &\leqslant BKc_\alpha \| y^* - y_0 \|^{\alpha+2} \left(1 + \frac{c_\alpha r^\alpha}{2}\right) \\ &\leqslant c_{\alpha+1} \| y^* - y_0 \|^{\alpha+2}. \end{aligned}$$

Since $c_{\alpha+1} \leqslant 1$,† $y_1 = \psi_{\alpha+1}(y_0) \in \bar{S}$. Suppose that $y_0, \ldots, y_n$ are in $\bar{S}$. Then $\psi_\alpha(y_n) \in \bar{S}$ by the induction hypothesis and we have $\| \psi_{\alpha+1}(y_n) - y^* \| \leqslant c_{\alpha+1} \| y^* - y_n \|^{\alpha+2}$ [by an argument exactly the same as that used to derive (5.21) and (5.22)]. It follows that $y_{n+1} = \psi_{\alpha+1}(y_n) \in \bar{S}$ for all n. Repeated application of the inequality $\| \psi_{\alpha+1}(y_n) - y^* \| \leqslant c_{\alpha+1} \| y^* - y_n \|^{\alpha+2}$ allows us to conclude that the M sequence $\{\psi_{\alpha+1}(y_n)\}$ converges to y^* with rate of convergence given by (5.16). The theorem is now established.

We now turn our attention to convergence theorems for the multipoint algorithms beginning with some simple lemmas.

LEMMA 5.23. Suppose that T is differentiable and that $(I - T_y')^{-1}$ exists for all y in a subset $\bar{S}$ of Y. Then $y^* \in \bar{S}$ is a fixed point of T if and only if y^* is a fixed point of ψ_α for all $\alpha \geqslant 1$.

Proof. If $y^* = T(y^*)$, then $y^* - T'_{y^*}(y^*) = T(y^*) - T'_{y^*}(y^*)$, and so $y^* = [(I - T'_{y^*})^{-1}(T - T'_{y^*})](y^*) = \psi_1(y^*)$. If we assume that $\psi_\beta(y^*) = y^*$ for $\beta \leqslant \alpha$, then $\psi_{\alpha+1}(y^*) = Q(y^*, \psi_\alpha(y^*)) = Q(y^*, y^*) = \psi_1(y^*) = y^*$, and so $\psi_\alpha(y^*) = y^*$ for all $\alpha \geqslant 1$ by induction.

† This follows by induction on α for if $c_{\alpha-1} \leqslant 1$, then $c_\alpha \leqslant (1 + \frac{1}{2})BKc_{\alpha-1} \leqslant 1$.

Conversely, if $\psi_1(y^*) = y^*$, then $(I - T'_{y^*})y^* = (I - T'_{y^*})\,\psi_1(y^*) = T(y^*) - T'_{y^*}(y^*)$ and y^* is a fixed point of T.

LEMMA 5.24. Suppose that (i) T is twice continuously differentiable on $\bar{S} = \bar{S}(y_0, r)$; (ii) $[I - T_y']^{-1}$ exists and is uniformly bounded on $\bar{S}$ with

$$\sup_{y\in\bar{S}}\{\|(I - T_y')^{-1}\|\} \leqslant D; \tag{5.25}$$

and (iii) T_y'' is uniformly bounded on $\bar{S}$ with

$$\sup_{y\in\bar{S}}\{\| T_y'' \|\} \leqslant M. \tag{5.26}$$

Then the mapping $Q(x, y)$ of (5.6) has partial derivatives $Q_1(x, y)(\cdot)$, $Q_2(x, y)(\cdot)$ with respect to x and y, respectively, and

$$Q_1(x, y)(\cdot) = (I - T_x')^{-1}\, T_x''(\cdot)(I - T_x')^{-1}\,(T - I)\,y \tag{5.27}$$

$$Q_2(x, y)(\cdot) = (I - T_x')^{-1}\,(T_y' - T_x')(\cdot) \tag{5.28}$$

for all x, y in $\bar{S}$.

Proof. Let x, y be elements of $\bar{S}$ and let h, k be increments in x and y, respectively, with $x + h$ and $y + k$ in $\bar{S}$. Then

$$\begin{aligned} Q(x + h, y) - Q(x, y) &= (I - T'_{x+h})^{-1}\,(T - T'_{x+h})\,y - (I - T_x')^{-1}\,(T - T_x')y \\ &= [(I - T_x') - (T'_{x+h} - T_x')]^{-1}\,[(T - T_x') - (T'_{x+h} - T_x')]y \\ &\quad - (I - T_x')^{-1}\,(T - T_x')y. \end{aligned} \tag{5.29}$$

However,

$$\begin{aligned} &[(I - T_x') - (T'_{x+h} - T_x')]^{-1} \\ &\quad = [I - (I - T_x')^{-1}\,(T'_{x+h} - T_x')]^{-1}\,[(I - T_x')] - I \\ &\quad = [I - U]^{-1}\,(I - T_x')^{-1} \end{aligned}$$

where

$$U = (I - T_x')^{-1}\,(T'_{x+h} - T_x') \tag{5.30}$$

provided that $(I - U)^{-1}$ exists. Now (i), (ii), and (iii) together imply that $\| U \| \leqslant DM \| h \|$ and so $(I - U)^{-1}$ will exist for all h with $\| h \| \leqslant \delta/DM$ where $\delta < 1$. Moreover, we then have $(I - U)^{-1} = I + U + U^2 + \cdots$. We also note that

$$U = (I - T_x')^{-1}\, T_x''(h) + \mathfrak{o}(\| h \|^2) \tag{5.31}$$

as $\|(I - T_x')^{-1}\| \leqslant D$. It follows that

$$\begin{aligned} Q(x + h, y) - Q(x, y) &\\ &= (I - U)^{-1}\,(I - T_x')^{-1}\,[(T - T_x') - (T'_{x+h} - T_x')]y \\ &\quad - (I - T_x')^{-1}\,(T - T_x')y \\ &= (I - U)^{-1}\,[(I - T_x')^{-1}\,(T - T_x') - U \\ &\quad - (I - U)(I - T_x')^{-1}\,(T - T_x')] \\ &= (I + U + U^2 + \cdots)[U\{(I - T_x')^{-1}\,(T - T_x') - I\}]y \\ &= (U + U^2 + \cdots)(I - T_x')^{-1}\,(T - I)y \\ &= (I - T_x')^{-1}\, T_x''(h)(I - T_x')^{-1}\,(T - I)y + \mathfrak{o}(\| h \|) \end{aligned} \tag{5.32}$$

and hence that the partial derivative of Q with respect to x exists and is given by (5.27). As for the partial derivative with respect to y, we have

$$\begin{aligned} Q(x, y + k) - Q(x, y) &\\ &= (I - T_x')^{-1}\,[T(y + k) - T_x'(y + k) - T(y) - T_x'y] \end{aligned} \tag{5.33}$$

and

$$\begin{aligned} \| Q(x, y + k) - Q(x, y) - (I - T_x')^{-1}\,(T_y' - T_x')k \| &\\ &= \|(I - T_x')^{-1}\,[T(y + k) - T(y) - T_y'k]\| \\ &\leqslant \frac{DM}{2} \| k \|^2. \end{aligned} \tag{5.34}$$

It follows that the partial derivative of Q with respect to y exists and is given by (5.28).

COROLLARY 5.35. Suppose that conditions (i), (ii), and (iii) of the lemma are satisfied. If y is an element of $\bar{S}$ such that $\psi_{\alpha-1}(\cdot)$ is differentiable at y and $\psi_{\alpha-1}(y)$ is in $\bar{S}$, then $\psi_{\alpha}(\cdot)$ is differentiable at y and

$$(5.36) \qquad \psi'_{\alpha,y}(\cdot) = Q_1(y, \psi_{\alpha-1}(y))(\cdot) + Q_2(y, \psi_{\alpha-1}(y))\, \psi'_{\alpha-1,y}(\cdot).$$

Proof. Simply apply the lemma and the chain rule for Frechet derivatives.

We now have the following.

THEOREM 5.37. Suppose that (i) T is twice continuously differentiable on $\bar{S} = \bar{S}(y_0, r)$; (ii) $(I - T_y')^{-1}$ exists and is uniformly bounded on $\bar{S}$ with

$$(5.38) \qquad \sup_{y \in \bar{S}}\{\|(I - T_y')^{-1}\|\} \leqslant B;$$

(iii) T''_y is uniformly bounded on $\bar{S}$ with

$$(5.39) \qquad \sup_{y \in \bar{S}}\{\| T''_y \|\} \leqslant K;$$

(iv) $T - I$ is uniformly bounded on $\bar{S}$ with

$$(5.40) \qquad \sup_{y \in \bar{S}}\{\|(T - I)y\|\} \leqslant M;$$

and (v) there is an $\eta_\alpha > 0$ such that

$$(5.41) \qquad \| \psi_\alpha(y_0) - y_0 \| \leqslant \eta_\alpha$$

$$(5.42) \qquad \eta_\alpha \leqslant (1 - h_\alpha)r$$

where $h_\alpha = \alpha(B^2KM) < 1$ for all $\alpha \leqslant \hat{\alpha}$. Then the M sequence $\{\psi_\alpha(y_n)\}$ based on y_0 converges to the unique fixed point y^* of T in $\bar{S}$ and the rate of convergence is given by

$$(5.43) \qquad \| y^* - \psi_\alpha(y_n)\| \leqslant \frac{h_\alpha}{1 - h_\alpha} \| \psi_\alpha(y_n) - \psi_\alpha(y_{n-1})\| \leqslant \frac{h_\alpha^{n+1}}{1 - h_\alpha} \| y_1 - y_0 \|$$

for all α with $1 \leqslant \alpha \leqslant \hat{\alpha}$.

Proof. We first show that $\psi_\alpha(\cdot)$ is differentiable on $\bar{S}$ and that

$$\sup_{y\in\bar{S}}\{\|\psi'_{\alpha,y}\|\} \leqslant h_\alpha < 1 \tag{5.44}$$

for all $\alpha \leqslant \hat{\alpha}$. Suppose that $\alpha = 1$. Then $\psi_1(\cdot)$ is differentiable on $\bar{S}$ (as $\psi_0(y) = Iy$) and

$$\begin{aligned}\sup_{y\in\bar{S}}\{\|\psi'_{1,y}\|\} &\leqslant \sup_{y\in\bar{S}}\{\|Q_1(y,y)\| + \|Q_2(y,y)\|\ 1\} \\ &\leqslant B^2KM = h_1 < 1\end{aligned} \tag{5.45}$$

by virtue of Corollary 5.35 and the hypotheses of the theorem. Since $\|\psi_1(y) - y_0\| \leqslant \|\psi_1(y) - \psi_1(y_0)\| + \|\psi_1(y_0) - y_0\|$, it follows from the mean value theorem (Dieudonné [D1]) that $\|\psi_1(y) - y_0\| \leqslant h_1r + (1 - h_1)r = r$. Thus, $\psi_1(\bar{S}) \subset \bar{S}$. Now assume that $\psi_\beta(\cdot)$ is differentiable on $\bar{S}$, $\psi_\beta(\bar{S}) \subset \bar{S}$, and that (5.44) holds if $\beta \leqslant \alpha < \hat{\alpha}$. Then $\psi_{\alpha+1}(\cdot)$ is differentiable on $\bar{S}$ and

$$\begin{aligned}\sup_{y\in\bar{S}}\{\|\psi'_{\alpha+1,y}\|\} &\leqslant \sup_{y\in\bar{S}}\{\|Q_1(y,\psi_\alpha(y))\| + \|Q_2(y,\psi_\alpha(y))\|\cdot\|\psi'_{\alpha,y}\|\} \\ &\leqslant B^2KM + BK\sup_{y\in\bar{S}}\{\|\psi_\alpha(y) - y\|\}\ h_\alpha\end{aligned} \tag{5.46}$$

by virtue of Corollary 5.35. But $\|\psi_\alpha(y) - y\| \leqslant \sum_{j=1}^{\alpha}\|\psi_j(y) - \psi_{j-1}(y)\|$ and $\|\psi_j(y) - \psi_{j-1}(y)\| = \|(I - T_y')^{-1}(T - I)\,\psi_{j-1}(y)\|$ so that

$$\sup_{y\in\bar{S}}\{\|\psi'_{\alpha+1,y}\|\} \leqslant B^2KM + B^2KM\alpha h_\alpha \leqslant (\alpha+1)\,h_1 = h_{\alpha+1} < 1. \tag{5.47}$$

Thus, (5.44) holds for all $\alpha \leqslant \hat{\alpha}$ by induction and $\psi_\alpha(\bar{S}) \subset \bar{S}$. It now follows from Corollary 2.10 that $\{\psi_\alpha(y_n)\}$ converges to the unique fixed point $y_\alpha{}^*$ of ψ_α in $\bar{S}$. However, the proof of Lemma 5.23 shows that $y_1{}^* = y^*$ is a fixed point of T and, hence, $y^* = y_\alpha{}^*$ for all α. The rate of convergence inequality follows from Corollary 2.10 and the theorem is established.

We now state and prove a basic convergence theorem for the multipoint algorithm (5.1). We write $y_{n,\alpha}$ to indicate that we are considering a particular element of the class of algorithms (5.1).

THEOREM 5.48. Suppose that (i) F is twice continuously differentiable on $\bar{S}_\alpha = \bar{S}(y_{0,\alpha}, r_\alpha)$; (ii) $(F'_{y_{0,\alpha}})^{-1}$ exists and $\|(F'_{y_{0,\alpha}})^{-1}\| \leqslant B_{0,\alpha}$; (iii) $\|(F'_{y_{0,\alpha}})^{-1}\| \, \|F(y_{0,\alpha})\| \leqslant d_{0,\alpha}$; (iv) F''_y is uniformly bounded on $\bar{S}_\alpha$ with

$$\sup_{y \in \bar{S}_\alpha}\{\|F''_y\|\} \leqslant K_\alpha; \tag{5.49}$$

(v) $\eta_{0,\alpha} = \gamma_{0,\alpha}^{(\alpha)} d_{0,\alpha}$ where $\gamma_{0,\alpha}^{(1)} = 1$ and $\gamma_{0,\alpha}^{(j)}$ is given by

$$\gamma_{0,\alpha}^{(j)} = 1 + \tfrac{1}{2} \sum_{i=1}^{j-1} \left\{ (K_\alpha B_{0,\alpha}\, d_{0,\alpha})^i \left(\prod_{k=1}^{i} \gamma_{0,\alpha}^{(k)} \right) \right\} \tag{5.50}$$

for $2 \leqslant j \leqslant \alpha$; and (vi) the following relations are satisfied

$$h_{0,\alpha} = K_\alpha B_{0,\alpha} \eta_{0,\alpha} \leqslant \tfrac{1}{2} \tag{5.51}$$

$$r_\alpha = \tfrac{16}{11}\, \eta_{0,\alpha} \tag{5.52}$$

$$\gamma_{0,\alpha}^{(\alpha)} \leqslant 2 \tag{5.53}$$

for $\alpha = 1, 2, \ldots$. Then the M sequence $\{\psi_\alpha(y_{n,\alpha})\}$ converges to a zero $y_\alpha{}^*$ of F in $\bar{S}_\alpha$ and the rate of convergence is given by

$$\| y_\alpha{}^* - y_{n,\alpha} \| \leqslant \tfrac{16}{11} \left(\tfrac{5}{16}\right)^n (2h_{0,\alpha})^{(\alpha+1)^n - 1}\, \eta_{0,\alpha} \tag{5.54}$$

for $\alpha = 1, 2, \ldots$.

Proof. We give the proof in three steps. We first show that all the inverses $(F'_{y_{n,\alpha}})^{-1}$ exist and that all the $y_{n,\alpha}$ are in $\bar{S}_\alpha$. Next we prove that $\{y_{n,\alpha}\}$ is a Cauchy sequence in $\bar{S}_\alpha$ and hence has a limit $y_\alpha{}^*$ in $\bar{S}_\alpha$. Finally we show that $F(y_\alpha{}^*) = 0$ and that (5.54) holds.

For each $\alpha \geqslant 1$, we define $B_{n,\alpha}$, $d_{n,\alpha}$, $\eta_{n,\alpha}$, and $h_{n,\alpha}$, recursively, by setting

$$B_{n,\alpha} = B_{n-1,\alpha}/(1 - h_{n-1,\alpha}) \tag{5.55}$$

$$d_{n,\alpha} = 2^{\alpha-2} h_{n-1,\alpha}^{\alpha} \eta_{n-1,\alpha} \tag{5.56}$$

$$\eta_{n,\alpha} = \tfrac{5}{16}\, 2^\alpha h_{n-1,\alpha}^{\alpha} \eta_{n-1,\alpha} \tag{5.57}$$

$$h_{n,\alpha} = K_\alpha B_{n,\alpha} \eta_{n,\alpha} \tag{5.58}$$

for $n \geqslant 1$. We now prove by induction that

$$(F'_{y_{n,\alpha}})^{-1} \quad \text{exists;} \tag{5.59}$$

$$\|(F'_{y_{n,\alpha}})^{-1}\| \leqslant B_{n,\alpha}; \tag{5.60}$$

$$\|(F'_{y_{n,\alpha}})^{-1}\| \, \|F(y_{n,\alpha})\| \leqslant d_{n,\alpha}; \tag{5.61}$$

$$\| y_{n+1,\alpha} - y_{n,\alpha} \| \leqslant \eta_{n,\alpha}; \tag{5.62}$$

$$h_{n,\alpha} \leqslant \tfrac{1}{2}; \tag{5.63}$$

and

$$\| y_{n+1,\alpha} - y_{0,\alpha} \| \leqslant r_\alpha \tag{5.64}$$

for $n = 0, 1, 2, \ldots$. For $n = 0$, (5.59)–(5.61) and (5.63) are hypotheses and (5.64) will follow from (5.52) and (5.62). Thus, we need only show that $\| y_{1,\alpha} - y_{0,\alpha} \| \leqslant \eta_{0,\alpha}$.

We begin by showing that $\psi_j(y_{0,\alpha})$ is an element of $\bar{S}_\alpha$ for $1 \leqslant j \leqslant \alpha - 1$. This is done by induction on α. For $\alpha = 2$, we have $\| \psi_1(y_{0,\alpha}) - y_{0,\alpha} \| = \|(F'_{y_{0,\alpha}})^{-1} F(y_{0,\alpha})\| \leqslant d_{0,\alpha} \leqslant \eta_{0,\alpha} < r_\alpha$ so that $\psi_1(y_{0,\alpha}) \in \bar{S}_\alpha$. By expanding $F(\psi_1(y_{0,\alpha}))$ about $y_{0,\alpha}$, we find that

$$\| F(\psi_1(y_{0,\alpha}))\| \leqslant K_\alpha d_{0,\alpha}^2 \tag{5.65}$$

and hence that

$$\| \psi_2(y_{0,\alpha}) - y_{0,\alpha} \| \leqslant d_{0,\alpha} \left(1 + \frac{K_\alpha}{2} B_{0,\alpha}\, d_{0,\alpha}\right) = d_{0,\alpha}\gamma_{0,\alpha}^{(2)} \leqslant r_\alpha \tag{5.66}$$

so that $\psi_2(y_{0,\alpha}) \in \bar{S}_\alpha$. This argument can be repeated to show that $\| \psi_j(y_{0,\alpha}) - y_{0,\alpha} \| \leqslant d_{0,\alpha}\gamma_{0,\alpha}^{(j)} \leqslant r_\alpha$ and consequently, that $\psi_j(y_{0,\alpha}) \in \bar{S}_\alpha$ for $1 \leqslant j \leqslant \alpha - 1$. Moreover, by expanding $F(\psi_j(y_{0,\alpha}))$ about $y_{0,\alpha}$, we have

$$\| F(\psi_j(y_{0,\alpha}))\| \leqslant K_\alpha \frac{\| F(\psi_{j-1}(y_{0,\alpha}))\| \, \| \psi_{j-1}(y_{0,\alpha}) - y_{0,\alpha} \|}{\| F'_{y_{0,\alpha}} \|} + \frac{K_\alpha}{2} \frac{\| F(\psi_{j-1}(y_{0,\alpha}))\|^2}{\| F'_{y_{0,\alpha}} \|^2} \tag{5.67}$$

for $1 \leqslant j \leqslant \alpha - 1$. It follows that

$$\|F(\psi_j(y_{0,\alpha}))\| \leqslant K_\alpha{}^j B_{0,\alpha}^{j-1} d_{0,\alpha}^{j+1} \left(\prod_{i=1}^{j} \gamma_{0,\alpha}^{(i)}\right) \tag{5.68}$$

for $1 \leqslant j \leqslant \alpha - 1$. Since $y_{1,\alpha} - y_{0,\alpha} = -\sum_{j=0}^{\alpha-1} (F'_{y_{0,\alpha}})^{-1} F(\psi_j(y_{0,\alpha}))$, $\| y_{1,\alpha} - y_{0,\alpha} \| \leqslant \eta_{0,\alpha}$ and so (5.62) holds for $n = 0$.

We now examine the transition from $n = 0$ to $n = 1$. Since $y_{1,\alpha}$ and $y_{0,\alpha}$ are in the convex set $\bar{S}_\alpha$, $\| F'_{y_{0,\alpha}} - F'_{y_{1,\alpha}} \| \leqslant K_\alpha \| y_{1,\alpha} - y_{0,\alpha} \|$. It follows that $\| F'_{y_{0,\alpha}} \| - \| F'_{y_{1,\alpha}} \| \leqslant K_\alpha \eta_{0,\alpha}$ and hence

$$\| F'_{y_{1,\alpha}} \| \geqslant \left(1 - \frac{K_\alpha \eta_{0,\alpha}}{\| F'_{y_{0,\alpha}} \|}\right) \| F'_{y_{0,\alpha}} \| \geqslant (1 - h_{0,\alpha}) \| F'_{y_{0,\alpha}} \| > 0. \tag{5.69}$$

But (5.69) implies that $(F'_{y_{1,\alpha}})^{-1}$ exists and satisfies

$$\|(F'_{y_{1,\alpha}})^{-1}\| \leqslant \frac{B_{0,\alpha}}{1 - h_{0,\alpha}} = B_{1,\alpha} \tag{5.70}$$

so that (5.59) and (5.60) hold for $n = 1$. To verify (5.61) for $n = 1$, we expand $F(y_{1,\alpha})$ about $\psi_{\alpha-1}(y_{0,\alpha})$ to obtain

$$\begin{aligned} &\|F(y_{1,\alpha}) - F(\psi_{\alpha-1}(y_{0,\alpha})) + F'_{\psi_{\alpha-1}(y_{0,\alpha})}(F'_{y_{0,\alpha}})^{-1} F(\psi_{\alpha-1}(y_{0,\alpha}))\| \\ &\qquad \leqslant \frac{K_\alpha}{2} \frac{\|F(\psi_{\alpha-1}(y_{0,\alpha}))\|^2}{\|F'_{y_{0,\alpha}}\|^2} \end{aligned} \tag{5.71}$$

and

$$\|F(y_{1,\alpha})\| \leqslant \frac{K_\alpha{}^\alpha B_{0,\alpha}^{\alpha-1} d_{0,\alpha}^{\alpha+1}}{2} \left(\prod_{j=1}^{\alpha} \gamma_{0,\alpha}^{(j)}\right). \tag{5.72}$$

Since $\eta_{0,\alpha} = \gamma_{0,\alpha}^{(\alpha)} d_{0,\alpha}$, $\gamma_{0,\alpha}^{(\alpha)} \leqslant 2$, and $\gamma_{0,\alpha}^{(j)} \leqslant \gamma_{0,\alpha}^{(\alpha)}$, we have

$$\begin{aligned} \|(F'_{y_{1,\alpha}})^{-1}\| \, \|F(y_{1,\alpha})\| &\leqslant \frac{K_\alpha{}^\alpha B_{0,\alpha}^\alpha d_{0,\alpha}^\alpha}{2(1 - h_{0,\alpha})} \left(\prod_{j=1}^{\alpha-1} \gamma_{0,\alpha}^{(j)}\right) \eta_{0,\alpha} \\ &\leqslant 2^{\alpha-2} h_{0,\alpha}^\alpha \eta_{0,\alpha} = d_{1,\alpha} \end{aligned} \tag{5.73}$$

so that (5.61) holds for $n = 1$. Now to verify that (5.62) holds for $n = 1$, we show that

$$\| y_{2,\alpha} - y_{1,\alpha} \| = \| \psi_\alpha(y_{1,\alpha}) - y_{1,\alpha} \| \leqslant \gamma_{1,\alpha}^{(\alpha)} d_{1,\alpha} \tag{5.74}$$

where $\gamma_{1,\alpha}^{(1)} = 1$ and $\gamma_{1,\alpha}^{(j)}$ is given by

$$\gamma_{1,\alpha}^{(j)} = 1 + \tfrac{1}{2} \sum_{i=1}^{j-1} \left\{ (K_\alpha B_{1,\alpha}\, d_{1,\alpha})^i \left(\prod_{k=1}^{i} \gamma_{1,\alpha}^{(k)} \right) \right\} \tag{5.75}$$

for $2 \leqslant j \leqslant \alpha$. We note that $\gamma_{1,\alpha}^{(j)} \leqslant \gamma_{0,\alpha}^{(j)} \leqslant 2$ for all $j \leqslant \alpha$ (by a simple calculation). Assuming for the moment that (5.74) holds, we have

$$\begin{aligned} \| y_{2,\alpha} - y_{1,\alpha} \| &\leqslant d_{1,\alpha} \left[1 + \tfrac{1}{2} \sum_{j=1}^{\alpha-1} \left\{ (K_\alpha B_{1,\alpha}\, d_{1,\alpha})^j \left(\prod_{k=1}^{j} \gamma_{1,\alpha}^{(k)} \right) \right\} \right. \\ &\leqslant d_{1,\alpha} \left[1 + \tfrac{1}{2} \sum_{j=1}^{\alpha-1} \left\{ \left(\frac{K_\alpha B_{0,\alpha} 2^{\alpha-2} h_{0,\alpha}^{\alpha} \eta_{0,\alpha}}{1 - h_{0,\alpha}} \right)^j 2^j \right\} \right. \\ &\leqslant d_{1,\alpha} \left[1 + \tfrac{1}{2} \sum_{j=1}^{\alpha-1} \{ (2^\alpha h_0^{\alpha+1})^j \} \right] \\ &\leqslant d_{1,\alpha} \left[1 + \tfrac{1}{2} \sum_{j=1}^{\alpha-1} 2^{-j} \right] \leqslant \tfrac{5}{4}\, d_{1,\alpha} . \end{aligned} \tag{5.76}$$

Since $d_{1,\alpha} = 2^{\alpha-2} h_{0,\alpha}^{\alpha} \eta_{0,\alpha}$,

$$\| y_{2,\alpha} - y_{1,\alpha} \| \leqslant \tfrac{5}{16}\, 2^\alpha h_{0,\alpha}^{\alpha} \eta_{0,\alpha} = \eta_{1,\alpha} \tag{5.77}$$

so that (5.62) holds for $n = 1$. We now establish (5.74). We observe that

$$\psi_\alpha(y_{1,\alpha}) - y_{1,\alpha} = -(F'_{y_{1,\alpha}})^{-1} \sum_{j=0}^{\alpha-1} F(\psi_j(y_{1,\alpha})) \tag{5.78}$$

and hence, that (5.74) will hold if

$$\| F(\psi_j(y_{1,\alpha})) \| \leqslant \frac{K_\alpha{}^j B_{1,\alpha}^{j-1} d_{1,\alpha}^{j+1}}{2} \left(\prod_{k=1}^{j} \gamma_{1,\alpha}^{(k)} \right) \tag{5.79}$$

for $1 \leqslant j \leqslant \alpha - 1$. Now (5.79) can be established in exactly the same way as (5.68) once we have shown that $\psi_j(y_{1,\alpha}) \in \bar{S}_\alpha$ for $1 \leqslant j \leqslant \alpha - 1$. But this is done by induction on α. For $\alpha = 2$,

$\| \psi_1(y_{1,\alpha}) - y_{0,\alpha} \| \leqslant \| \psi_1(y_{1,\alpha}) - y_{1,\alpha} \| + \| y_{1,\alpha} - y_{0,\alpha} \| \leqslant d_{1,\alpha} + \eta_{0,\alpha} \leqslant (1 + 2^{\alpha-2} h_{0,\alpha}^{\alpha}) \eta_{0,\alpha} \leqslant \frac{5}{4} \eta_{0,\alpha} \leqslant r_\alpha$ so that $\psi_1(y_{1,\alpha}) \in \bar{S}_\alpha$. Expanding $F(\psi_1(y_{1,\alpha}))$ about $y_{1,\alpha}$, we find that $\| F(\psi_1(y_{1,\alpha}))\| \leqslant (K_\alpha/2)\, d_{1,\alpha}^2$ and consequently, that

$$\begin{aligned} \| \psi_2(y_{1,\alpha}) - y_{0,\alpha} \| &\leqslant \| \psi_2(y_{1,\alpha}) - \psi_1(y_{1,\alpha})\| \\ &\quad + \| \psi_1(y_{1,\alpha}) - y_{1,\alpha} \| + \| y_{1,\alpha} - y_{0,\alpha} \| \\ &\leqslant \frac{K_\alpha}{2} B_{1,\alpha}\, d_{1,\alpha}^2 + d_{1,\alpha} + \eta_{0,\alpha} \\ &\leqslant \tfrac{5}{4}\, d_{1,\alpha} + \eta_{0,\alpha} \leqslant \tfrac{16}{11}\, \eta_{0,\alpha} = r_\alpha . \end{aligned}$$

Thus, $\psi_2(y_{1,\alpha}) \in \bar{S}_\alpha$. The argument can be repeated to show that $\psi_j(y_{1,\alpha}) \in \bar{S}_\alpha$ for $j \leqslant \alpha - 1$ since $\gamma_{1,\alpha}^{(j)} \leqslant \frac{5}{4}$ [see Eq. (5.76)]. It follows that (5.62) holds for $n = 1$. As for (5.63), we have

$$\begin{aligned} h_{1,\alpha} = K_\alpha B_{1,\alpha} \eta_{1,\alpha} &= \frac{K_\alpha B_{0,\alpha}}{1 - h_{0,\alpha}} \frac{5}{16}\, 2^\alpha h_{0,\alpha}^\alpha \eta_{0,\alpha} \\ &\leqslant \tfrac{5}{8}\, 2^\alpha h_{0\ \alpha}^{\alpha+1} \leqslant \tfrac{5}{8}\, h_{0,\alpha} \leqslant \tfrac{1}{2} . \end{aligned} \tag{5.80}$$

Now,

$$\begin{aligned} \| y_{2,\alpha} - y_{0,\alpha} \| &\leqslant \| y_{2,\alpha} - y_{1,\alpha} \| + \| y_{1,\alpha} - y_{0,\alpha} \| \\ &\leqslant (\tfrac{5}{16}\, 2^\alpha h_{0,\alpha}^\alpha + 1)\, \eta_{0,\alpha} \leqslant \tfrac{21}{16}\, \eta_{0,\alpha} < r_\alpha \end{aligned}$$

and so (5.64) holds for $n = 1$.

If we now assume that (5.59)–(5.64) hold for $m \leqslant n - 1$, then we can show by exactly the same arguments used in going from $n = 0$ to $n = 1$ that (5.59)–(5.64) are satisfied for n. Thus, by induction, the relations (5.59)–(5.64) hold for all $n \geqslant 0$.

Now, it follows from (5.57) and (5.63) that $\eta_{n,\alpha} \leqslant (\frac{5}{16})^n\, \eta_{0,\alpha}$ and hence that the series $\sum_{n=0}^{\infty} \eta_{n,\alpha}$ is convergent. Since

$$\| y_{n+m,\alpha} - y_{n,\alpha} \| \leqslant \sum_{j=0}^{m-1} \eta_{n+j,\alpha} \tag{5.81}$$

we conclude that $\{y_{n,\alpha}\}$ is a Cauchy sequence in $\bar{S}_\alpha$ and so converges to an element $y_\alpha{}^*$ of $\bar{S}_\alpha$.

We claim that $y_\alpha{}^*$ is a zero of F. In view of the analog of (5.72) for arbitrary n, we have

$$\|F(y_{n+1,\alpha})\| \leqslant K_\alpha{}^\alpha B_{n,\alpha}^{\alpha-1}\, d_{n\ \alpha}^{\alpha+1}\, 2^{\alpha-2}\gamma_{n,\alpha}^{(\alpha)} \tag{5.82}$$

$$\leqslant \frac{h_{n,\alpha}^\alpha\, 2^{\alpha-2} d_{n,\alpha}\gamma_{n,\alpha}^{(\alpha)}}{B_{n,\alpha}}$$

$$\leqslant \frac{h_{n,\alpha}^\alpha\, 2^{\alpha-2}}{B_{0,\alpha}}\,\eta_{n,\alpha} \leqslant \frac{1}{4B_{0,\alpha}}\left(\frac{5}{16}\right)^n \eta_{0,\alpha}$$

[using the analog of (5.74)]. It follows that $\lim_{n\to\infty}\|F(y_{n,\alpha})\| = \|F(y_\alpha{}^*)\| = 0$ as F is continuous.

All that remains is the establishment of the rate of convergence inequality (5.54). But, since

$$\|y_\alpha{}^* - y_{n,\alpha}\| \leqslant \sum_{j=0}^{\infty} \eta_{n+j,\alpha}\,,$$

(5.54) will follow from the estimate

$$\eta_{n,\alpha} \leqslant (\tfrac{5}{16})^n\,(2h_{0,\alpha})^{(\alpha+1)^n-1}\,\eta_{0,\alpha} \tag{5.83}$$

and the fact that $h_{0,\alpha} \leqslant \frac{1}{2}$. But (5.83) is a direct consequence of the relations

$$\eta_{n,\alpha} = \tfrac{5}{16}\,(2h_{n-1,\alpha})^\alpha\,\eta_{n-1,\alpha} \tag{5.84}$$

$$h_{n,\alpha} \leqslant \tfrac{1}{2}\,(2h_{0,\alpha})^{(\alpha+1)^n} \tag{5.85}$$

which follow from the definitions of $\eta_{n,\alpha}$ and $h_{n,\alpha}$.* Thus, the proof of the theorem is complete.

We use this theorem in Chapters 4 and 5.

* The argument is as follows:

$$\begin{aligned}
\eta_{n,\alpha} &= (\tfrac{5}{16})(2h_{n-1,\alpha})^\alpha\eta_{n-1,\alpha}\\
&\leqslant (\tfrac{5}{16})^n(2^\alpha)^n[(2h_{0,\alpha})^{(\alpha+1)^{n-1}+\cdots+(\alpha+1)}]^\alpha(2^{-\alpha})^{n-1}h_{0,\alpha}^\alpha\eta_{0,\alpha}\\
&\leqslant (\tfrac{5}{16})^n[(2h_{0,\alpha})]^{\{[(\alpha+1)^n-(\alpha+1)]\alpha\}/\alpha}(2h_{0,\alpha})^\alpha\eta_{0,\alpha}\\
&\leqslant (\tfrac{5}{16})^n(2h_{0,\alpha})^{(\alpha+1)^n-1}\eta_{0,\alpha}\,.
\end{aligned}$$

CHAPTER 3

REPRESENTATION OF BOUNDARY VALUE PROBLEMS

3.1. Introduction

We noted in Chapter 2 that two-point boundary value problems (TPBVP's) can be represented by operator equations. Here, we shall examine, in detail, the problem of developing suitable representations for continuous and discrete TPBVP's. More precisely, we consider TPBVP's of the form

$$\dot{y} = F(y, t), \qquad g(y(0)) + h(y(1)) = c \tag{1.1}$$

or of the form

$$y(j+1) - y(j) = F(y(j), y(j+1), j), \qquad g(y(0)) + h(y(q)) = c \tag{1.2}$$

where F, g, and h are suitable vector valued functions and c is a constant vector. We note that (1.1) and (1.2) are normalized with respect to time. We show that (1.1) can be represented by a variety of integral equations and that (1.2) can be represented by a variety of "summation equations." These representations involve linear TPBVP's in a crucial way. Thus, we devote some attention to linear TPBVP's, i.e., to problems of the form

$$\dot{y} = V(t)\,y + f(t), \qquad My(0) + Ny(1) = c \tag{1.3}$$

or of the form

$$\begin{aligned} &y(j+1) - y(j) = A(j)\,y(j+1) + B(j)\,y(j) + f(j), \\ &My(0) + Ny(q) = c \end{aligned} \tag{1.4}$$

where $V(t)$, $f(t)$, $A(j)$, $B(j)$, and $f(j)$ are suitable vector and matrix valued functions, M and N are matrices, and c is a constant vector. We use the results of this chapter throughout the sequel.

3.2. Continuous Linear Two-Point Boundary Value Problems

We consider a linear TPBVP of the form

$$\dot{y} = V(t)\,y + f(t), \qquad My(0) + Ny(1) = c \tag{2.1}$$

where $V(t)$, M, and N are $p \times p$ matrices and $f(t)$ and c are p vectors. We suppose that $V(t)$ and $f(t)$ are defined and measurable on an open interval I containing $[0, 1]$ and that there is a (Lebesgue) integrable function $m(t)$ on I such that $\| V(t)\| \leqslant m(t)$ and $\| f(t)\| \leqslant m(t)$. We then have the following.

DEFINITION 2.2. A p vector valued function $\psi(t)$ is called a solution of (2.1) if (i) $\psi(t)$ is absolutely continuous, (ii) $\dot{\psi}(t) = V(t)\,\psi(t) + f(t)$ for almost all t, and (iii) $M\psi(0) + N\psi(1) = c$.

LEMMA 2.3. Let $\mathscr{S}$ denote the set of all solutions of (2.1). Then $\mathscr{S}$ is nonempty if and only if $c - N\int_0^1 \Phi^V(1, s)\,f(s)\,ds = \xi$ is an element of the range of $M + N\Phi^V(1, 0)$ where $\Phi^V(t, s)$ is the fundamental matrix of the linear system $\dot{y} = V(t)y$. Moreover, if γ is any p vector with $[M + N\Phi^V(1, 0)]\,\gamma = \xi$, then $\mathscr{S}$ is "isomorphic with" $\gamma + \mathscr{N}(M + N\Phi^V(1, 0))$ where $\mathscr{N}(M + N\Phi^V(1, 0))$ is the null space of $M + N\Phi^V(1, 0)$.

Proof. By virtue of the standard existence and uniqueness theorem for initial value problems [C4], we can write the *unique* solution of $\dot{y} = V(t)y + f(t)$ for a given initial value $y(0)$ as

$$y(t) = \Phi^V(t, 0)\,y(0) + \Phi^V(t, 0)\int_0^t \Phi^V(0, s)\,f(s)\,ds. \tag{2.4}$$

For $t = 1$, this solution will pass through the point

$$y(1) = \Phi^V(1, 0)\,y(0) + \Phi^V(1, 0)\int_0^1 \Phi^V(0, s)\,f(s)\,ds.$$

Thus, $y(t)$ [as given by (2.4)] will be a solution of (2.1) if and only if

$$My(0) + N\Phi^V(1,0)\left[y(0) + \int_0^1 \Phi^V(0,s)f(s)\,ds\right] = c \tag{2.5}$$

i.e., if and only if

$$[M + N\Phi^V(1,0)]\,y(0) = c - N\int_0^1 \Phi^V(1,s)f(s)\,ds = \xi \tag{2.6}$$

or, equivalently, if and only if ξ is an element of the range of $M+N\Phi^V(1,0)$. Finally, if γ is any p vector with $[M+N\Phi^V(1,0)]\gamma = \xi$ and $\psi(t)$ is any element of $\mathscr{S}$, then $\psi(0) - \gamma$ is an element of $\mathscr{N}(M + N\Phi^V(1,0))$ and the lemma is established.

COROLLARY 2.7. If $\det([M + N\Phi^V(1,0)]) \neq 0$, then (2.1) has a unique solution $\psi(t)$ which can be expressed in the following form

$$\psi(t) = H^{V_{MN}}(t)\,c + \int_0^1 G^{V_{MN}}(t,s)f(s)\,ds \tag{2.8}$$

where the Green's matrices $H^{V_{MN}}(t)$ and $G^{V_{MN}}(t,s)$ are given by

$$H^{V_{MN}}(t) = \Phi^V(t,0)[M + N\Phi^V(1,0)]^{-1} \tag{2.9}$$

and

$$G^{V_{MN}}(t,s) = \begin{cases} \Phi^V(t,0)[M + N\Phi^V(1,0)]^{-1}\,M\Phi^V(0,s), & 0 \leqslant s < t \\ -\,\Phi^V(t,0)[M + N\Phi^V(1,0)]^{-1}\,N\Phi^V(1,s), & t < s \leqslant 1 \end{cases} \tag{2.10}$$

respectively.

Proof. By virtue of Lemma 2.3, (2.1) has a unique solution $\psi(t)$ which is given by

$$\begin{aligned} \psi(t) = {} & \Phi^V(t,0)[M + N\Phi^V(1,0)]^{-1}\,c \\ & - \Phi^V(t,0)[M + N\Phi^V(1,0)]^{-1}\,N\Phi^V(1,0)\int_0^1 \Phi^V(0,s)f(s)\,ds \\ & + \Phi^V(t,0)[M + N\Phi^V(1,0)]^{-1}\,[M + N\Phi^V(1,0)] \\ & \times [\Phi^V(t,0)]^{-1}\,\Phi^V(t,0)\int_0^t \Phi^V(0,s)f(s)\,ds. \end{aligned} \tag{2.11}$$

Cancellation of the terms

$$\Phi^V(t, 0)[M + N\Phi^V(1, 0)]^{-1} N\Phi^V(1, 0) \int_0^t \Phi^V(0, s) f(s)\, ds$$

in (2.11) yields the desired result. Thus, the corollary is proved.

In order to avoid needless repetition of the conditions of existence and uniqueness, we introduce the following.

DEFINITION 2.12. Let $V(t)$, M, and N be $p \times p$ matrices. Then the set $\{V(t), M, N\}$ will be called boundary compatible if (i) $V(t)$ is measurable with $\| V(t)\| \leqslant m(t)$ for an integrable $m(t)$, and (ii) $\det(M + N\Phi^V(1, 0)) \neq 0$ where $\Phi^V(t, s)$ is the fundamental matrix of $\dot{y} = V(t)y$; or, equivalently, if (2.1) has a unique solution for all $f(t)$ and c.

In the sequel we shall often be given two boundary related matrices M and N and will be required to determine a matrix $V(t)$ so that the set $\{V(t), M, N\}$ is boundary compatible. With a view toward making such a determination, we prove the following simple lemma which gives a necessary and sufficient condition for the existence of a matrix $V(t)$ such that $\{V(t), M, N\}$ is boundary compatible.

LEMMA 2.13. Let M and N be $p \times p$ matrices. A necessary and sufficient condition that there be a $V(t)$ with $\{V(t), M, N\}$ boundary compatible is that the $p \times 2p$ matrix $[M\,N]$ have full rank p.

Proof. We prove the lemma with some well known results from linear algebra (see, for example, Nering [N1]). If $[M\,N]$ is of rank less than p, say of rank r, then there are only r linearly independent columns in $[M\,N]$. These r columns (column vectors) span an r dimensional subspace D_r of R^p. Any column obtained by adding a column of M to a linear combination of columns of N lies in this subspace D_r. Therefore, for any $V(t)$ and corresponding fundamental matrix $\Phi^V(1, 0)$, all columns of the matrix $(M + N\Phi^V(1, 0))$ belong to D_r. This implies that $(M + N\Phi^V(1, 0))$ has at most $r(<p)$ linearly independent columns, and hence that

$$\det(M + N\Phi^V(1, 0)) = 0$$

for all $V(t)$. It follows that there is no matrix $V(t)$ which is boundary compatible with M and N in view of Definition 2.12. This proves necessity.

If $[M\,N]$ is of rank p, then there are p linearly independent columns in $[M\,N]$. Let M have q ($\leqslant p$) linearly independent columns; then N has $p - q$ columns which are linearly independent of the columns of M. By postmultiplication of N by a product of elementary matrices $Q([N\,1])$, we can assure that: (1) the $p - q$ columns of N, which are linearly independent of the columns of M, have the same position in the matrix NQ as the linearly dependent columns in the matrix M, and (2) the remaining q columns of NQ are multiples of the original columns of N. In this manner we find that the sum $M + NQ$ has p linearly independent columns, or equivalently, that

$$\det(M + NQ) \neq 0.$$

Since any product of elementary matrices is nonsingular, Q is nonsingular and hence the logarithm of Q exists [G1, p. 239]. If we choose

$$V(t) = V = \log Q, \tag{2.14}$$

then, in view of the expression for the fundamental matrix of a time-invariant system, we have

$$\Phi^V(t, s) = e^{V(t-s)} \qquad \text{and} \qquad \Phi^V(1, 0) = e^V = e^{\log Q} = Q$$

so that

$$\det(M + N\Phi^V(1, 0)) = \det(M + NQ) \neq 0 \tag{2.15}$$

which proves that $\{V, M, N\}$ is boundary compatible. Thus, the lemma is established.

We shall use the results of this section to obtain integral representations for continuous TPBVP's of the form (1.1) in Section 4.

3.3. Discrete Linear Two-Point Boundary Value Problems

We consider a discrete linear TPBVP of the form

$$\begin{aligned} &y(j+1) - y(j) = A(j)\,y(j+1) + B(j)\,y(j) + f(j), \\ &My(0) + Ny(q) = c \end{aligned} \tag{3.1}$$

with $j \in \{0, 1, \ldots, q-1\}$ where $A(j)$, $B(j)$, M, and N are $p \times p$

matrices and $f(j)$ and c are p vectors. We suppose that $A(j)$, $B(j)$, and $f(j)$ are defined for $j \in \{0, 1, \ldots, q-1\}$ and that

$$\det(I - A(j)) \neq 0 \tag{3.2}$$

for $j \in \{0, 1, \ldots, q-1\}$, i.e., that $I - A(j)$ is nonsingular for all j. We then have the following.

DEFINITION 3.3. A p vector valued function $\psi(j)$ is called a solution of (3.1) if (i) $\psi(j+1) - \psi(j) = A(j)\,\psi(j+1) + B(j)\,\psi(j) + f(j)$ for $j = 0, 1, \ldots, q-1$, and (ii) $M\psi(0) + N\psi(q) = c$.

LEMMA 3.4. Let $\mathscr{S}$ denote the set of all solutions of (3.1). Then $\mathscr{S}$ is nonempty if and only if

$$c - N\left\{\sum_{i=0}^{q-1} \Phi^V(q, i+1)[I - A(i)]^{-1} f(i)\right\} = \xi$$

is an element of the range of $M + N\Phi^V(q, 0)$ where $\Phi^V(j, i)$ is the transition matrix of the linear system $y(j+1) - y(j) = V(j)\,y(j)$ with $V(j) = [I - A(j)]^{-1}\,[A(j) + B(j)]$.* Moreover, if γ is any p vector with $[M + N\Phi^V(q, 0)]\,\gamma = \xi$, then $\mathscr{S}$ is "isomorphic with" $\gamma + \mathscr{N}(M + N\Phi^V(q, 0))$ where $\mathscr{N}(M + N\Phi^V(q, 0))$ is the null space of $M + N\Phi^V(q, 0)$.

Proof. By virtue of the standard existence and uniqueness theorems for discrete initial value problems [P4], we can write the *unique* solution of $y(j+1) - y(j) = V(j)\,y(j) + f(j)$ for a given initial value $y(0)$ as

$$y(j) = \Phi^V(j, 0)\,y(0) + \sum_{i=0}^{j-1} \Phi^V(j, i+1)[I - A(i)]^{-1} f(i). \tag{3.5}$$

For $j = q$, this solution will pass through the point

* The transition matrix $\Phi^V(j, i)$ is given by

$$\Phi^V(j,i) = \begin{cases} [I + V(j-1)] \cdots [I + V(i)], & j \geqslant i+1 \\ I, & j = i. \end{cases}$$

$$y(q) = \Phi^V(q, 0)\, y(0) + \sum_{i=0}^{q-1} \Phi^V(q, i+1)[I - A(i)]^{-1} f(i).$$

Thus, $y(j)$ [as given by (3.5)] will be a solution of (3.1) if and only if

$$\text{(3.6)} \quad My(0) + N\Phi^V(q, 0)\, y(0) + N \left\{ \sum_{i=0}^{q-1} \Phi^V(q, i+1)[I - A(i)]^{-1} f(i) \right\} = c$$

i.e., if and only if

$$\text{(3.7)} \quad [M + N\Phi^V(q, 0)]\, y(0) = c - N \left\{ \sum_{i=0}^{q-1} \Phi^V(q, i+1)[I - A(i)]^{-1} f(i) \right\} = \xi$$

or, equivalently, if and only if ξ is an element of the range of $M+N\Phi^V(q, 0)$. Finally, if γ is any p vector with $[M+N\Phi^V(q, 0)]\gamma = \xi$ and $\psi(j)$ is any element of $\mathscr{S}$, then $\psi(0) - \gamma$ is an element of $\mathscr{N}(M + N\Phi^V(q, 0))$ and the lemma is established.

COROLLARY 3.8. If $\det([M + N\Phi^V(q, 0)]) \neq 0$, then (3.1) has a unique solution $\psi(j)$ which can be expressed in the following form

$$\text{(3.9)} \qquad \psi(j) = H^{V_{MN}}(j)\, c + \sum_{i=0}^{q-1} G^{V_{MN}}(j, i) f(i)$$

where the Green's matrices $H^{V_{MN}}(j)$ and $G^{V_{MN}}(j, i)$ are given by

$$\text{(3.10)} \qquad H^{V_{MN}}(j) = \Phi^V(j, 0)[M + N\Phi^V(q, 0)]^{-1}$$

and

$$\text{(3.11)} \quad G^{V_{MN}}(j, i) = \begin{cases} -H^{V_{MN}}(j)\, N\Phi^V(q, i+1)[I - A(i)]^{-1} & \\ \quad + \Phi^V(j, i+1)[I - A(i)]^{-1}, & 0 \leqslant i \leqslant j-1 \\ -H^{V_{MN}}(j)\, N\Phi^V(q, i+1)[I - A(i)]^{-1}, & j \leqslant i \leqslant q-1 \end{cases}$$

respectively.

Proof. By virtue of Lemma 3.4, (3.1) has a unique solution $\psi(j)$ which is given by

(3.12)

$$\psi(j) = \Phi^V(j, 0)[M + N\Phi^V(q, 0)]^{-1} c - \Phi^V(j, 0)[M + N\Phi^V(q, 0)]^{-1} N$$

$$\times \left\{ \sum_{i=0}^{q-1} \Phi^V(q, i+1)[I - A(i)]^{-1} f(i) \right\} + \sum_{i=0}^{j-1} \Phi^V(j, i+1)[I - A(i)]^{-1} f(i)$$

and so the corollary is proved.

COROLLARY 3.13. If, in addition to the assumptions of Corollary 3.8, it is assumed that the matrix $I + V(j) = [I - A(j)]^{-1} [I + B(j)]$ is nonsingular for $j \in \{0, 1, \ldots, q-1\}$, then (3.1) has a unique solution $\psi(j)$ which can be expressed in the form $\psi(j) = H^V{}_{MN}(j)\, c + \sum_{i=0}^{q-1} G^V{}_{MN}(j, i) f(i)$ where $H^V{}_{MN}(j)$ is given by (3.10) and $G^V{}_{MN}(j, i)$ is given by

$$\text{(3.14)}\quad G^V{}_{MN}(j, i) = \begin{cases} H^V{}_{MN}(j)\, M\Phi^V(0, i+1)[I - A(i)]^{-1}, & 0 \leqslant i \leqslant j-1 \\ -H^V{}_{MN}(j)\, N\Phi^V(q, i+1)[I - A(i)]^{-1}, & j \leqslant i \leqslant q-1. \end{cases}$$

Proof. By virtue of the additional assumption, we have $\Phi^V(i, j) = \Phi^V(i, k)\, \Phi^V(k, j)$ and $\Phi^V(j, i) = [\Phi^V(i, j)]^{-1}$. It follows that, for $0 \leqslant i \leqslant j-1$,

$$\begin{aligned}
\text{(3.15)}\quad & -H^V{}_{MN}(j)\, N\Phi^V(q, i+1)[I - A(i)]^{-1} + \Phi^V(j, i+1)[I - A(i)]^{-1} \\
&= -\Phi^V(j, 0)[M + N\Phi^V(q, 0)]^{-1} N\Phi^V(q, i+1)[I - A(i)]^{-1} \\
&\quad + \Phi^V(j, 0)[M + N\Phi^V(q, 0)]^{-1} \\
&\quad \times M\Phi^V(0, j)\, \Phi^V(j, i+1)[I - A(i)]^{-1} \\
&\quad + \Phi^V(j, 0)[M + N\Phi^V(q, 0)]^{-1} \\
&\quad \times N\Phi^V(q, 0)\, \Phi^V(0, j)\, \Phi^V(j, i+1)[I - A(i)]^{-1} \\
&= H^V{}_{MN}(j)\, M\Phi^V(0, i+1)[I - A(i)]^{-1}
\end{aligned}$$

and hence, by (3.11), that the corollary is valid.

We now have the following.

DEFINITION 3.16. Let $A(j)$, $B(j)$, M, and N be $p \times p$ matrices. Then the set $\{A(j), B(j), M, N\}$ is called boundary compatible if (i) $[I - A(j)]$ is nonsingular for $j \in \{0, 1, \ldots, q-1\}$, and (ii)

$\det(M + N\Phi^V(q, 0)) \neq 0$ where $\Phi^V(j, i)$ is the transition matrix of the linear system $y(j + 1) - y(j) = V(j)\, y(j)$ with

$$V(j) = [I - A(j)]^{-1} [A(j) + B(j)];$$

or, equivalently, if (3.1) has a unique solution for all $f(j)$ and c.

By analogy with Lemma 2.13, we have the following simple lemma which gives a necessary and sufficient condition for the existence of matrices $A(j)$ and $B(j)$ such that $\{A(j), B(j), M, N\}$ is boundary compatible.

LEMMA 3.17. Let M and N be $p \times p$ matrices. A necessary and sufficient condition that there be matrices $A(j)$ and $B(j)$ with $\{A(j), B(j), M, N\}$ boundary compatible is that the $p \times 2p$ matrix $[M\, N]$ have full rank p.

Proof. The proof of necessity is exactly the same as the proof of necessity in Lemma 2.13. As for sufficiency, we again determine a nonsingular matrix Q with $\det(M + NQ) \neq 0$. Then the logarithm of Q, $\log Q$, exists and the matrix $S = (\log Q)/q$ has the property that $(e^S)^q = Q$. If we let $A(j) = 0$ and $B(j) = -I + e^S$, then $V(j) = -I + e^S$ and $\Phi^V(q, 0) = [I + V(q - 1)] \cdots [I + V(0)] = (e^S)^q = Q$. It follows that $\det(M + N\Phi^V(q, 0)) = \det(M + NQ) \neq 0$ and thus the lemma is established.

We shall use the results of this section to obtain summation representations for discrete TPBVP's of the form (1.2) in Section 5.

We observe that there is considerable similarity between the results of this section and the results of Section 2. This is no accident. In fact, similar results can be derived in a very general context for abstract linear boundary value problems in Banach spaces (see, for example, Conti [C5]). Such a generalization is particularly useful in the treatment of boundary value problems for distributed systems.

3.4. Representation of Continuous Two-Point Boundary Value Problems

We now develop integral equation representations for TPBVP's of the form (1.1) using the results of Section 2. The equivalence between differential equation and integral equation representations of

TPBVP's has been known for a long time. In fact, Picard [P2] used this equivalence to prove the convergence of various iterative methods for the solution of nonlinear TPBVP's. We now have the following.

THEOREM 4.1. Let D be an open set in R_p and let I be an open set in R containing $[0, 1]$. Suppose that (i) $F(y, t)$ is a map of $D \times I$ into D which is measurable in t for each fixed y and continuous in y for each fixed t; (ii) there is an integrable function $m(t)$ such that $\|F(y, t)\| \leqslant m(t)$ on $D \times I$; (iii) $g(y)$ and $h(y)$ are maps of D into D; and (iv) $\{V(t), M, N\}$ is a boundary-compatible set of dimension p. Then the boundary value problem

$$\dot{y} = F(y, t), \qquad g(y(0)) + h(y(1)) = c \tag{4.2}$$

has the equivalent representation

$$\begin{aligned} y(t) = {} & H^{VMN}(t)\{c - g[y(0)] - h[y(1)] + My(0) + Ny(1)\} \\ & + \int_0^1 G^{VMN}(t, s)\{F(y(s), s) - V(s)\, y(s)\}\, ds \end{aligned} \tag{4.3}$$

where the Green's functions $H^{VMN}(t)$ and $G^{VMN}(t, s)$ are given by

$$H^{VMN}(t) = \Phi^V(t, 0)[M + N\Phi^V(1, 0)]^{-1} \tag{4.4}$$

and

$$G^{VMN}(t, s) = \begin{cases} \Phi^V(t, 0)[M + N\Phi^V(1, 0)]^{-1} M\Phi^V(0, s), & 0 \leqslant s < t \\ -\Phi^V(t, 0)[M + N\Phi^V(1, 0)]^{-1} N\Phi^V(1, s), & t < s \leqslant 1 \end{cases} \tag{4.5}$$

where $\Phi^V(t, s)$ is the fundamental matrix of the linear system $\dot{y} = V(t)y$.

Proof. We must show that a solution of (4.2) is also a solution of (4.3) and, conversely, that an absolutely continuous solution of the integral equation (4.3) is a solution of the TPBVP (4.2).

Let $\psi(t)$ be a solution of (4.2). Then $\psi(t)$ is also a solution of the linear TPBVP

$$\dot{y} = V(t)\, y + f(t), \qquad My(0) + Ny(1) = d \tag{4.6}$$

where

$$\begin{aligned} f(t) &= F(\psi(t), t) - V(t)\,\psi(t) \\ d &= c - g(\psi(0)) - h(\psi(1)) + M\psi(0) + N\psi(1). \end{aligned} \tag{4.7}$$

Since $F(y, t)$ satisfies (i) and (ii) and $V(t)$ is measurable and dominated by an integrable function, $f(t)$ is measurable and dominated by an integrable function. Moreover, $\det(M + N\Phi^V(1, 0)) \neq 0$ in view of (iv). Thus, all the conditions of Corollary 2.7 are satisfied for the linear TPBVP (4.6). It follows that the solution of (4.6) is unique and is given by

$$\psi(t) = H^{V_{MN}}(t)\, d + \int_0^1 G^{V_{MN}}(t, s) f(s)\, ds \tag{4.8}$$

where $H^{V}{}_{MN}(t)$ and $G^{V}{}_{MN}(t, s)$ are given by (4.4) and (4.5). From (4.7) and (4.8), we then deduce that

$$\begin{aligned} \psi(t) = {} & H^{V_{MN}}(t)\{c - g[\psi(0)] - h[\psi(1)] + M\psi(0) + N\psi(1)\} \\ & + \int_0^1 G^{V_{MN}}(t, s)\{F(\psi(s), s) - V(s)\,\psi(s)\}\, ds \end{aligned} \tag{4.9}$$

which shows that $\psi(t)$ is also a solution of the integral equation (4.3).

Conversely, let $\phi(t)$ be an absolutely continuous function which satisfies the integral equation (4.3). In view of (4.4) and (4.5) we see that

$$\begin{aligned} \phi(t) = {} & \Phi^V(t, 0)[M + N\Phi^V(1, 0)]^{-1} \\ & \times \{c - g[\phi(0)] - h[\phi(1)] + M\phi(0) + N\phi(1)\} \\ & + \Phi^V(t, 0)[M + N\Phi^V(1, 0)]^{-1} \\ & \times M \int_0^t \Phi^V(0, s)\{F(\phi(s), s) - V(s)\,\phi(s)\}\, ds \\ & - \Phi^V(t, 0)[M + N\Phi^V(1, 0)]^{-1} \\ & \times N\Phi^V(1, 0) \int_t^1 \Phi^V(0, s)\{F(\phi(s), s) - V(s)\,\phi(s)\}\, ds. \end{aligned} \tag{4.10}$$

Straightforward substitution gives

$$
\begin{aligned}
M\phi(0) &+ N\phi(1) \\
&= M\Phi^V(0,0)[M + N\Phi^V(1,0)]^{-1} \\
&\quad \times \{c - g[\phi(0)] - h[\phi(1)] + M\phi(0) + N\phi(1)\} \\
&\quad + N\Phi^V(1,0)[M + N\Phi^V(1,0)]^{-1} \\
&\quad \times \{c - g[\phi(0)] - h[\phi(1)] + M\phi(0) + N\phi(1)\} \\
&\quad - M\Phi^V(0,0)[M + N\Phi^V(1,0)]^{-1} \\
&\quad \times N\Phi^V(1,0) \int_0^1 \Phi^V(0,s)\{F(\phi(s),s) - V(s)\,\phi(s)\}\,ds \\
&\quad + N\Phi^V(1,0)[M + N\Phi^V(1,0)]^{-1} \\
&\quad \times M \int_0^1 \Phi^V(0,s)\{F(\phi(s),s) - V(s)\,\phi(s)\}\,ds \\
&\quad - N\Phi^V(1,0)[M + N\Phi^V(1,0)]^{-1} \\
&\quad \times N\Phi^V(1,0) \int_0^1 \Phi^V(0,s)\{F(\phi(s),s) - V(s)\,\phi(s)\}\,ds \\
&\quad + N\Phi^V(1,0)[M + N\Phi^V(1,0)]^{-1} \\
&\quad \times N\Phi^V(1,0) \int_0^1 \Phi^V(0,s)\{F(\phi(s),s) - V(s)\,\phi(s)\}\,ds \\
&= c - g[\phi(0)] - h[\phi(1)] + M\phi(0) + N\phi(1)
\end{aligned}
$$

and so

$$g[\phi(0)] + h[\phi(1)] = c.$$

This shows that $\phi(t)$ satisfies the boundary conditions of (4.2).

Differentiation of both sides of the expression (4.10) for $\phi(t)$ (which is possible a.e. because $\phi(t)$ is absolutely continuous) leads to

$$
\begin{aligned}
\dot{\phi}(t) = V(t)\,&\Phi^V(t,0)[M + N\Phi^V(1,0)]^{-1} \\
&\times \{c - g[\phi(0)] - g[\phi(1)] + M\phi(0) + N\phi(1)\} \\
&+ V(t)\,\Phi^V(t,0)[M + N\Phi^V(1,0)]^{-1} \\
&\times M \int_0^t \Phi^V(0,s)\{F(\phi(s),s) - V(s)\,\phi(s)\}\,ds
\end{aligned}
$$

$$
\begin{aligned}
&- V(t)\,\Phi^V(t,0)[M + N\Phi^V(1,0)]^{-1} \\
&\times N\Phi^V(1,0)\int_t^1 \Phi^V(0,s)\{F(\phi(s),s) - V(s)\,\phi(s)\}\,ds \\
&+ \Phi^V(t,0)[M + N\Phi^V(1,0)]^{-1}\,M\Phi^V(0,t)\{F(\phi(t),t) - V(t)\,\phi(t)\} \\
&+ \Phi^V(t,0)[M + N\Phi^V(1,0)]^{-1}\,N\Phi^V(1,0)\,\Phi^V(0,t)\{F(\phi(t),t) - V(t)\,\phi(t)\} \\
= {}& V(t)\,\phi(t) + F(\phi(t),t) - V(t)\,\phi(t) \\
= {}& F(\phi(t),t)
\end{aligned}
$$

and so $\phi(t)$ satisfies the differential equation of (4.2). This completes the proof of the theorem.

We observe that Theorem 4.1 remains true if the hypothesis (i) is replaced by the following hypothesis: (i') $F(y, t)$ is a map of $D \times I$ into D which is Borel measurable in the pair (y, t).

3.5. Representation of Discrete Two-Point Boundary Value Problem

We now develop summation equation representation for TPBVP's of the form (1.2) using the results of Section 3. The development is entirely analogous to that of Section 4. In particular, we have the following.

THEOREM 5.1. Let D be a subset of R_p and let $\mathbf{Q}' = \{0, 1, \ldots, q-1\}$. Suppose that (i) $F(u, v, j)$ is a map of $D \times D \times \mathbf{Q}'$ into D; (ii) $g(y)$ and $h(y)$ are maps of D into D; and (iii) $\{A(j), B(j), M, N\}$ is a boundary-compatible set of dimension p. Then the boundary value problem

$$y(j+1) - y(j) = F(y(j+1), y(j), j), \qquad g(y(0)) + h(y(q)) = c \tag{5.2}$$

has the equivalent representation

(5.3)

$$
\begin{aligned}
y(j) = {}& H^{VMN}(j)\{c - g(y(0)) - h(y(q)) + My(0) + Ny(q)\} \\
&+ \sum_{k=0}^{q-1} G^{VMN}(j,k)\,\{F(y(k+1), y(k), k) - A(k)\,y(k+1) - B(k)\,y(k)\}
\end{aligned}
$$

for $j = 0, 1, \ldots, q$ where the Green's functions $H^{V_{MN}}(j)$ and $G^{V_{MN}}(j, k)$ are given by

$$(5.4) \quad H^{V_{MN}}(j) = \Phi^V(j, 0)[M + N\Phi^V(q, 0)]^{-1}$$

and

$$(5.5) \quad G^{V_{MN}}(j, k) = \begin{cases} -H^{V_{MN}}(j)\, N\Phi^V(q, k+1)[I - A(k)]^{-1} & \\ \quad + \Phi^V(j, k+1)[I - A(k)]^{-1}, & 0 \leqslant k \leqslant j-1 \\ -H^{V_{MN}}(j)\, N\Phi^V(q, k+1)[I - A(k)]^{-1}, & j \leqslant k \leqslant q-1 \end{cases}$$

where $\Phi^V(j, i)$ is the transition matrix of the linear system $y(j+1) - y(j) = V(j)\, y(j)$ with $V(j) = [I - A(j)]^{-1}\, [A(j) + B(j)]$.

Proof. We must show that if a sequence $\psi(0), \ldots, \psi(q)$ satisfies (5.2), then it also satisfies (5.3) and, conversely, that a solution of the summation equation (5.3) is also a solution of the TPBVP (5.2).

Now let $\psi(0), \ldots, \psi(q)$ be a solution of (5.2). Then $\psi(0), \ldots, \psi(q)$ is also a solution of the linear TPBVP

$$(5.6) \quad \begin{aligned} & y(j+1) - y(j) = A(j)\, y(j+1) + B(j)\, y(j) + f(j) \\ & My(0) + Ny(q) = d \end{aligned}$$

where

$$(5.7) \quad \begin{aligned} f(j) &= F(\psi(j+1), \psi(j), j) - A(j)\, \psi(j+1) - B(j)\, \psi(j) \\ d &= c - g(\psi(0)) - h(\psi(q)) + M\psi(0) + N\psi(q). \end{aligned}$$

Since $f(j)$ is defined for all j in $\mathbf{Q}'$ and since $\{A(j), B(j), M, N\}$ is a boundary-compatible set, all the conditions of Corollary 3.8 are satisfied by the linear TPBVP (5.6). It follows that $\psi(0), \ldots, \psi(q)$ is the *unique* solution of (5.6) and hence, can be written in the form

$$(5.8) \quad \psi(j) = H^{V_{MN}}(j)\, d + \sum_{k=0}^{q-1} G^{V_{MN}}(j, k)\, f(k)$$

where $H^{V_{MN}}(j)$ and $G^{V_{MN}}(j, k)$ are given by (5.4) and (5.5), respectively. From (5.7) and (5.8), we then deduce that $\psi(0), \ldots, \psi(q)$ is a solution of the summation equation (5.3).

Conversely, let us suppose that $\phi(0), \ldots, \phi(q)$ is a solution of (5.3). Then, for any k in $\mathbf{Q}'$,

$$\phi(k+1) - \phi(k) = [H^{V_{MN}}(k+1) - H^{V_{MN}}(k)]\, d_\phi + \sum_{l=0}^{q-1} [G^{V_{MN}}(k+1, l) - G^{V_{MN}}(k, l)]\, f_\phi(l) \tag{5.9}$$

where

$$\begin{aligned} f_\phi(l) &= F(\phi(l+1), \phi(l), l) - A(l)\,\phi(l+1) - B(l)\,\phi(l) \\ d_\phi &= c - g(\phi(0)) - h(\phi(q)) + M\phi(0) + N\phi(q). \end{aligned} \tag{5.10}$$

In view of (5.4), we can see that

$$H^{V_{MN}}(k+1) - H^{V_{MN}}(k) = [\Phi^V(k+1, 0) - \Phi^V(k, 0)] \times [M + N\Phi^V(q, 0)]^{-1} \tag{5.11}$$

for k in $\mathbf{Q}'$. Now, for $k \geqslant l$, $\Phi^V(k+1, l) - \Phi^V(k, l) = V(k)\,\Phi^V(k, l)$ (since $\Phi^V(j, i) = [I + V(j-1)] \cdots [I + V(i)]$ if $j \geqslant i+1$ and $\Phi^V(j, i) = I$ if $j = i$). Thus,

$$\begin{aligned} H^{V_{MN}}(k+1) - H^{V_{MN}}(k) &= V(k)\,\Phi^V(k, 0)[M + N\Phi^V(q, 0)]^{-1} \\ &= V(k)\, H^{V_{MN}}(k) \end{aligned} \tag{5.12}$$

for k in $\mathbf{Q}'$. Similarly, we deduce from (5.5) that

$$G^{V_{MN}}(k+1, l) - G^{V_{MN}}(k, l)$$

is given by the following formulas:

$$\begin{aligned} &G^{V_{MN}}(k+1, l) - G^{V_{MN}}(k, l) \\ &\quad = -[H^{V_{MN}}(k+1) - H^{V_{MN}}(k)]\, N\Phi^V(q, l+1)[I - A(l)]^{-1} \\ &\qquad + [\Phi^V(k+1, l+1) - \Phi^V(k, l+1)][I - A(l)]^{-1} \\ &\quad = -V(k)\, H^{V_{MN}}(k)\, N\Phi^V(q, l+1)[I - A(l)]^{-1} \\ &\qquad + V(k)\,\Phi^V(k, l+1)[I - A(l)]^{-1} \\ &\quad = V(k)\, G^{V_{MN}}(k, l) \end{aligned} \tag{5.13}$$

if $k \geqslant l+1$;

$$\text{(5.14)}\quad G^{VMN}(k+1, l) - G^{VMN}(k, l)$$
$$= -[H^{VMN}(k+1) - H^{VMN}(k)]\, N\Phi^V(q, l+1)[I - A(l)]^{-1}$$
$$= V(k)\, G^{VMN}(k, l)$$

if $k \leqslant l-1$; and

$$\text{(5.15)}\quad G^{VMN}(k+1, l) - G^{VMN}(k, l)$$
$$= -[H^{VMN}(k+1) - H^{VMN}(k)]\, N\Phi^V(q, l+1)[I - A(l)]^{-1}$$
$$+ \Phi^V(k+1, l+1)[I - A(l)]^{-1}$$
$$= V(k)\, G^{VMN}(k, l) + [I - A(l)]^{-1}$$

if $k = l$. Substitution of (5.12) and (5.13)–(5.15) into (5.9) leads to

$$\text{(5.16)}\qquad \phi(k+1) - \phi(k) = V(k)\,\phi(k) + [I - A(k)]^{-1} f_\phi(k)$$

for k in $\mathbf{Q}'$ since $\phi(0), \ldots, \phi(q)$ is a solution of (5.3). However, $V(k) = [I - A(k)]^{-1}[A(k) + B(k)]$ and so we have

$$\text{(5.17)}\quad \phi(k+1) - \phi(k)$$
$$= [I - A(k)]^{-1}\{A(k)\,\phi(k) + B(k)\,\phi(k) + F(\phi(k+1), \phi(k), k)$$
$$- A(k)\,\phi(k+1) - B(k)\,\phi(k)\}$$

or, equivalently,

$$\text{(5.18)}\qquad \phi(k+1) - \phi(k) = F(\phi(k+1), \phi(k), k))$$

for any k in $\mathbf{Q}'$. Thus, $\phi(0), \ldots, \phi(q)$ satisfies the difference equation (5.2).

The proof that $\phi(0), \ldots, \phi(q)$ satisfies the boundary condition of (5.2) proceeds along similar lines. We observe that

$$\text{(5.19)}\quad M\phi(0) + N\phi(q) = [MH^{VMN}(0) + NH^{VMN}(q)]\, d_\phi$$
$$+ \sum_{l=0}^{q-1} [MG^{VMN}(0, l) + NG^{VMN}(q, l)]\, f_\phi(l)$$

where

$$d_\phi = c - g(\phi(0)) - h(\phi(q)) + M\phi(0) + N\phi(q)$$

and

$$f_\phi(l) = F(\phi(l+1), \phi(l), l) - A(l)\phi(l+1) - B(l)\phi(l).$$

Since

$$(5.20)\quad MH^{V_{MN}}(0) + NH^{V_{MN}}(q) = [M\Phi^V(0,0) + N\Phi^V(q,0)][M + N\Phi^V(q,0)]^{-1} = I$$

by virtue of (5.4) and since

$$(5.21)\quad MG^{V_{MN}}(0,l) + NG^{V_{MN}}(q,l) = -[MH^{V_{MN}}(0) + NH^{V_{MN}}(q)]\, N\Phi^V(q, l+1)[I - A(l)]^{-1} + N\Phi^V(q, l+1)[I - A(l)]^{-1} = 0$$

by virtue of (5.5) and (5.20), we deduce that

$$(5.22)\quad M\phi(0) + N\phi(q) = c - g(\phi(0)) - h(\phi(q)) + M\phi(0) + N\phi(q)$$

and hence that

$$(5.23)\quad g(\phi(0)) + h(\phi(q)) = c.$$

Thus, the proof of the theorem is complete.

3.6. A Continuous Example

We illustrate the results of Sections 2 and 4 with a simple example. We proceed as follows. First, we illustrate Lemma 2.13 by the choice of a matrix V which is boundary compatible with the matrices M and N of the example. Then we use Corollary 2.7 to determine an expression for the linear TPBVP corresponding to the boundary-compatible set $\{V, M, N\}$. Finally, we use Theorem 4.1 to obtain an integral equation which is equivalent to the original TPBVP.

We consider the nonlinear TPBVP

$$\begin{bmatrix} \dot{y}_1 \\ \dot{y}_2 \end{bmatrix} = \begin{bmatrix} -\epsilon\sqrt{y_1} - b^2 y_2 \\ \epsilon y_2/2\sqrt{y_1} \end{bmatrix} \tag{6.1}$$

$$\begin{bmatrix} 1 & 0 \\ 0 & 0 \end{bmatrix}\begin{bmatrix} y_1(0) \\ y_2(0) \end{bmatrix} + \begin{bmatrix} 0 & 0 \\ 1 & 0 \end{bmatrix}\begin{bmatrix} y_1(1) \\ y_2(1) \end{bmatrix} = \begin{bmatrix} c_1 \\ c_2 \end{bmatrix}$$

with $\epsilon > 0$. Obvious choices for M and N are given by

$$M = \begin{bmatrix} 1 & 0 \\ 0 & 0 \end{bmatrix}, \qquad N = \begin{bmatrix} 0 & 0 \\ 1 & 0 \end{bmatrix} \tag{6.2}$$

and the matrix $[M\,N]$ has rank 2. It follows from Lemma 2.13 that there is a matrix $V(t)$ such that $\{V(t), M, N\}$ forms a boundary-compatible set.

We first try the simplest matrix $V = 0$. Then $\Phi^V(t, s) = e^{0(t-s)} = I$ and $\det(M + N\Phi^V(1, 0)) = \det(M + NI) = 0$. Thus, the choice $V = 0$ does not result in a boundary compatible set. This shows that not every matrix of the proper dimension leads to a boundary-compatible set. We next try the matrix

$$V = \begin{bmatrix} 0 & 1 \\ 0 & 0 \end{bmatrix}. \tag{6.3}$$

Then

$$\Phi^V(t, s) = e^{V(t-s)} = \begin{bmatrix} 1 & t-s \\ 0 & 1 \end{bmatrix} \tag{6.4}$$

for all t, s and so

$$M + N\Phi^V(1, 0) = \begin{bmatrix} 1 & 0 \\ 0 & 0 \end{bmatrix} + \begin{bmatrix} 0 & 0 \\ 1 & 0 \end{bmatrix}\begin{bmatrix} 1 & 1 \\ 0 & 1 \end{bmatrix} = \begin{bmatrix} 1 & 0 \\ 1 & 1 \end{bmatrix} \tag{6.5}$$

is nonsingular. It follows that $\{V, M, N\}$ is a boundary-compatible set.

Since $[M + N\Phi^V(1, 0)]^{-1}$ is given by

$$[M + N\Phi^V(1,0)]^{-1} = \begin{bmatrix} 1 & 0 \\ -1 & 1 \end{bmatrix} \tag{6.6}$$

we have

$$H^{V_{MN}}(t) = \Phi^V(t,0)[M + N\Phi^V(1,0)]^{-1} = \begin{bmatrix} 1-t & t \\ -1 & 1 \end{bmatrix} \tag{6.7}$$

and

$$G^{V_{MN}}(t,s) = H^{V_{MN}}(t)\, M\Phi^V(0,s) = \begin{bmatrix} 1-t & -(1-t)s \\ -1 & s \end{bmatrix} \tag{6.8}$$

for $0 \leqslant s < t$, and

$$G^{V_{MN}}(t,s) = -H^{V_{MN}}(t)\, N\Phi^V(1,s) = \begin{bmatrix} -t & -t(1-s) \\ -1 & -(1-s) \end{bmatrix} \tag{6.9}$$

for $t < s \leqslant 1$. It follows that the solution of the linear TPBVP

$$\begin{bmatrix} \dot{y}_1 \\ \dot{y}_2 \end{bmatrix} - \begin{bmatrix} 0 & 1 \\ 0 & 0 \end{bmatrix} \begin{bmatrix} y_1 \\ y_2 \end{bmatrix} = \begin{bmatrix} f_1(t) \\ f_2(t) \end{bmatrix}, \tag{6.10}$$

$$\begin{bmatrix} 1 & 0 \\ 0 & 0 \end{bmatrix} \begin{bmatrix} y_1(0) \\ y_2(0) \end{bmatrix} + \begin{bmatrix} 0 & 0 \\ 1 & 0 \end{bmatrix} \begin{bmatrix} y_1(1) \\ y_2(1) \end{bmatrix} = \begin{bmatrix} c_1 \\ c_2 \end{bmatrix}$$

is given by

$$\begin{bmatrix} y_1(t) \\ y_2(t) \end{bmatrix} = \begin{bmatrix} 1-t & t \\ -1 & 1 \end{bmatrix} \begin{bmatrix} c_1 \\ c_2 \end{bmatrix} + \int_0^t \begin{bmatrix} 1-t & -(1-t)s \\ -1 & s \end{bmatrix} \begin{bmatrix} f_1(s) \\ f_2(s) \end{bmatrix} ds + \int_t^1 \begin{bmatrix} -t & -t(1-s) \\ -1 & -(1-s) \end{bmatrix} \begin{bmatrix} f_1(s) \\ f_2(s) \end{bmatrix} ds \tag{6.11}$$

or componentwise, by

$$
(6.12)\qquad
\begin{aligned}
y_1(t) &= c_1 + (c_2 - c_1)\, t + \int_0^t \{(1 - t) f_1(s) - (1 - t)\, s f_2(s)\}\, ds \\
&\quad + \int_t^1 \{- t f_1(s) - t(1 - s) f_2(s)\}\, ds \\
y_2(t) &= c_2 - c_1 + \int_0^t \{- f_1(s) + s f_2(s)\}\, ds \\
&\quad + \int_t^1 \{- f_1(s) - (1 - s) f_2(s)\}\, ds
\end{aligned}
$$

for t in $[0, 1]$. We note that if $f_1(t) = 0$, then (6.12) reduces to the well-known solution [A1] of the linear TPBVP $\ddot{y}_1(t) = f_2(t)$, $y_1(0) = c_1$, $y_1(1) = c_2$.

Using (6.11) and Theorem 4.1, we find that the original nonlinear TPBVP (6.1) is equivalent to the following integral equation:

$$
(6.13)\qquad
\begin{aligned}
\begin{bmatrix} y_1(t) \\ y_2(t) \end{bmatrix} &= \begin{bmatrix} c_1 + (c_2 - c_1)t \\ c_2 - c_1 \end{bmatrix} \\
&\quad + \int_0^t \left\{ \begin{bmatrix} 1 - t & -(1 - t)s \\ -1 & +s \end{bmatrix} \right. \\
&\qquad \left. \times \begin{bmatrix} -\epsilon \sqrt{y_1(s)} - (b^2 + 1)\, y_2(s) \\ \epsilon y_2(s)/2\sqrt{y_1(s)} \end{bmatrix} \right\} ds \\
&\quad + \int_t^1 \left\{ \begin{bmatrix} -t & -t(1 - s) \\ -1 & -(1 - s) \end{bmatrix} \right. \\
&\qquad \left. \times \begin{bmatrix} -\epsilon \sqrt{y_1(s)} - (b^2 + 1)\, y_2(s) \\ \epsilon y_2(s)/2\sqrt{y_1(s)} \end{bmatrix} \right\} ds
\end{aligned}
$$

with $\epsilon > 0$ and $0 \leqslant t \leqslant 1$. This type of integral representation will play an important role in the sequel.

3.7. A Discrete Example

To illustrate the results of Sections 3 and 5 we discuss a simple discrete example which is very similar to the continuous example of Section 6. Our approach is also very similar. First, we illustrate Lemma 3.4 by the choice of two matrices $A(j)$ and $B(j)$ [which determine the matrix $V(j)$] which are boundary compatible with the matrices M and N of the example. Then, we determine the expression for the solution of the linear TPBVP corresponding to the boundary-compatible set $\{A(j), B(j), M, N\}$ with the aid of Corollary 3.8. Finally, we use Theorem 5.1 to obtain a summation equation which is equivalent to the original discrete TPBVP.

We consider the nonlinear discrete TPBVP

$$\begin{bmatrix} y_1(k+1) \\ y_2(k+1) \end{bmatrix} - \begin{bmatrix} y_1(k) \\ y_2(k) \end{bmatrix} = \begin{bmatrix} -y_2(k) \\ -y_1^3(k) \end{bmatrix}, \tag{7.1}$$

$$\begin{bmatrix} y_1(0) \\ 0 \end{bmatrix} + \begin{bmatrix} 0 \\ y_1(q) \end{bmatrix} = \begin{bmatrix} c_1 \\ c_2 \end{bmatrix}.$$

Obvious choices for the matrices M and N are

$$M = \begin{bmatrix} 1 & 0 \\ 0 & 0 \end{bmatrix}, \qquad N = \begin{bmatrix} 0 & 0 \\ 1 & 0 \end{bmatrix} \tag{7.2}$$

which results in a matrix $[M\,N]$ with rank 2. Lemma 3.17 then implies the existence of matrices $A(j)$ and $B(j)$ which form a boundary-compatible set with these matrices M and N.

Just as in the continuous case, we first try the simple matrices $A(j) = 0$ and $B(j) = 0$. This choice results in a matrix $V(j) = [I - A(j)]^{-1}[A(j)+B(j)] = 0$, $\Phi^V(j, k) = I$, and $\det(M+N\Phi^V(q, 0)) = 0$. The resulting set $\{A(j), B(j), M, N\}$ is thus not boundary compatible, which shows that not every set of matrices of the proper dimension is boundary compatible. We next try the matrices

$$A = \begin{bmatrix} 0 & -1 \\ 0 & 0 \end{bmatrix}, \qquad B = \begin{bmatrix} 0 & 0 \\ 0 & 0 \end{bmatrix}. \tag{7.3}$$

This choice leads to

$$V(j) = \begin{bmatrix} 0 & -1 \\ 0 & 0 \end{bmatrix}, \tag{7.4}$$

$$\Phi^V(j, i) = \begin{bmatrix} 1 & -(j-i) \\ 0 & 1 \end{bmatrix}, \tag{7.5}$$

and

$$\begin{aligned} M + N\Phi^V(q, 0) &= \begin{bmatrix} 1 & 0 \\ 0 & 0 \end{bmatrix} + \begin{bmatrix} 0 & 0 \\ 1 & 0 \end{bmatrix} \begin{bmatrix} 1 & -q \\ 0 & 1 \end{bmatrix} \\ &= \begin{bmatrix} 1 & 0 \\ 1 & -q \end{bmatrix}. \end{aligned} \tag{7.6}$$

Since $\det(M + N\Phi^V(q, 0)) = -q$, the last matrix is nonsingular. This implies that the choice (7.3) results in a boundary-compatible set.

With $[M + N\Phi(q, 0)]^{-1}$ given by

$$[M + N\Phi(q, 0)]^{-1} = \begin{bmatrix} 1 & 0 \\ q^{-1} & -q^{-1} \end{bmatrix} \tag{7.7}$$

we have

$$H^{VMN}(j) = \Phi^V(j, 0)[M + N\Phi^V(q, 0)]^{-1} = \begin{bmatrix} 1 - jq^{-1} & jq^{-1} \\ q^{-1} & -q^{-1} \end{bmatrix} \tag{7.8}$$

and with Corollary 3.13 being applicable

$$\begin{aligned} G^{VMN}(j, i) &= H^{VMN}(j)\, M\Phi^V(0, i+1)[I - A(i)]^{-1} \\ &= \begin{bmatrix} 1 - jq^{-1} & (1 - jq^{-1})i \\ q^{-1} & q^{-1}i \end{bmatrix} \end{aligned} \tag{7.9}$$

for $0 \leqslant i \leqslant j - 1$, and

$$\begin{aligned} G^{VMN}(j, i) &= -H^{VMN}(j)\, N\Phi^V(q, i+1)[I - A(i)]^{-1} \\ &= \begin{bmatrix} -jq^{-1} & jq^{-1}(q-i) \\ q^{-1} & -q^{-1}(q-i) \end{bmatrix} \end{aligned} \tag{7.10}$$

for $j \leqslant i \leqslant q$. According to Corollary 3.8, the solution of the discrete linear TPBVP

$$\begin{bmatrix} y_1(k+1) \\ y_2(k+1) \end{bmatrix} - \begin{bmatrix} y_1(k) \\ y_2(k) \end{bmatrix} = \begin{bmatrix} 0 & -1 \\ 0 & 0 \end{bmatrix} \begin{bmatrix} y_1(k+1) \\ y_2(k+1) \end{bmatrix} + \begin{bmatrix} 0 & 0 \\ 0 & 0 \end{bmatrix} \begin{bmatrix} y_1(k) \\ y_2(k) \end{bmatrix} + \begin{bmatrix} f_1(j) \\ f_2(j) \end{bmatrix} \tag{7.11}$$

$$\begin{bmatrix} 1 & 0 \\ 0 & 0 \end{bmatrix} \begin{bmatrix} y_1(0) \\ y_2(0) \end{bmatrix} + \begin{bmatrix} 0 & 0 \\ 1 & 0 \end{bmatrix} \begin{bmatrix} y_1(q) \\ y_2(q) \end{bmatrix} = \begin{bmatrix} c_1 \\ c_2 \end{bmatrix}$$

is now given by

$$\begin{bmatrix} y_1(k) \\ y_2(k) \end{bmatrix} = \begin{bmatrix} 1 - jq^{-1} & jq^{-1} \\ q^{-1} & -q^{-1} \end{bmatrix} \begin{bmatrix} c_1 \\ c_2 \end{bmatrix} + \sum_{i=0}^{j-1} \begin{bmatrix} 1 - jq^{-1} & (1 - jq^{-1})i \\ q^{-1} & q^{-1}i \end{bmatrix} \begin{bmatrix} f_1(i) \\ f_2(i) \end{bmatrix} + \sum_{i=j}^{q-1} \begin{bmatrix} -jq^{-1} & jq^{-1}(q-i) \\ q^{-1} & -q^{-1}(q-i) \end{bmatrix} \begin{bmatrix} f_1(i) \\ f_2(i) \end{bmatrix}. \tag{7.12}$$

Using this result, (7.12), and Theorem 5.1, we find that the original nonlinear, discrete TPBVP (7.1) is equivalent to the summation equation

$$\begin{bmatrix} y_1(k) \\ y_2(k) \end{bmatrix} = \begin{bmatrix} c_1 + (c_2 - c_1)\,jq^{-1} \\ -(c_2 - c_1)\,q^{-1} \end{bmatrix} + \sum_{i=0}^{j-1} \begin{bmatrix} 1 - jq^{-1} & (1 - jq^{-1})i \\ q^{-1} & -q^{-1}i \end{bmatrix} \begin{bmatrix} 0 \\ -y_1^{3}(i) \end{bmatrix} \tag{7.13}$$

$$+\sum_{i=j}^{q-1}\begin{bmatrix} -jq^{-1} & jq^{-1}(q-i) \\ q^{-1} & -q^{-1}(q-i) \end{bmatrix}\begin{bmatrix} 0 \\ -y_1{}^3(i) \end{bmatrix}.$$

Summation equation representations of this type play the same role in the discrete case as the integral equation representations play in the continuous case.

3.8. Computation of Derivatives: Continuous Case

We have seen that if the conditions of Theorem 4.1 are satisfied, then the TPBVP

$$\dot{y} = F(y, t), \qquad g(y(0)) + h(y(1)) = c \tag{8.1}$$

is equivalent to the integral equation

$$\begin{aligned} y(t) = {} & H^{VMN}(t)\{c - g[y(0)] - h[y(1)] + My(0) + Ny(1)\} \\ & + \int_0^1 G^{VMN}(t, s)\{F(y(s), s) - V(s)\, y(s)\}\, ds \end{aligned} \tag{8.2}$$

where $H^{VMN}(t)$ and $G^{VMN}(t, s)$ are the Green's matrices of the linear TPBVP corresponding to the boundary-compatible set $J = \{V(t), M, N\}$. Assuming that the conditions of Theorem 4.1 are satisfied, we can define a mapping T^J of the Banach space $Y = \mathscr{C}([0, 1], R_p)$ into itself by setting

$$\begin{aligned} T^J(\varphi)(t) = {} & H^J(t)\{c - g[\varphi(0)] - h[\varphi(1)] + M\varphi(0) + N\varphi(1)\} \\ & + \int_0^1 G^J(t, s)\{F(\varphi(s), s) - V(s)\, \varphi(s)\}\, ds \end{aligned} \tag{8.3}$$

where $\varphi(\cdot) \in \mathscr{C}([0, 1], R_p)$ and

$$H^J(t) = H^{VMN}(t),$$

$$G^J(t, s) = G^{VMN}(t, s).^*$$

Then (8.2) is equivalent to the fixed-point problem

$$y = T^J(y) \tag{8.4}$$

* $T^J(\varphi)(\cdot)$ is continuous in view of (4.4) and (4.5) and the continuity of $\Phi^V(t, 0)$.

on $\mathscr{C}([0, 1], R_p)$ and we can apply the various algorithms of Chapter 2 to (8.4). We shall actually make this application in Chapter 4. However, in order to interpret the theorems and algorithms of Chapter 2 explicitly in terms of F, g, and h, we require the (Frechet) derivatives of the operator T^J and estimates on the norms of these derivatives. We obtain the required derivatives and estimates in this section. We begin with the following.

LEMMA 8.5. Let D be an open set in R_P and let I be an open set in R containing $[0, 1]$. Suppose that (i) $K(t, y, s)$ is a map of $I \times D \times I$ into R_P which is measurable in s for each fixed y and t and continuous in y for each fixed s and t; (ii) $(\partial K/\partial y)(t, y, s)$ is a map of $I \times D \times I$ into $\mathscr{M}(R_P, R_P)$* which is measurable in s for each fixed y and t and continuous in y for each fixed s and t; (iii) there is an integrable function $m(t, s)$ of s with

$$\sup_t \int_0^1 m(t, s)\, ds < \infty$$

such that $\| K(t, y, s)\| \leqslant m(t, s)$ and $\|(\partial K/\partial y)(t, y, s)\| \leqslant m(t, s)$ on $I \times D \times I$; and (iv) $\lim_{t \to t'} \int_0^1 \| K(t, y(s), s) - K(t', y(s), s)\| \, ds = 0$, and $\lim_{t \to t'} \int_0^1 \|(\partial K/\partial y)(t, y(s), s) - (\partial K/\partial y)(t', y(s), s)\| \, ds = 0$ for all t, t' in $[0, 1]$ and $y(\cdot)$ in $\mathscr{C}([0, 1], D)$. Then the mapping T given by

$$T(u)(t) = \int_0^1 K(t, u(s), s)\, ds \tag{8.6}$$

is a differentiable mapping of $\mathscr{C}([0, 1], D)$ into $\mathscr{C}([0, 1], R_P)$ with derivative

$$(T_u'v)(t) = \int_0^1 \frac{\partial K}{\partial y}(t, u(s), s)\, v(s)\, ds \tag{8.7}$$

where $u(\cdot)$ is in $\mathscr{C}([0, 1], D)$.

Proof. We first observe that the mappings T and T_u' carry $\mathscr{C}([0, 1], D)$ into $\mathscr{C}([0, 1], R_P)$ in view of (i), (ii), and (iv) [B0]. Now let $u(\cdot)$ be an element of $\mathscr{C}([0, 1], D)$ and let $w(\cdot)$ be any element of $\mathscr{C}([0, 1], R_p)$ with the segment $u(\cdot) + \theta w(\cdot)$, $0 \leqslant \theta \leqslant 1$, in $\mathscr{C}([0, 1], D)$.

* The set of $p \times p$ matrices.

Then

$$\sup_t \| T(u + w)(t) - T(u)(t) - (T_u{}'w)(t)\|$$
$$= \sup_t \left\| \int_0^1 \{K(t, u(s) + w(s), s) - K(t, u(s), s) - \frac{\partial K}{\partial y}(t, u(s), s)\, w(s)\}\, ds \right\|$$
$$\leqslant \sup_t \int_0^1 \| \psi(t, s, w(s))\|\, ds$$

where

$$\psi(t, s, w(s)) = K(t, u(s) + w(s), s) - K(t, u(s), s) - \frac{\partial K}{\partial y}(t, u(s), s)\, w(s).$$

Let $\| w(\cdot)\| = \sup_s \| w(s)\|$. Then $\| \psi(t, s, w(s))\| / \| w(\cdot)\| \to 0$ pointwise in s as $\| w(\cdot)\| \to 0$ since $\| w(\cdot)\| \geqslant \| w(s)\|$ and $\partial K/\partial y$ is defined. Moreover, it follows from the mean-value theorem that

$$\| \psi(t, s, w(s))\| \leqslant \| w(s)\| \sup_{0<\theta<1} \left[\left\| \frac{\partial K}{\partial y}(t, u(s) + \theta w(s), s) - \frac{\partial K}{\partial y}(t, u(s), s) \right\| \right]$$

and hence, that $\| \psi(t, s, w(s))\| \leqslant 2 \| w(s)\|\, m(t, s)$ in view of (iii). This implies that $(\| \psi(t, s, w(s))\| / \| w(\cdot)\|) \leqslant 2m(t, s)$. Since $m(t, s)$ is integrable,

$$\lim_{\|w(\cdot)\| \to 0} \left\{ \sup_t \int_0^1 \frac{\| \psi(t, s, w(s))\|}{\| w(\cdot)\|}\, ds \right\} = 0 \tag{8.8}$$

by the Lebesque dominated-convergence theorem. Thus, the lemma is established.*

We observe that the lemma remains true if the hypotheses (i) and/or (ii) are replaced by the conditions: (i)′ $K(t, y, s)$ is a map of $I \times D \times I$ into D which is Borel measurable in the pair (y, s) for each t; and (ii)′ $(\partial K/\partial y)(t, y, s)$ is a map of $I \times D \times I$ into $\mathcal{M}(R_p, R_p)$ which is Borel measurable in the pair (y, s) for each t. We now have the following.

COROLLARY 8.9. Suppose that the function $K(t, y, s) = G^J(t, s)\{F(y, s) - V(s)y\}$ satisfies the conditions of Lemma 8.5 and that g, h are differentiable. Then the operator T^J is differentiable and

* Note that $\int_0^1 \| \psi(t, s, w(s)) \|\, ds$ is continuous in t by virtue of (iv).

(8.10) $$[(T_\varphi{}^J)'\,v](t) = H^J(t)\left\{\left[M - \frac{\partial g}{\partial y}(\varphi(0))\right]v(0) + \left[N - \frac{\partial h}{\partial y}(\varphi(1))\right]v(1)\right\} + \int_0^1 G^J(t, s)\left\{\left[\frac{\partial F}{\partial y}(\varphi(s), s) - V(s)\right]v(s)\right\}ds$$

where $\varphi(\cdot) \in \mathscr{C}([0, 1], D)$.

COROLLARY 8.11. Suppose that the functions

$$K(t, y, s) = G^J(t, s)\{F(y, s) - V(s)\,y\}$$

and

$$\frac{\partial K}{\partial y}(t, y, s) = G^J(t, s)\left\{\frac{\partial F}{\partial y}(y, s) - V(s)\right\}$$

satisfy the conditions of Lemma 8.5* and that g and h are twice differentiable. Then the operator T^J is twice differentiable with $(T_\varphi{}^J)'$ given by (8.10) and $(T_\varphi{}^J)''$ given by

(8.12) $$(T_\varphi{}^J)''\,(u, v)(t) = H^J(t)\{[-\,\mathbf{g}^j_{kl}(\varphi(0)), u(0)]\,v(0) + [-\,\mathbf{h}^j_{kl}(\varphi(1)), u(1)]\,v(1)\} + \int_0^1 G^J(t, s)\{[\mathbf{F}^j_{kl}(\varphi(s), s), u(s)]\,v(s)\}\,ds$$

where $\varphi(\cdot) \in \mathscr{C}([0, 1], D)$ and where

(8.13) $$[-\,\mathbf{g}^j_{kl}(\varphi(0)), u(0)] = -\sum_{l=1}^{p}\left(\frac{\partial}{\partial y_l}\left[\frac{\partial g_j}{\partial y_k}\right]\right)(\varphi(0))\,u_l(0)$$

(8.14) $$[-\,\mathbf{h}^j_{kl}(\varphi(1)), u(1)] = -\sum_{l=1}^{p}\left(\frac{\partial}{\partial y_l}\left[\frac{\partial g_j}{\partial y_k}\right]\right)(\varphi(0))\,u_l(1)$$

(8.15) $$[\mathbf{F}^j_{kl}(\varphi(s), s), u(s)] = \sum_{l=1}^{p}\left(\frac{\partial}{\partial y_l}\left[\frac{\partial F_j}{\partial y_k}\right]\right)(\varphi(s), s)\,u_l(s).$$

[Note that, for example, $\mathbf{F}^j_{kl}(\varphi(s), s)$ is the three-entry matrix with elements $(\partial^2 F_j/\partial x_k\,\partial x_l)(\varphi(s), s)$.]

* As regards $(\partial K/\partial y)\,(t, y, s)$, the hypothesis (ii) becomes the following: $(\partial^2 K/\partial y^2)$ (t, y, s) is a map of $I \times D \times I$ into $\mathscr{B}(R_p, R_p)$ which is measurable in s for each fixed y and t and continuous in y for each fixed s and t where $\mathscr{B}(R_p, R_p)$ is the space of bilinear forms on $R_p \oplus R_p$.

We can obtain estimates of the norms of the operators $(T_\varphi{}^J)'$ and $(T_\varphi{}^J)''$ from Corollaries 8.9 and 8.11. We recall first of all that if $w(\cdot) \in \mathscr{C}([0, 1], R_p)$, then

$$\|w(\cdot)\| = \sup_{i\in\mathscr{P}} \sup_{t\in[0,1]} |w_i(t)| \tag{8.16}$$

is the norm of $w(\cdot)$ where $\mathscr{P} = \{1, 2, \ldots, p\}$ and $w_i(\cdot)$ is the ith component of $w(\cdot)$. Noting that $\|(T_\varphi{}^J)'\| = \sup_{\|u\|\leqslant 1}\{\|(T_\varphi{}^J)'u\|\}$ and letting $H^J(t) = [H_{ij}^J(t)]$, $G^J(t, s) = [G_{ij}^J(t, s)]$, $M = [m_{jk}]$, $N = [n_{jk}]$, $V(s) = [v_{jk}(s)]$, we have

$$
\begin{aligned}
\|(T_\phi{}^J)'\| &= \sup_{\|u\|\leqslant 1}\{\|(T_\phi{}^J)'\, u\,\|\} \\
&= \sup_{\|u\|\leqslant 1}\sup_{i\in\mathscr{P}}\sup_{t}\Bigg\{\Bigg|\sum_{k=1}^{p}\sum_{j=1}^{p}\Bigg\{H_{ij}^J(t)\Bigg(\Bigg[m_{jk}-\frac{\partial g_j}{\partial y_k}(\varphi(0))\Bigg]u_k(0) \\
&\quad + \Bigg[n_{jk}-\frac{\partial h_j}{\partial y_k}(\varphi(1))\Bigg]u_k(1)\Bigg) \\
&\quad + \int_0^1 G_{ij}^J(t, s)\Bigg[\frac{\partial F_j}{\partial y_k}(\varphi(s), s)-v_{jk}(s)\Bigg]u_k(s)\,ds\Bigg\}\Bigg|\Bigg\} && \text{(a)} \\
&\leqslant \sup_{i\in\mathscr{P}}\sup_{t}\Bigg\{\sum_{k=1}^{p}\Bigg(\Bigg|\sum_{j=1}^{p}H_{ij}^J(t)\Bigg[m_{jk}-\frac{\partial g_j}{\partial y_k}(\varphi(0))\Bigg]\Bigg| \\
&\quad + \Bigg|\sum_{j=1}^{p}H_{ij}^J(t)\Bigg[n_{jk}-\frac{\partial h_j}{\partial y_k}(\varphi(1))\Bigg]\Bigg|\Bigg) \\
&\quad + \sum_{k=1}^{p}\int_0^1\Bigg|\sum_{j=1}^{p}G_{ij}^J(t, s)\Bigg[\frac{\partial F_j}{\partial y_k}(\varphi(s), s)-v_{jk}(s)\Bigg]\Bigg|\,ds\Bigg\} && \text{(b)} \\
&\leqslant \sup_{i\in\mathscr{P}}\sup_{t}\Bigg\{\sum_{j=1}^{p}\Bigg(\Big|H_{ij}^J(t)\Big|\Bigg)\cdot\Bigg(\sum_{k=1}^{p}\Bigg\{\Bigg|m_{jk}-\frac{\partial g_j}{\partial y_k}(\varphi(0))\Bigg| \\
&\quad + \Bigg|n_{jk}-\frac{\partial h_j}{\partial y_k}(\varphi(1))\Bigg|\Bigg\}\Bigg) + \sum_{j=1}^{p}\Bigg(\int_0^1 |G_{ij}^J(t, s)|\,ds\Bigg) \\
&\quad \times\Bigg(\sup_{s}\Bigg\{\sum_{k=1}^{p}\Bigg|\frac{\partial F_j}{\partial y_k}(\varphi(s), s)-v_{jk}(s)\Bigg|\Bigg\}\Bigg)\Bigg\}. && \text{(c)}
\end{aligned} \tag{8.17}
$$

Since the actual estimate (a) and the somewhat coarser estimate (b) are often difficult to evaluate in practice, we frequently use the coarse estimate (c). Similarly, since the norm of the bilinear operator $(T_\varphi{}^J)''(u, v)$ is given by

$$\|(T_\varphi{}^J)''\| = \sup_{\substack{\|u\|\leqslant 1\\ \|v\|\leqslant 1}} \{\|(T_\varphi{}^J)''(u, v)\|\},$$

we have

$$\begin{aligned}
(8.18)\quad \|(T_\varphi{}^J)''\| &= \sup_{\substack{\|u\|\leqslant 1\\ \|v\|\leqslant 1}} \{\|(T_\varphi{}^J)''(u, v)\|\} \\
&= \sup_{\substack{\|u\|\leqslant 1\\ \|v\|\leqslant 1}} \sup_{i\in\mathscr{P}} \sup_t \Bigg\{\Bigg| \sum_{k=1}^p \sum_{j=1}^p \sum_{l=1}^p \\
&\quad \Bigg\{ H_{ij}^J(t) \Bigg(-\frac{\partial^2 g_j}{\partial y_k\, \partial y_l}(\varphi(0))\, u_l(0)\, v_k(0) \\
&\quad - \frac{\partial^2 h_j}{\partial y_k\, \partial y_l}(\varphi(1))\, u_l(1)\, v_k(1)\Bigg) \\
&\quad + \int_0^1 G_{ij}^J(t, s) \frac{\partial^2 F_j}{\partial y_k\, \partial y_l}(\varphi(s), s)\, u_l(s)\, v_k(s)\, ds\Bigg\} \Bigg|\Bigg\} && \text{(a)} \\
&\leqslant \sup_{i\in\mathscr{P}} \sup_t \Bigg\{ \sum_{k=1}^p \sum_{l=1}^p \Bigg(\Bigg| \sum_{j=1}^p H_{ij}^J(t) \frac{\partial^2 g_j}{\partial y_k\, \partial y_l}(\varphi(0)) \Bigg| \\
&\quad + \Bigg| \sum_{j=1}^p H_{ij}^J(t) \frac{\partial^2 h_j}{\partial y_k\, \partial y_l}(\varphi(1)) \Bigg| \Bigg) \\
&\quad + \sum_{k=1}^p \sum_{l=1}^p \int_0^1 \Bigg| \sum_{j=1}^p G_{ij}^J(t, s) \frac{\partial^2 F_j}{\partial y_k\, \partial y_l}(\varphi(s), s) \Bigg|\, ds \Bigg\} && \text{(b)} \\
&\leqslant \sup_{i\in\mathscr{P}} \sup_t \Bigg\{ \sum_{j=1}^p (|H_{ij}^J(t)|) \cdot \Bigg(\sum_{k=1}^p \sum_{l=1}^p \Bigg\{ \Bigg| \frac{\partial^2 g_j}{\partial y_k\, \partial y_l}(\varphi(0)) \Bigg| \\
&\quad + \Bigg| \frac{\partial^2 h_j}{\partial y_k\, \partial y_l}(\varphi(1)) \Bigg| \Bigg\} \Bigg) + \sum_{j=1}^p \Bigg(\int_0^1 |G_{ij}^J(t, s)|\, ds \Bigg) \\
&\quad \times \Bigg(\sup_s \Bigg\{ \sum_{k=1}^p \sum_{l=1}^p \Bigg| \frac{\partial^2 F_j}{\partial y_k\, \partial y_l}(\varphi(s), s) \Bigg| \Bigg\} \Bigg) \Bigg\}. && \text{(c)}
\end{aligned}$$

Again the actual estimate (a) and the somewhat coarser estimate (b) are often difficult to evaluate in practice and so the coarse estimate (c) is frequently used.

We use the estimates (8.17) and (8.18) quite often in the sequel. To avoid repetition of these cumbersome formulas, *we write* $\|(T_\varphi{}^J)'\|_{(a)}$, $\|(T_\varphi{}^J)'\|_{(b)}$, and $\|(T_\varphi{}^J)'\|_{(c)}$ *in place of the right-hand sides of* (8.17), (a), (b), *and* (c), *respectively, and* $\|(T_\varphi{}^J)''\|_{(a)}$, $\|(T_\varphi{}^J)''\|_{(b)}$, and $\|(T_\varphi{}^J)''\|_{(c)}$ *in place of the right-hand sides of* (8.18), (a), (b), *and* (c), *respectively*. Thus, for example, $\|(T_\varphi{}^J)'\|_{(c)} \leqslant \delta$ means that the right-hand side of (8.17) (c) is no greater than δ.

3.9. Computation of Derivatives: Discrete Case

We have seen that if the conditions of Theorem 5.1 are satisfied, then the TPBVP

$$(9.1) \qquad y(j+1) - y(j) = F(y(j+1), y(j), j), \qquad g(y(0)) + h(y(q)) = c$$

is equivalent to the summation equation

$$(9.2) \qquad y(j) = H^{V_{MN}}(j)\{c - g(y(0)) - h(y(q)) + My(0) + Ny(q)\} + \sum_{k=0}^{q-1} G^{V_{MN}}(j, k)\{F(y(k+1), y(k), k) - A(k)\, y(k+1) - B(k)\, y(k)\}$$

where $H^{V_{MN}}(j)$ and $G^{V_{MN}}(j, k)$ are the Green's matrices of the linear TPBVP corresponding to the boundary-compatible set

$$J = \{A(j), B(j), M, N\}.$$

Assuming then that the conditions of Theorem 5.1 are satisfied and letting $\mathbf{Q} = \{0, 1, \ldots, q\}$, we can define a mapping T^J of the Banach space $Y = \mathscr{S}(\mathbf{Q}, R_p)$ into itself by setting

$$(9.3) \qquad T^J(\varphi)(j) = H^J(j)\{c - g[\varphi(0)] - h[\varphi(q)] + M\varphi(0) + N\varphi(q)\} + \sum_{k=0}^{q-1} G^J(j, k)\{F(\varphi(k+1), \varphi(k), k) - A(k)\, \varphi(k+1) - B(k)\, \varphi(k)\}$$

where $\varphi(\cdot) \in \mathscr{S}(\mathbf{Q}, R_p)$ and $H^J(j) = H^{V_{MN}}(j)$, $G^J(j, k) = G^{V_{MN}}(j, k)$. Then, (9.2) is equivalent to the fixed-point problem

$$y = T^J(y) \tag{9.4}$$

on $\mathscr{S}(\mathbf{Q}, R_p)$ and we can apply the various algorithms of Chapter 2 to (9.4). We shall actually make this application in Chapter 4. However, in order to interpret the theorems and algorithms of Chapter 2 explicitly in terms of F, g, and h, we require the (Frechet) derivatives of the operator T^J and estimates on the norms of these derivatives. We obtain the required derivatives and estimates in this section. We begin with the following.

LEMMA 9.5. Let D be an open set in R_p and let $\mathbf{Q} = \{0, 1, \ldots, q\}$ and $\mathbf{Q}' = \{0, 1, \ldots, q-1\}$. Suppose that (i) $K(j, x, y, k)$ is a map of $\mathbf{Q} \times D \times D \times \mathbf{Q}'$ into R_p; (ii) $(\partial K/\partial x)(j, x, y, k)$ and $(\partial K/\partial y)(j, x, y, k)$ are maps of $\mathbf{Q} \times D \times D \times \mathbf{Q}'$ into $\mathscr{M}(R_p, R_p)$ with (say) $(\partial K/\partial y)(j, x, y, k)$ continuous in x for fixed j, y, and k*; and (iii) there is a function $m(j, k)$ such that

$$\| K(j, x, y, k)\| \leqslant m(j, k),$$

$$\left\| \frac{\partial K}{\partial x}(j, x, y, k) \right\| \leqslant m(j, k),$$

and

$$\left\| \frac{\partial K}{\partial y}(j, x, y, k) \right\| \leqslant m(j, k)$$

on $\mathbf{Q} \times D \times D \times \mathbf{Q}'$. Then the mapping T given by

$$T(u)(j) = \sum_{k=0}^{q-1} K(j, u(k+1), u(k), k) \tag{9.6}$$

is a differentiable mapping of $\mathscr{S}(\mathbf{Q}, D)$ into $\mathscr{S}(\mathbf{Q}, R_p)$ with derivative

$$(T_u{}'v)(j) = \sum_{k=0}^{q-1} \left\{ \frac{\partial K}{\partial x}(j, u(k+1), u(k), k)\, v(k+1) + \frac{\partial K}{\partial y}(j, u(k+1), u(k), k)\, v(k) \right\} \tag{9.7}$$

where $u(\cdot)$ is in $\mathscr{S}(\mathbf{Q}, D)$.

* Or with $(\partial K/\partial x)(j, x, y, k)$ continuous in y for fixed j, x, and k.

Proof. It is obvious that the mappings T and T_u' carry $\mathscr{S}(\mathbf{Q}, D)$ into $\mathscr{S}(\mathbf{Q}, R_p)$. Now let $u(\cdot)$ be an element of $\mathscr{S}(\mathbf{Q}, D)$ and let $w(\cdot)$ be any element of $\mathscr{S}(\mathbf{Q}, R_p)$ with the segment $u(\cdot) + \theta w(\cdot)$, $0 \leqslant \theta \leqslant 1$, in $\mathscr{S}(\mathbf{Q}, D)$. Then

$$\sup_j \| T(u + w)(j) - T(u)(j) - (T_u'w)(j)\|$$

$$= \sup_j \left\| \sum_{k=0}^{q-1} \{\psi_1(j, k, w(k)) + \psi_2(j, k, w(k)) + \psi_3(j, k, w(k))\} \right\|$$

where

$$\begin{aligned}\psi_1(j, k, w(k)) = {} & K(j, u(k + 1) + w(k + 1), u(k) + w(k), k) \\ & - K(j, u(k + 1) + w(k + 1), u(k), k) \\ & - \frac{\partial K}{\partial y} (j, u(k + 1) + w(k + 1), u(k), k)\, w(k),\end{aligned}$$

$$\begin{aligned}\psi_2(j, k, w(k)) = {} & K(j, u(k + 1) + w(k + 1), u(k), k) \\ & - K(j, u(k + 1), u(k), k) \\ & - \frac{\partial K}{\partial x} (j, u(k + 1), u(k), k)\, w(k + 1),\end{aligned}$$

and

$$\begin{aligned}\psi_3(j, k, w(k)) = {} & \left\{\frac{\partial K}{\partial y} (j, u(k + 1) + w(k + 1), u(k), k)\right. \\ & \left. - \frac{\partial K}{\partial y} (j, u(k + 1), u(k), k)\right\} w(k).\end{aligned}$$

Application of the mean-value theorem and the hypothesis (iii) leads to the estimates $\| \psi_1(j, k, w(k)\| \leqslant 2m(j, k) \| w(k)\|$ and $\| \psi_2(j, k, w(k))\| \leqslant 2m(j, k) \| w(k)\|$. Moreover, it follows directly from (iii) that $\| \psi_3(j, k, w(k))\| \leqslant 2m(j, k) \| w(k)\|$. Let $\| w(\cdot)\|_\infty = \sup_l \| w(l)\|$. Then $\| \psi_i(j, k, w(k))\|/\| w(\cdot)\|_\infty \to 0$ pointwise in k as $\| w(\cdot)\|_\infty \to 0$ for $i = 1, 2, 3$ since $\| w(\cdot)\|_\infty \geqslant \| w(k)\|$, $\partial K/\partial x$ and $\partial K/\partial y$ are defined, and $\partial K/\partial y$ is continuous in x. Since $\sum_k m(j, k) < \infty$, we have

$$\lim_{\|w(\cdot)\|_\infty \to 0} \sup_j \left\{ \sum_{k=0}^{q-1} \frac{[\psi_1(j, k, w(k)) + \psi_2(j, k, w(k)) + \psi_3(j, k, w(k))]}{\| w(\cdot)\|_\infty} \right\} = 0 \tag{9.8}$$

by the Lebesque dominated convergence theorem.* Thus, the lemma is established.

We observe that Lemma 9.5 is entirely analogous to Lemma 8.5 and that both can be viewed as special cases of a lemma on Banach space-valued integrals. We now have the following.

COROLLARY 9.9. Suppose that the function

$$K(j, x, y, k) = G^J(j, k)\{F(x, y, k) - A(k)\,x - B(k)y\}$$

satisfies the conditions of Lemma 9.5 and that g and h are differentiable. Then the mapping T^J is differentiable and

$$(9.10)\quad [(T_\varphi{}^J)'v](j) = H^J(j)\left\{\left[M - \frac{\partial g}{\partial y}(\varphi(0))\right]v(0) + \left[N - \frac{\partial h}{\partial y}(\varphi(q))\right]v(q)\right\}$$
$$+ \sum_{k=0}^{q-1} G^J(j, k)\left\{\left[\frac{\partial F}{\partial x}(\varphi(k+1), \varphi(k), k) - A(k)\right]\right.$$
$$\left.\times\, v(k+1) + \left[\frac{\partial F}{\partial y}(\varphi(k+1), \varphi(k), k) - B(k)\right]v(k)\right\}$$

where $\varphi(\cdot) \in \mathscr{S}(\mathbf{Q}, D)$.

COROLLARY 9.11. Suppose that the functions

$$K(j, x, y, k) = G^J(j, k)\{F(x, y, k) - A(k)x - B(k)y\}$$

and

$$\frac{\partial K}{\partial x}(j, x, y, k) = G^J(j, k)\left\{\frac{\partial F}{\partial x}(x, y, k) - A(k)\right\}$$

and

$$\frac{\partial K}{\partial y}(j, x, y, k) = G^J(j, k)\left\{\frac{\partial F}{\partial y}(x, y, k) - B(k)\right\}$$

satisfy the conditions of Lemma 9.5 and that g and h are twice

* The measure μ on $\mathbf{Q}'$ is given by $\mu(k) = 1$ for $k \in \mathbf{Q}'$ and $\mu(\phi) = 0$.

differentiable. Then the mapping T^J is twice differentiable with $(T_\varphi{}^J)'$ given by (9.10) and $(T_\varphi{}^J)''$ given by

(9.12)* $$(T_\varphi{}^J)''(u, v)(j) = H^J(j)\{[-\mathbf{g}^i_{kl}(\varphi(0)), u(0)]\, v(0) + [-\mathbf{h}^i_{kl}(\varphi(q)), u(q)]\, v(q)\} + \sum_{k=0}^{q-1} G^J(j, k) \times \{[\mathbf{F}^{i,xx}_{kl}(\varphi(k+1), \varphi(k), k), u(k+1)]\, v(k+1) + [\mathbf{F}^{i,xy}_{kl}(\varphi(k+1), \varphi(k), k), u(k+1)]\, v(k) + [\mathbf{F}^{i,yx}_{kl}(\varphi(k+1), \varphi(k), k), u(k)]\, v(k+1) + [\mathbf{F}^{i,yy}_{kl}(\varphi(k+1), \varphi(k), k), u(k)]\, v(k)\}.$$

[Note that, for example, $\mathbf{F}^{i,xy}_{kl}(\varphi(k+1), \varphi(k), k)$ is the three-entry matrix with elements $(\partial^2 F_i/\partial x_k\, \partial y_l)(\varphi(k+1), \varphi(k), k)$.]

We can obtain estimates of the norms of the operators $(T_\varphi{}^J)'$ and $(T_\varphi{}^J)''$ from Corollaries (9.9) and (9.11). We recall first of all that if $w(\cdot) \in \mathscr{S}(\mathbf{Q}, R_p)$, then

(9.13) $$\| w(\cdot)\| = \sup_{i \in \mathscr{P}} \sup_{j \in \mathbf{Q}} | w_i(j)|$$

is the norm of $w(\cdot)$ where $\mathscr{P} = \{1, 2, \ldots, p\}$ and $w_i(\cdot)$ is the ith component of $w(\cdot)$. The matrix norm which corresponds to (9.13) is given by

(9.14) $$\| P(j)\| = \sup_{i \in \mathscr{P}} \sup_{j \in \mathbf{Q}} \left\{ \sum_{k=1}^{p} | p_{ik}(j)| \right\}$$

where $P(j) = (p_{ik}(j))$. We also use the notation $| P(j)|$ for the matrix $(| p_{ik}(j)|)$. Noting that $\|(T_\varphi{}^J)'\| = \sup_{\|u(\cdot)\| \leq 1} \{\|(T_\varphi{}^J)'u\|\}$ and letting $H^J(\alpha) = [H^J_{ik}(\alpha)]$, $G^J(\alpha, \beta) = [G^J_{ik}(\alpha, \beta)]$, $M = [m_{k\mu}]$, $N = [n_{k\mu}]$, $A(l) = [a_{k\mu}(l)]$, and $B(l) = [b_{k\mu}(l)]$, we have

* The notation is the same as in Corollary 8.11.

$$\text{(9.15)}\quad \|(T_\varphi{}^J)'\| = \sup_{\|u\|\leqslant 1}\{\|(T_\varphi{}^J)'\,u\,\|\}$$

$$= \sup_{\|u\|\leqslant 1}\ \sup_{i\in\mathscr{P}}\ \sup_{\alpha\in\mathbf{Q}} \left\{\left| \sum_{\mu=1}^{p}\sum_{k=1}^{p}\left\{ H^J_{ik}(\alpha)\left(\left[m_{k\mu} - \frac{\partial g_k}{\partial y_\mu}\right]u_\mu(0)\right.\right.\right.\right.$$

$$\left. + \left[n_{k\mu} - \frac{\partial h_k}{\partial y_\mu}\right]u_\mu(q)\right) + \sum_{\beta=0}^{q-1} G^V_{ik}(\alpha,\beta)$$

$$\left.\left.\left.\times\left(\left[\frac{\partial F_k}{\partial x_\mu} - a_{k\mu}(\beta)\right]u_\mu(\beta+1) + \left[\frac{\partial F_k}{\partial y_\mu} - b_{k\mu}(\beta)\right]u_\mu(\beta)\right)\right|\right\} \tag{a}$$

$$\leqslant \sup_{i\in\mathscr{P}}\ \sup_{\alpha\in\mathbf{Q}}\left\{\sum_{\mu=1}^{p}\left(\left|\sum_{k=1}^{p} H^J_{ik}(\alpha)\left[m_{k\mu} - \frac{\partial g_k}{\partial y_\mu}\right]\right|\right.\right.$$

$$\left. + \left|\sum_{k=1}^{p} H^J_{ik}(\alpha)\left[n_{k\mu} - \frac{\partial h_k}{\partial y_\mu}\right]\right|\right)$$

$$+ \sum_{\mu=1}^{p}\sum_{\beta=0}^{q-1}\left(\left|\sum_{k=1}^{p} G^V_{ik}(\alpha,\beta)\left[\frac{\partial F_k}{\partial x_\mu} - a_{k\mu}(\beta)\right]\right|\right.$$

$$\left.\left. + \left|\sum_{k=1}^{P} G^V_{ik}(\alpha,\beta)\left[\frac{\partial F_k}{\partial y_\mu} - b_{k\mu}(\beta)\right]\right|\right)\right\} \tag{b}$$

$$\leqslant \left\| \,|\, H^J(\alpha)| \cdot \left\{\left| M - \frac{\partial g}{\partial y}\right| + \left| N - \frac{\partial h}{\partial y}\right|\right\}\right.$$

$$+ \left(\sum_{\beta=0}^{q-1} |\, G^J(\alpha,\beta)| \left(\sup_\beta \left\{\left|\frac{\partial F}{\partial x} - A(\beta)\right|\right.\right.\right.$$

$$\left.\left.\left.\left. + \left|\frac{\partial F}{\partial y} - B(\beta)\right|\right\}\right)\right)\right\| \tag{c}$$

where the various partial derivatives are evaluated at the proper values of $\varphi(\cdot)$. For example, $\partial F_k/\partial x_\mu = (\partial F_k/\partial x_\mu)(\varphi(\beta+1), \varphi(\beta), \beta)$. The comments made in Section 8 also apply to these estimates.

Similarly, we can obtain analogous estimates for the norm of $(T_\varphi{}^J)''$ using the fact that

$$\|(T_\varphi{}^J)''\| = \sup_{\substack{\|u\|\leqslant 1\\ \|v\|\leqslant 1}} \{\|(T_\varphi{}^J)''(u, v)\|\}.$$

We leave this to the reader. Again to avoid repetition of cumbersome formulas, *we use the simplified notation* $\|(T_\varphi{}^J)'\|_{(a)}$, $\|(T_\varphi{}^J)'\|_{(b)}$, $\|(T_\varphi{}^J)'\|_{(c)}$, $\|(T_\varphi{}^J)''\|_{(a)}$, $\|(T_\varphi{}^J)''\|_{(b)}$, *and* $\|(T_\varphi{}^J)''\|_{(c)}$ *in the sequel.*

3.10. A Lemma on Equivalence: Continuous Case

We now prove a lemma which will play a role in our treatment of Newton's method. This lemma involves the relation between the operators $T^{\tilde J}$ and $T^{\tilde J}$ for different boundary-compatible sets $J = \{V(t), M, N\}$ and $\tilde J = \{U(t), K, L\}$. We have the following.

LEMMA 10.1. Let $J = \{V(t), M, N\}$ and $\tilde J = \{U(t), K, L\}$ be boundary-compatible sets. Let $F(y, t)$ be continuous in y for each fixed t and measurable in t for each fixed y with $\|F(y, t)\| \leqslant m(t)$, $m(t)$ integrable. Let Γ be the linear manifold of absolutely continuous functions in $\mathscr{C}([0, 1], R_p)$. Let U_{KL}^J be the operator given by

$$(10.2)\qquad (U_{KL}^J y)(t) = H^J(t)\{-Ky(0) - Ly(1) + My(0) + Ny(1)\} + \int_0^1 G^J(t, s)\{U(s)\, y(s) - V(s)\, y(s)\}\, ds$$

for $y(\cdot)$ in $\mathscr{C}([0, 1], R_p)$. Then (i) U_{KL}^J maps $\mathscr{C}([0, 1], R_p)$ into $\mathscr{C}([0, 1], R_p)$ and Γ into Γ; (ii) the operator $I - U_{KL}^J$ has a bounded linear inverse on Γ with

$$(10.3)^*\qquad [I - U_{KL}^J]^{-1} y = [I - V_{MN}^{\tilde J}]y$$

for $y(\cdot)$ in Γ; (iii) if $y(\cdot)$ is in $\mathscr{C}([0, 1], R_p)$, then

$$(10.4)\qquad [I - U_{KL}^J]^{-1}[T^J(y) - U_{KL}^J(y)] = T^{\tilde J}(y);$$

* Note that $V_{MN}^{\tilde J}$ is given by

$$V_{MN}^{\tilde J} y = H^{\tilde J}(t)\{-My(0) - Ny(1) + Ky(0) + Ly(1)\} + \int_0^1 G^{\tilde J}(t, s)\{V(s)y(s) - U(s)y(s)\}\, ds.$$

and (iv) under the assumptions of Corollaries 8.9 and 8.11,

$$[I - U_{KL}^J]^{-1}[(T_y^J)' - U_{KL}^J] = (T_y^{\tilde{J}})' \tag{10.5}$$

$$[I - U_{KL}^J]^{-1}(T_y^J)'' = (T_y^{\tilde{J}})'' \tag{10.6}$$

for all $y(\cdot)$.

Proof. We note that (i) is an immediate consequence of the properties of the Green's matrices H^J and G^J. Now let $\Psi = I - U_{KL}^J$. It is clear that Ψ is linear and maps $\mathscr{C}([0, 1], R_p)$ into $\mathscr{C}([0, 1], R_p)$ and Γ into Γ. As is well known [V2], Ψ^{-1} will exist if only if the equation $\Psi u = w$ has a unique solution $u(\cdot)$ in Γ for all $w(\cdot)$ in Γ. But, since Ψ is linear, this is equivalent to the condition that

$$\Psi(u) = [I - U_{KL}^J](u) = 0 \tag{10.7}$$

has zero as its unique solution. However, by virtue of Corollary 2.7 and the definition of U_{KL}^J, (10.7) is equivalent to the linear TPBVP

$$\dot{u} - V(t)u = [U(t) - V(t)]u,$$
$$Mu(0) + Nu(1) = [M - K]\,u(0) + [N - L]\,u(1)$$

which can be written as

$$\dot{u} = U(t)u, \qquad Ku(0) + Lu(1) = 0. \tag{10.8}$$

Since $\{U(t), K, L\}$ is a boundary-compatible set, it follows that $u(\cdot) \equiv 0$ and hence that Ψ^{-1} exists on Γ. To determine the form of Ψ^{-1}, we note that $\Psi u = w$ is equivalent to the equation $w = u - q$ where $q = U_{KL}^J(u)$ is a solution of the linear TPBVP

$$\begin{aligned} \dot{q} - V(t)q &= [U(t) - V(t)]u, \\ Mq(0) + Nq(1) &= [M - K]\,u(0) + [N - L]\,u(1). \end{aligned} \tag{10.9}$$

Since $u - w = q$, it follows that $u - w$ is a solution of the linear TPBVP

$$[\dot{u} - \dot{w}] - U(t)[u - w] = [U(t) - V(t)]w,$$
$$K[u(0) - w(0)] + L[u(1) - w(1)] = [M - K]\,w(0) + [N - L]\,w(1)$$

and hence by Corollary 2.7, that

$$u(t) - w(t) = -H^J(t)\{[K - M]\, w(0) + [L - N]\, w(1)\} - \int_0^1 G^J(t, s)\{V(s)\, w(s) - U(s)\, w(s)\}\, ds \tag{10.10}$$

or, equivalently, that

$$u = [I - V^J_{MN}](w). \tag{10.11}$$

Since $\Psi u = w$, we have established (10.3) and since $[I - V^J_{MN}]$ is linear and bounded, Ψ^{-1} is linear and bounded.

The proof of (10.4), (10.5), and (10.6) is now rather simple. The basis for these relations is the equivalence between the integral equation $\Psi u = w$ and the linear TPBVP for $u - w$, i.e., the linear TPBVP

$$\begin{aligned} \dot{u} - U(t)u &= \dot{w} - V(t)w, \\ Ku(0) + Lu(1) &= Mw(0) + Nw(1). \end{aligned} \tag{10.12}$$

In order to prove (10.4), let $y(\cdot)$ be an element of $\mathscr{C}([0, 1], R_p)$ and let $w(\cdot) = T^J(y) - U^J_{KL}(y)$. Then

$$w(t) = H^J(t)\{c - g(y(0)) - h(y(1)) + Ky(0) + Ly(1)\} + \int_0^1 G^J(t, s)\{F(y(s), s) - U(s)\, y(s)\}\, ds \tag{10.13}$$

and, by Corollary 2.7,

$$\begin{aligned} \dot{w} - V(t)w &= F(y(t), t) - U(t)y, \\ Mw(0) + Nw(1) &= c - g(y(0)) - h(y(1)) + Ky(0) + Ly(1). \end{aligned}$$

If $u = \Psi^{-1}w$, then it follows from (10.12) that

$$\begin{aligned} \dot{u} - U(t)u &= F(y(t), t) - U(t)y, \\ Ku(0) + Lu(1) &= c - g(y(0)) - h(y(1)) + Ky(0) + Ly(1) \end{aligned}$$

and hence, that $u = T^J(y)$ by virtue of Corollary 2.7. Thus, (10.4) is established.

Equations (10.5) and (10.6) are established in a similar way. We shall treat (10.5) and shall leave (10.6) to the reader. In order to prove (10.5), let $y(\cdot)$ and $v(\cdot)$ be elements of $\mathscr{C}([0, 1], R_p)$ and set $w(\cdot) = [(T_y{}^J)'v - U^J_{KL}v]$. Then

$$w(t) = H^J(t)\left\{\left[K - \frac{\partial g}{\partial y}(y(0))\right]v(0) + \left[L - \frac{\partial h}{\partial y}(y(1))\right]v(1)\right\} + \int_0^1 G^J(t, s)\left\{\left[\frac{\partial F}{\partial y}(y(s), s) - U(s)\right]v(s)\right\} ds \tag{10.14}$$

by virtue of Corollary 8.9. It follows that $w(\cdot)$ is a solution of the linear TPBVP

$$\dot{w} - V(t)w = \left[\frac{\partial F}{\partial y}(y(t), t) - U(t)\right]v,$$

$$Mw(0) + Nw(1) = \left[K - \frac{\partial g}{\partial y}(y(0))\right]v(0) + \left[L - \frac{\partial h}{\partial y}(y(1))\right]v(1).$$

If $u = \Psi^{-1}w$, then it follows from (10.12) that

$$\dot{u} - U(t)u = \left[\frac{\partial F}{\partial y}(y(t), t) - U(t)\right]v,$$

$$Ku(0) + Lu(1) = \left[K - \frac{\partial g}{\partial y}(y(0))\right]v(0) + \left[L - \frac{\partial h}{\partial y}(y(1))\right]v(1)$$

and hence, that $u = (T_y{}^{\tilde{J}})'v$ by virtue of Corollary 2.7.

Lemma 10.1 is essentially a confirmation of the fact that for every boundary-compatible set there is a (possibly) different integral representation of the same TPBVP and that these representations are equivalent, with the equivalence given by (10.4).

3.11. A Lemma on Equivalence: Discrete Case

We now prove a lemma, which is entirely analogous to Lemma 10.1, for the discrete case. We have the following.

LEMMA 11.1. Let

$$J = \{A(j), B(j), M, N\} \quad \text{and} \quad \tilde{J} = \{C(j), D(j), K, L\}$$

be boundary-compatible sets. Let $F(x, y, k)$ be defined on

$R_p \times R_p \times \mathbf{Q}'$ where $\mathbf{Q}' = \{0, 1, \ldots, q-1\}$ and let U^J_{KL} be the operator given by

$$(11.2) \qquad (U^J_{KL}y)(j) = H^J(j)\{-Ky(0) - Ly(q) + My(0) + Ny(q)\}$$
$$+ \sum_{k=0}^{q-1} G^J(j,k)\{[C(k) - A(k)]\,y(k+1)$$
$$+ [D(k) - B(k)]\,y(k)\}$$

for $y(\cdot)$ in $\mathscr{S}(\mathbf{Q}, R_p)$ with $\mathbf{Q} = \{0, 1, \ldots, q\}$. Then (i) U^J_{KL} maps $\mathscr{S}(\mathbf{Q}, R_p)$ into $\mathscr{S}(\mathbf{Q}, R_p)$; (ii) the operator $I - U^J_{KL}$ has a bounded linear inverse with

$$(11.3)^* \qquad [I - U^J_{KL}]^{-1}y = [I - V^{\tilde{J}}_{MN}]y$$

for $y(\cdot)$ in $\mathscr{S}(\mathbf{Q}, R_p)$; (iii) if $y(\cdot)$ is in $\mathscr{S}(\mathbf{Q}, R_p)$, then

$$(11.4) \qquad [I - U^J_{KL}]^{-1}[T^J(y) - U^J_{KL}(y)] = T^{\tilde{J}}(y);$$

and (iv) under the assumptions of Corollaries 9.9 and 9.11,

$$(11.5) \qquad [I - U^J_{KL}]^{-1}[(T_y{}^J)' - U^J_{KL}] = (T_y{}^{\tilde{J}})'$$

$$(11.6) \qquad [I - U^J_{KL}]^{-1}(T_y{}^J)'' = (T_y{}^{\tilde{J}})''$$

for all $y(\cdot)$.

Proof. Assertion (i) is obvious. Now let $\Psi = I - U^J_{KL}$. It is clear that Ψ maps $\mathscr{S}(\mathbf{Q}, R_p)$ into itself and that Ψ is linear. Again, Ψ^{-1} will exist if and only if $\Psi u = w$ has a unique solution for all $w(\cdot)$. Since Ψ is linear, this is equivalent to the condition that

$$(11.7) \qquad \Psi u = [I - U^J_{KL}]u = 0$$

has zero as its unique solution. However, by virtue of Theorem 5.1

* Note that $V^{\tilde{J}}_{MN}$ is given by

$$V^{\tilde{J}}_{MN}y = H^{\tilde{J}}(j)\{-My(0) - Ny(q) + Ky(0) + Ly(q)\}$$
$$+ \sum_{k=0}^{q-1} G^{\tilde{J}}(j,k)\{[A(k) - C(k)]y(k+1) +]B(k) - D(k)]y(k)\}.$$

and the definition of U^J_{KL}, (11.7) is equivalent to the linear TPBVP

$$u(j+1) - u(j) = C(j)\,u(j+1) + D(j)\,u(j), \qquad (11.8)$$
$$Ku(0) + Lu(q) = 0.$$

Since $\{C(j), D(j), K, L\}$ is a boundary compatible set, it follows that $u(\cdot) \equiv 0$ and hence, that Ψ^{-1} exists. To determine the form of Ψ^{-1}, we note that, when written out, $\Psi u = w$ becomes

$$w(j) = u(j) - H^J(j)\{[M-K]\,u(0) + [N-L]\,u(q)\} \qquad (11.9)$$
$$- \sum_{k=0}^{q-1} G^J(j,k)\{[C(k) - A(k)]\,u(k+1)$$
$$+ [D(k) - B(k)]\,u(k)\}.$$

However, (11.9) is, in view of Theorem 5.1, equivalent to the TPBVP

$$u(j+1) - w(j+1) - u(j) + w(j)$$
$$= A(j)[u(j+1) - w(j+1)] + B(j)[u(j) - w(j)]$$
$$+ [C(j) - A(j)]\,u(j+1) + [D(j) - B(j)]\,u(j),$$
$$M[u(0) - w(0)] + N[u(q) - w(q)] = [M-K]\,u(0) + [N-L]\,u(q).$$

After some rearrangement and addition, this TPBVP can be written as

$$u(j+1) - w(j+1) - u(j) + w(j)$$
$$= C(j)[u(j+1) - w(j+1)] + D(j)[u(j) - w(j)]$$
$$+ [C(j) - A(j)]\,w(j+1) + [D(j) - B(j)]\,w(j),$$
$$K[u(0) - w(0)] + L[u(q) - w(q)] = [M-K]\,w(0) + [N-L]\,w(q).$$

It follows from Corollary 3.8 that the solution of this TPBVP is given by

$$u(j) - w(j) = H^{\tilde{J}}(j)\{[M-K]\,w(0) + [N-L]\,w(q)\} \qquad (11.10)$$
$$+ \sum_{k=0}^{q-1} G^{\tilde{J}}(j,k)\{[C(k) - A(k)]\,w(k+1)$$
$$+ [D(k) - B(k)]\,w(k)\}$$

or, equivalently, that

$$u = [I - V^{J}_{MN}](w) \tag{11.11}$$

Since $\Psi u = w$, we have established (11.3) and since $[I - V^{J}_{MN}]$ is linear and bounded, Ψ^{-1} is linear and bounded.

Now the proof of (11.4) (11.5), and (11.6) becomes rather simple. The basis for these relations is the equivalence between the operator equation $\Psi u = w$ and the linear TPBVP for $u - w$, i.e., the linear TPBVP

$$\begin{aligned} u(j+1) - u(j) - C(j)\,u(j+1) - D(j)\,u(j) \\ = w(j+1) - w(j) - A(j)\,w(j+1) - B(j)\,w(j) \\ Ku(0) + Lu(q) = Mw(0) + Nw(q). \end{aligned} \tag{11.12}$$

In order to prove (11.4), let $y(\cdot)$ be an element of $\mathscr{S}(\mathbf{Q}, R_p)$ and let $w(\cdot) = T^J(y) - U^J_{KL}(y)$. Then, by (9.3) and (11.2),

$$\begin{aligned} w(j) = H^J(j)\{c - g(y(0)) - h(y(q)) + Ky(0) + Ly(q)\} \\ + \sum_{k=0}^{q-1} G^J(j, k)\{F(y(k+1), y(k), k) \\ - C(k)\,y(k+1) - D(k)\,y(k)\} \end{aligned} \tag{11.13}$$

and, by Corollary 3.8,

$$\begin{aligned} w(j+1) - w(j) - A(j)\,w(j+1) - B(j)\,w(j) \\ = F(y(j+1), y(j), j) - C(j)\,y(j+1) - D(j)\,y(j), \\ Mw(0) + Nw(q) = c - g(y(0)) - h(y(q)) + Ky(0) + Ly(q). \end{aligned}$$

If $u = \Psi^{-1}w$, then it follows from (11.12) that

$$\begin{aligned} u(j+1) - u(j) = C(j)\,u(j+1) + D(j)\,u(j) + F(y(j+1), y(j), j) \\ - C(j)\,y(j+1) - D(j)\,y(k), \\ Ku(0) + Lu(q) = c - g(y(0)) - h(y(q)) + Ky(0) + Ly(q) \end{aligned}$$

and hence that $u = T^J(y)$. Thus, (11.4) holds.

Equations (11.5) and (11.6) are established in an entirely similar way. We treat (11.5) and we leave (11.6) to the reader. In order to prove (11.5), let $y(\cdot)$ and $v(\cdot)$ be elements of $\mathscr{S}(\mathbf{Q}, R_p)$ and set $w(\cdot) = [(T_y^J)'v - U_{KL}^J v]$. Then, using (9.10),

$$w(j) = H^J(j)\left\{\left[K - \frac{\partial g}{\partial y}(y(0))\right]v(0) + \left[L - \frac{\partial h}{\partial y}(y(q))\right]v(q)\right\} + \sum_{k=0}^{q-1} G^J(j,k)\left\{\left[\frac{\partial F}{\partial x}(y(k+1), y(k), k) - C(k)\right]v(k+1) + \left[\frac{\partial F}{\partial y}(y(k+1), y(k), k) - D(k)\right]v(k)\right\}. \tag{11.14}$$

It follows that $w(\cdot)$ is a solution of the TPBVP

$$\begin{aligned} w(j+1) - w(j) - A(j)\,w(j+1) - B(j)\,w(j) &= \left[\frac{\partial F}{\partial x}(y(k+1), y(k), k) - C(k)\right]v(k+1) \\ &\quad + \left[\frac{\partial F}{\partial y}(y(k+1), y(k), k) - D(k)\right]v(k), \\ Mw(0) + Nw(q) &= \left[K - \frac{\partial g}{\partial y}(y(0))\right]v(0) + \left[L - \frac{\partial h}{\partial y}(y(q))\right]v(q). \end{aligned}$$

If $u = \Psi^{-1}w$, then it follows from (11.12) that

$$\begin{aligned} u(j+1) - u(j) &= C(j)\,u(j+1) + D(j)\,u(j) \\ &\quad + \left[\frac{\partial F}{\partial x}(y(j+1), y(j), j) - C(j)\right]v(j+1) \\ &\quad + \left[\frac{\partial F}{\partial y}(y(j+1), y(j), j) - D(j)\right]v(j), \\ Ku(0) + Lu(q) &= \left[K - \frac{\partial g}{\partial y}(y(0))\right]v(0) + \left[L - \frac{\partial h}{\partial y}(y(q))\right]v(q) \end{aligned}$$

and hence that $u = (T_y^J)'v$ by virtue of (9.10) and Corollary 3.8.

Just as in the continuous case, the lemma is nothing more than a confirmation of the fact that for every boundary-compatible set there is a different summation representation of the same TPBVP and that these representations are equivalent, with the equivalence given by (11.4).

Appendix. Lipschitz Norms

Consider the TPBVP

$$\dot{y} = F(y, t), \qquad g(y(0)) + h(y(1)) = c \tag{A.1}$$

and let $J = \{V(t), M, N\}$ be a boundary-compatible set. Assuming that the conditions of Theorem 4.1 are satisfied, we can define a mapping T^J of $\mathscr{C}([0, 1], R_p)$ into itself by setting

$$\begin{aligned} T^J(\phi)(t) &= H^J(t)\{c - g(\phi(0)) - h(\phi(1)) + M\phi(0) + N\phi(1)\} \\ &\quad + \int_0^1 G^J(t, s)\{F(\phi(s), s) - V(s)\,\phi(s)\}\, ds \end{aligned} \tag{A.2}$$

for $\varphi(\cdot)$ in $\mathscr{C}([0, 1], R_p)$. We computed the Frechet derivatives of the operator T^J and estimates of the norms of these derivatives in Section 8. Here, under somewhat weaker smoothness conditions, we shall compute the Lipschitz norm of the operator T^J. We begin with the following.

LEMMA A.3. Let S be a bounded open set in $\mathscr{C}([0, 1], R_p)$ and let D be an open set in R_p containing the range of $\bar{S}$. Suppose that (i) $K(t, y, s)$ is a map of $[0, 1] \times D \times [0, 1]$ into D which is measurable in s for each fixed y and t and continuous in y for each fixed s and t; (ii) there is an integrable function $m(t, s)$ of s with $\sup_t \int_0^1 m(t, s)\, ds = \mu < \infty$ such that $\| K(t, y, s)\| \leqslant m(t, s)$ and $\| K(t, y_1, s) - K(t, y_2, s)\| \leqslant m(t, s)\| y_1 - y_2 \|$ on $[0, 1] \times D \times [0, 1]$; and (iii) $\lim_{t \to t'} \int_0^1 \| K(t, y(s), s) - K(t', y(s), s)\|\, ds = 0$ for all t, t' in $[0, 1]$ and $y(\cdot)$ in $\bar{S}$. Then the mapping T given by

$$T(u)(t) = \int_0^1 K(t, u(s), s)\, ds \tag{A.4}$$

maps $\mathscr{C}([0, 1], D)$ into $\mathscr{C}([0, 1], R_p)$ and the Lipschitz norm, $\Box\, T \,\Box_{\bar{S}}$, satisfies the inequality

$$\Box\, T \,\Box_{\bar{S}} \leqslant \mu. \tag{A.5}$$

Proof. We first observe that T maps $\mathscr{C}([0, 1], D)$ into $\mathscr{C}([0, 1], R_p)$ in view of (i) and (iii) [B0]. Now let $u(\cdot)$ and $v(\cdot)$ be elements of $\bar{S}$. Then

$$\begin{aligned} \| T(u)(t) - T(v)(t) \| &\leqslant \int_0^1 \| K(t, u(s), s) - K(t, v(s), s) \| \, ds \\ &\leqslant \int_0^1 m(t, s) \, \| u(s) - v(s) \| \, ds \\ &\leqslant \left(\int_0^1 m(t, s) \, ds \right) \| u - v \| . \end{aligned}$$

It follows that $\| T(u) - T(v) \| \leqslant \mu \| u - v \|$ and hence that

$$\Box\, T \,\Box_{\bar{S}} = \sup_{u,v} \{ \| T(u) - T(v) \| / \| u - v \| \} \leqslant \mu.$$

COROLLARY A.6. Suppose that the function

$$K(t, y, s) = G^J(t, s)\{F(y, s) - V(s)y\}$$

satisfies the conditions of Lemma A.3 and that

$$\| g(y_1) - g(y_2) \| \leqslant \mu_1 \| y_1 - y_2 \| \quad \text{and} \quad \| h(y_1) - h(y_2) \| \leqslant \mu_2 \| y_1 - y_2 \| .$$

Let $\alpha = \max\{\mu, \| H^J(\cdot) \| \mu_1, \| H^J(\cdot) \| \mu_2, \| H^J(\cdot) M \|, \| H^J(\cdot) N \|\}$. Then $\Box\, T^J \,\Box_{\bar{S}} \leqslant \alpha$.

The estimate of Corollary A.6 can often be used in connection with the contraction mapping method. Similar results can be obtained in the discrete case and we leave this to the reader.

CHAPTER 4

APPLICATION TO CONTROL PROBLEMS

4.1. Introduction

We discussed iterative methods for the solution of operator equations in Chapter 2 and we showed how TPBVP's can be represented by such operator equations in Chapter 3. Here, we shall combine the results of these chapters to obtain convergence theorems for the iterative solution of TPBVP's of the type that arise in optimal control problems.

We begin with a brief discussion of the way in which optimal control problems can be reduced to TPBVP's. Continuous control problems are treated in Section 4.2 and discrete control problems are treated in Section 4.4. We then consider the application of the results of Chapters 2 and 3 to these TPBVP's in Sections 4.5–4.11. In the last section, we summarize the results obtained.

4.2. Continuous Control Problems

An optimal control problem is a composite concept consisting of four basic elements: (1) a dynamical system, (2) a set of initial states and a set of final states, (3) a set of admissible controls, and (4) a cost functional to be minimized. The problem consists of finding the admissible control which transfers the state of the dynamical system from the set of initial states to the set of final states and, in so doing, minimizes the cost functional. In this section we discuss the way in which optimal control problems may be reduced to TPBVP's by means of Pontryagin's principle [P3]. Our discussion will be brief and the details of the theory will be omitted.

DEFINITION 2.1. An optimal control problem is the composite concept consisting of (i) a dynamical system

$$\dot{\mathbf{x}} = \mathbf{f}(\mathbf{x}, \mathbf{u}, \mathbf{t}) \tag{2.2}$$

where $\mathbf{x}$ is an n vector, called the state, and $\mathbf{u}(t)$ is an m vector, called the control; (ii) a set S_0 of initial states and a set S_f of final states with

$$\begin{aligned} S_0 &= \{(\mathbf{x}, t): g_i(\mathbf{x}, t) = c_i\,, \quad i = 1, \ldots, k\} \\ S_f &= \{(\mathbf{x}, t): h_j(\mathbf{x}, t) = d_j\,, \quad j = 1, \ldots, l\} \end{aligned} \tag{2.3}$$

where both S_0 and S_f are smooth manifolds; (iii) a set U of admissible controls with $U \subset L_\infty(R, \Omega)$ where Ω is a subset of R_m; (iv) a cost functional

$$J(\mathbf{u}(\cdot)) = G(\mathbf{x}_\mathbf{u}(t_0), t_0) + K(\mathbf{x}_\mathbf{u}(t_f), t_f) + \int_{t_0}^{t_f} L(\mathbf{x}_\mathbf{u}(s), \mathbf{u}(s), s)\, ds \tag{2.4}$$

where G, K, L are real-valued functions; and (v) the statement, "determine the admissible control $\mathbf{u}(\cdot)$ which transfers the state of the dynamical system from S_0 to S_f and which, in so doing, minimizes the cost functional $J(\cdot)$." A solution $\mathbf{u}^*(\cdot)$ of the optimal control problem is called an optimal control.

A common approach to the solution of optimal control problems consists of the following steps: (1) the determination of necessary conditions for optimality; (2) the determination of functions (extremals) which satisfy these necessary conditions and thus qualify as candidates for the solution; and (3) the determination of those (if any) extremals which are optimal. Necessary conditions for optimality have been derived in a number of ways [B4, C0, H4, N3]. In general, the derivation involves the assumption of an optimal solution followed by an investigation of the effects of suitable variations. The resulting conditions for optimality lead to a TPBVP as we shall see.

Let us now suppose that (i) $\mathbf{f}(\mathbf{x}, \mathbf{u}, t)$, $(\partial\mathbf{f}/\partial t)(\mathbf{x}, \mathbf{u}, t)$, $(\partial\mathbf{f}/\partial\mathbf{x})(\mathbf{x}, \mathbf{u}, t)$, $L(\mathbf{x}, \mathbf{u}, t)$, $(\partial F/\partial t)(\mathbf{x}, \mathbf{u}, t)$, and $(\partial L/\partial\mathbf{x})(\mathbf{x}, \mathbf{u}, t)$ are continuous on $R_n \times \bar{\Omega} \times R$; and (ii) $G(\mathbf{x}, t)$, $(\partial G/\partial t)(\mathbf{x}, t)$, $(\partial G/\partial\mathbf{x})(\mathbf{x}, t)$, $K(\mathbf{x}, t)$, $(\partial K/\partial t)(\mathbf{x}, t)$, and $(\partial K/\partial\mathbf{x})(\mathbf{x}, t)$ are continuous on (neighborhoods of) S_0 and S_f, respectively. In that case, we call the control problem *smooth*. We shall assume from now on that the term "control problem" means "smooth control problem." We now have the following.

DEFINITION 2.5. The real-valued function $H(\mathbf{x}, \mathbf{p}, \mathbf{u}, p_0, t)$ given by

$$H(\mathbf{x}, \mathbf{p}, \mathbf{u}, p_0, t) = p_0 L(\mathbf{x}, \mathbf{u}, t) + \langle \mathbf{p}, \mathbf{f}(\mathbf{x}, \mathbf{u}, t)\rangle \tag{2.6}$$

is called the Hamiltonian of the (given) control problem.

THEOREM 2.7 (The Pontryagin principle [P3]). Let $\mathbf{u}^*(\cdot)$ be an admissible control which transfers the state of the dynamical system (2.2) from S_0 to S_f and let $\mathbf{x}^*(\cdot)$ be the corresponding trajectory. Suppose that $\mathbf{u}^*(\cdot)$ is optimal. Then there are a vector-valued function $\mathbf{p}^*(\cdot)$, a vector $\boldsymbol{\alpha}$ in R_k, a vector $\boldsymbol{\beta}$ in R_l, and a number $p_0^* \geqslant 0$ such that the following conditions are satisfied:

(a) $(p_0^*, \mathbf{p}^*(t))$ is not identically zero;

(b) $\mathbf{x}^*(t)$ and $p_0^*, \mathbf{p}^*(t)$ satisfy the canonical system of differential equations, i.e.,

$$\begin{aligned} \dot{\mathbf{x}}^*(t) &= \frac{\partial H}{\partial \mathbf{p}}(\mathbf{x}^*(t), \mathbf{p}^*(t), \mathbf{u}^*(t), p_0^*, t) \\ &= \mathbf{f}(\mathbf{x}^*(t), \mathbf{u}^*(t), t) \end{aligned} \tag{2.8}$$

$$\begin{aligned} \dot{\mathbf{p}}^*(t) &= -\frac{\partial H}{\partial \mathbf{x}}(\mathbf{x}^*(t), \mathbf{p}^*(t), \mathbf{u}^*(t), p_0^*, t) \\ &= -p_0^* \frac{\partial L}{\partial \mathbf{x}}(\mathbf{x}^*(t), \mathbf{u}^*(t), t) - \left(\frac{\partial \mathbf{f}}{\partial \mathbf{x}}\right)'(\mathbf{x}^*(t), \mathbf{u}^*(t), t)\, \mathbf{p}^*(t); \end{aligned} \tag{2.9}$$

(c) $\mathbf{x}^*(\cdot)$ and $p_0^*, \mathbf{p}^*(\cdot)$ satisfy the boundary conditions

$$\begin{aligned} &\mathbf{g}(\mathbf{x}^*(t_0), t_0) = \mathbf{c}, \\ &\mathbf{p}^*(t_0) = -p_0^* \frac{\partial G}{\partial \mathbf{x}}(\mathbf{x}^*(t_0), t_0) - \frac{\partial \mathbf{g}}{\partial \mathbf{x}}(\mathbf{x}^*(t_0), t_0)\boldsymbol{\alpha} \end{aligned} \tag{2.10}$$

$$\begin{aligned} &\mathbf{h}(\mathbf{x}^*(t_f), t_f) = \mathbf{d}, \\ &\mathbf{p}^*(t_f) = p_0^* \frac{\partial K}{\partial \mathbf{x}}(\mathbf{x}^*(t_f), t_f) + \frac{\partial \mathbf{h}}{\partial \mathbf{x}}(\mathbf{x}^*(t_f), t_f)\boldsymbol{\beta} \end{aligned} \tag{2.11}$$

where $\mathbf{g}, \mathbf{h}, \mathbf{c}, \mathbf{d}$ are vectors with components g_i, h_j, c_i, and d_j, respectively;

(d) $\mathbf{u}^*(t)$ minimizes the Hamiltonian over Ω for (almost) all t, i.e.,

$$(2.12) \qquad H(\mathbf{x}^*(t), \mathbf{p}^*(t), \mathbf{u}^*(t), p_0^*, t) \leqslant H(\mathbf{x}^*(t), \mathbf{p}^*(t), \boldsymbol{\omega}, p_0^*, t)$$

for all $\boldsymbol{\omega}$ in Ω; and

(e) $H^*(t_0) = p_0^*(\partial G/\partial t)(\mathbf{x}^*(t_0), t_0) + \langle(\partial \mathbf{g}/\partial t)(\mathbf{x}^*(t_0), t_0), \boldsymbol{\alpha}\rangle$ and $H^*(t_f) = -p_0^*(\partial K/\partial t)(\mathbf{x}^*(t_f), t_f) - \langle(\partial \mathbf{h}/\partial t)(\mathbf{x}^*(t_f), t_f), \boldsymbol{\beta}\rangle$ where $H^*(t) = H(\mathbf{x}^*(t), \mathbf{p}^*(t), \mathbf{u}^*(t), p_0^*, t)$.

A proof of Theorem 2.7 is given by Pontryagin *et al.* [P3]. We now make some comments regarding Theorem 2.7. We first observe that the adjoint equation (2.9) is linear in $\mathbf{p}^*(t)$ and has a forcing function and boundary conditions proportional to p_0^*. Therefore, the constant p_0^* can be regarded as a scale factor for the adjoint functions. In theoretical work (if $p_0^* \neq 0$) this scale factor is usually assigned the value $p_0^* = 1$. In numerical work it may be preferable to carry p_0^* along as a scale factor. We next note that in [P3] p_0^* was chosen nonpositive, rather than nonnegative. With this choice, the Hamiltonian has the opposite sign and, instead of a minimum, has a maximum at the optimal control. Not counting the scale factor p_0^* or the function $H^*(t)$, which is fully defined by

$$H^*(t) = H(\mathbf{x}^*(t), \mathbf{p}^*(t), \mathbf{u}^*(t), p_0^*, t),$$

we have $2n + m$ functions of time to determine; namely, $\mathbf{x}^*(t)$, $\mathbf{p}^*(t)$ and $\mathbf{u}^*(t)$ and two values of the time, t_0 and t_f. To solve for these, we have $2n$ first-order differential equations, (2.8) and (2.9) with $k + (n - k) + l + (n - l) = 2n$ boundary conditions (assuming the elimination of $\boldsymbol{\alpha}$ and $\boldsymbol{\beta}$), m scalar equations resulting from (2.12) and finally, two equations involving t_0 and t_f. Hence, there are enough equations, in theory, to solve for $\mathbf{x}^*(t)$, $\mathbf{p}^*(t)$, and $\mathbf{u}^*(t)$. We can also readily see that the boundary conditions include terminal sets which are fixed points and the case where the terminal state is free. In the case of fixed end points, we have (for example), $\mathbf{g}(\mathbf{x}(t_0), t_0) = \mathbf{x}(t_0) = \mathbf{c}$ and $\mathbf{h}(\mathbf{x}(t_f), t_f) = \mathbf{x}(t_f) = \mathbf{d}$. In this case, there will be no cost functional terms G and K and so $\mathbf{p}^*(t_0) = \boldsymbol{\alpha}$, $\mathbf{p}^*(t_f) = \boldsymbol{\beta}$ which implies that the values of the adjoint function $\mathbf{p}^*(\cdot)$ are free at the end points.

Now, Let us call any triple $(\mathbf{x}(t), \mathbf{p}(t), \mathbf{u}(t))$ which satisfies (a)–(e) of Theorem 2.7, an *extremal* of the control problem. Since any optimal control gives rise to an extremal, one frequently used approach to the solution of control problems is to determine all extremals. As is apparent from Theorem 2.7, this involves the simultaneous solution of $2n$ differential equations, m minimization equations, and 2 algebraic equations. In general, this is a sizable problem. We examine some aspects of this problem in the remainder of this section.

The only analytical progress toward the determination of the extremals that usually can be made is the reduction of the set of $2n + m + 2$ equations to a set of $2n$ differential and 2 algebraic equations. This reduction is effected by solving the minimization equation (2.12) for the optimal control $\mathbf{u}$† in terms of $\mathbf{x}$, $\mathbf{p}$, and t, i.e.,

$$\mathbf{u} = \mathbf{u}^0(\mathbf{x}, \mathbf{p}, t). \tag{2.13}$$

This reduction is possible if the Hamiltonian is normal [A3]. Substitution of (2.13) into the differential equations (2.8) and (2.9) makes the problem of the determination of the extremals into a nonlinear two-point boundary value problem of the form

$$\dot{\mathbf{x}} = \boldsymbol{\psi}(\mathbf{x}, \mathbf{p}, t) \tag{2.14}$$

$$\dot{\mathbf{p}} = -\left(\frac{\partial \boldsymbol{\psi}}{\partial \mathbf{x}}\right)' \boldsymbol{\psi}(\mathbf{x}, \mathbf{p}, t)\, \mathbf{p} - \frac{\partial L}{\partial \mathbf{x}}(\mathbf{x}, \mathbf{p}, t)\, p_0 = \boldsymbol{\phi}(\mathbf{x}, \mathbf{p}, t) \tag{2.15}$$

with the boundary conditions (2.10) and (2.11).

For theoretical as well as practical (numerical) reasons, it is often advantageous to standardize the time interval over which the TPBVP (2.14), (2.15) is defined. This standardization is accomplished by the introduction of a new variable. Let (see Long [L2])

$$t = t_0 + (t_f - t_0)s = b + as. \tag{2.16}$$

Here s is the new variable which varies between 0 and 1; a (scale factor) and b (initial time) are two generally unknown constants. These constants a and b can conveniently be considered as new state variables given by the trivial equations

$$\frac{da}{ds} = 0, \qquad \frac{db}{ds} = 0 \tag{2.17}$$

† For simplicity we drop the asterisk (*) for the "optimal" values.

In terms of s, a, and b, the TPBVP becomes

$$(2.18)\qquad \begin{cases} \dfrac{d\mathbf{x}}{ds} = a\boldsymbol{\psi}(\mathbf{x}, \mathbf{p}, b + as) \\[2ex] \dfrac{d\mathbf{p}}{ds} = a\boldsymbol{\phi}(\mathbf{x}, \mathbf{p}, b + as) \\[2ex] \dfrac{da}{ds} = 0, \qquad \dfrac{db}{ds} = 0 \end{cases}$$

$$(2.19)\qquad \begin{cases} \mathbf{g}(\mathbf{x}(0), b) = \mathbf{c}, \qquad \mathbf{h}(\mathbf{x}(1), a + b) = \mathbf{d} \\[1ex] \mathbf{p}(0) = -p_0 \dfrac{\partial G}{\partial \mathbf{x}}(\mathbf{x}(0), b) - \dfrac{\partial \mathbf{g}}{\partial \mathbf{x}}(\mathbf{x}(0), b)\boldsymbol{\alpha} \\[2ex] \mathbf{p}(1) = p_0 \dfrac{\partial K}{\partial \mathbf{x}}(\mathbf{x}(1), a + b) + \dfrac{\partial \mathbf{h}}{\partial \mathbf{x}}(\mathbf{x}(1), a + b)\boldsymbol{\beta} \\[2ex] H(0) = p_0 \dfrac{\partial G}{\partial t}(\mathbf{x}(0), b) + \left\langle \dfrac{\partial \mathbf{g}}{\partial t}(\mathbf{x}(0), b), \boldsymbol{\beta} \right\rangle \\[2ex] H(1) = -p_0 \dfrac{\partial K}{\partial t}(\mathbf{x}(1), a + b) - \left\langle \dfrac{\partial \mathbf{h}}{\partial t}(\mathbf{x}(1), a + b), \boldsymbol{\beta} \right\rangle \end{cases}$$

where $H(s) = p_0 L(\mathbf{x}, \mathbf{p}, b + as) + \langle \mathbf{p}, \boldsymbol{\psi}(\mathbf{x}, \mathbf{p}, b + as)\rangle$. Since the sets S_0 and S_f are smooth manifolds, it is possible (at least in theory) to eliminate the unknown constants $\boldsymbol{\alpha}$ and $\boldsymbol{\beta}$ in (2.19). Assuming that this has been done and letting

$$(2.20)\qquad y = [\mathbf{x}, \mathbf{p}, a, b]$$

$$(2.21)\qquad F = [a\boldsymbol{\psi}, a\boldsymbol{\phi}, 0, 0]$$

$$(2.22)\qquad g = [\hat{\mathbf{g}}, \mathbf{0}]$$

$$(2.23)\qquad h = [\mathbf{0}, \hat{\mathbf{h}}]$$

$$(2.24)\qquad c = [\hat{\mathbf{c}}, \mathbf{d}]$$

where (2.19) is replaced by the conditions $\hat{\mathbf{g}}(\mathbf{x}(0), \mathbf{p}(0), b) = \hat{\mathbf{c}}$, $\hat{\mathbf{h}}(\mathbf{x}(1), \mathbf{p}(1), a + b) = \mathbf{d}$, we see that the TPBVP can be written in the standard form

$$(2.25)\qquad \frac{dy}{ds} = F(y(s), s), \qquad g(y(0)) + h(y(1)) = c.$$

We shall apply the results of Chapters 2 and 3 to the TPBVP (2.25) in the sequel.

4.3. A Continuous Example

Consider the scalar control system

$$\dot{x} = -\epsilon\sqrt{x} + bu \tag{3.1}$$

with state variable x and control variable u. Let $x(0) = x_0$ and $x(1) = x_1$ be the initial and final states, respectively. Let $U = L_\infty([0, 1], R)$ be the set of admissible controls and let the cost functional $J(u)$ be given by

$$J(u) = \tfrac{1}{2}\int_0^1 u^2(\tau)\, d\tau. \tag{3.2}$$

The control problem can now be stated as follows: determine a $u(\cdot)$ in U which transfers the state of (3.1) from x_0 to x_1 and, at the same time, minimizes (3.2).

The extremals of this optimal control problem are found with the aid of Pontryagin's principle. The first step is the formation of the Hamiltonian

$$H(x, p, u, p_0) = \tfrac{1}{2} p_0 u^2 + pbu - p\epsilon\sqrt{x}\,. \tag{3.3}$$

The corresponding canonical equations (2.8), (2.9) then have the form

$$\dot{x} = \frac{\partial H}{\partial p} = bu - \epsilon\sqrt{x} \tag{3.4}$$

$$\dot{p} = -\frac{\partial H}{\partial x} = +\epsilon\frac{1}{2\sqrt{x}}p. \tag{3.5}$$

Next, the Hamilton is minimized with respect to u. Since $H(x, p, u, p_0)$ is a parabola in u and since u is unconstrained, it follows that $H(x, p, u, p_0)$ has (for $p_0 \neq 0$) an absolute minimum at

$$u^0(x, p) = -\frac{1}{p_0}bp. \tag{3.6}$$

Substitution of (3.6) into (3.4) and (3.5) yields a TPBVP given by

$$\dot{x} = -\frac{b^2}{p_0} p - \epsilon \sqrt{x} \tag{3.7}$$

$$\dot{p} = + \epsilon \frac{1}{2\sqrt{x}} p \tag{3.8}$$

with the boundary conditions

$$x(0) = x_0 , \qquad x(1) = x_1 . \tag{3.9}$$

In standard form this TPBVP (see Section 6 of Chapter 3) can be written as

$$\begin{bmatrix} \dot{y}_1 \\ \dot{y}_2 \end{bmatrix} = \begin{bmatrix} -\dfrac{b^2}{p_0} y_2 - \epsilon \sqrt{y_1} \\ + \epsilon \dfrac{1}{2\sqrt{y_1}} y_2 \end{bmatrix} ,$$

$$\begin{bmatrix} y_1(0) \\ 0 \end{bmatrix} + \begin{bmatrix} 0 \\ y_1(1) \end{bmatrix} = \begin{bmatrix} x_1 \\ x_0 \end{bmatrix} . \tag{3.10}$$

The resulting TPBVP is so simple that an analytical solution can be found. The two first-order differential equations are converted into a single second-order equation by differentiating the first equation and substituting the second into the result. This yields

$$\ddot{y}_1 = - \epsilon \frac{1}{2\sqrt{y_1}} \dot{y}_1 - \frac{b^2}{p_0} \epsilon \frac{1}{2\sqrt{y_1}} y_2 . \tag{3.11}$$

In view of the first equation

$$-\frac{b^2}{p_0} y_2 = \dot{y}_1 + \epsilon \sqrt{y_1} . \tag{3.12}$$

Hence, by substitution of (3.12) into (3.11)

$$\ddot{y}_1 = \epsilon \frac{1}{2\sqrt{y_1}} [\dot{y}_1 + \epsilon \sqrt{y_1}] - \epsilon \frac{1}{2\sqrt{y_1}} \dot{y}_1 = \frac{\epsilon^2}{2} . \tag{3.13}$$

The solution of (3.13) is of the form $y_1(t) = (\epsilon^2/4)t^2 + C_1 t + C_2$ and the constants C_1 and C_2 are derived from the boundary conditions $y_1(0) = C_2 = x_0$, $y_1(1) = (\epsilon^2/4) + C_1 + C_2 = x_1$. This example illustrates the way in which TPBVP's arise in control problems.

4.4. Discrete Control Problems

We now examine the way in which discrete optimal control problems may be reduced to TPBVP's by means of the discrete maximum principle [C0, H4].

DEFINITION 4.1. A discrete optimal control problem is the composite concept consisting of (i) a discrete dynamical system

$$\mathbf{x}(j+1) - \mathbf{x}(j) = \mathbf{f}(\mathbf{x}(j), \mathbf{u}(j), j), \qquad j \in \mathbf{Q}' = \{0, 1, \ldots, q-1\} \tag{4.2}$$

where $\mathbf{x}(j)$ is an n vector, called the state, and $\mathbf{u}(j)$ is an m vector, called the control; (ii) a set S_0 of initial states and a set S_f of final states with

$$\begin{aligned} S_0 &= \{\mathbf{x}: \ g_i(\mathbf{x}) = c_i, \qquad i = 1, \ldots, k\} \\ S_f &= \{\mathbf{x}: \ h_i(\mathbf{x}) = d_i, \qquad i = 1, \ldots, l\} \end{aligned} \tag{4.3}$$

where both S_0 and S_f are smooth manifolds; (iii) a set U of admissible controls with $U \subset \mathscr{S}(\mathbf{Q}', \Omega)$ where Ω is a subset of R_m; (iv) a cost functional

$$J(\mathbf{u}(\cdot)) = K(\mathbf{x}_{\mathbf{u}}(q)) + \sum_{j=0}^{q-1} L(\mathbf{x}_{\mathbf{u}}(j), \mathbf{u}(j), j) \tag{4.4}$$

where K and L are real valued; and (v) the statement, "determine an admissible control $\mathbf{u}(\cdot)$ which transfers the state of the dynamical system from S_0 to S_f and which, in so doing, minimizes the cost functional $J(\cdot)$." A solution sequence $\{\mathbf{u}^*(0), \ldots, \mathbf{u}^*(q-1)\}$ is called an optimal control sequence.

Let us now suppose that (i) $\mathbf{f}(\cdot, \omega, j)$, $(\partial \mathbf{f}/\partial \mathbf{x})(\cdot, \omega, j)$, $L(\cdot, \omega, j)$, and $(\partial L/\partial \mathbf{x})(\cdot, \omega, j)$ are continuous for all ω in Ω and all j; (ii) $K(\mathbf{x})$ and $(\partial K/\partial \mathbf{x})(\mathbf{x})$ are continuous on (a neighborhood of) S_f; and (iii) the sets $\{(L(\mathbf{x}, \omega, j), \ \mathbf{f}(\mathbf{x}, \omega, j)): \ \omega \in \Omega\}$ are convex subsets of R_{n+1} for every $\mathbf{x}$ in R_n and j in $\mathbf{Q}'$. In that case, we call the discrete control problem *smooth*. We suppose from now on that our discrete control problems are smooth. We now have the following.

DEFINITION 4.5. The real-valued function $H(\mathbf{x}, \mathbf{p}, \mathbf{u}, p_0, j)$ given by

$$H(\mathbf{x}, \mathbf{p}, \mathbf{u}, p_0, j) = p_0 L(\mathbf{x}, \mathbf{u}, j) + \langle \mathbf{p}, \mathbf{f}(\mathbf{x}, \mathbf{u}, j) \rangle \tag{4.6}$$

is called the Hamiltonian of the control problem.

THEOREM 4.7 (The Discrete Pontryagin Principle [C0, H3]). If $\{\mathbf{u}^*(j)\}$ is an optimal control sequence with $\{\mathbf{x}^*(j)\}$ as corresponding optimal trajectory, then there are vectors $\mathbf{p}^*(0), \ldots, \mathbf{p}^*(q)$ in R_n, $\boldsymbol{\alpha}$ in R_k, $\boldsymbol{\beta}$ in R_l, and a number $p_0^* \geqslant 0$ such that the following conditions are satisfied:

(a) $p_0^*, \mathbf{p}^*(0), \ldots, \mathbf{p}^*(q), \boldsymbol{\alpha}, \boldsymbol{\beta}$ are not all zero;

(b) $\mathbf{x}^*(j)$ and $p_0^*, \mathbf{p}^*(j)$ satisfy the canonical system of difference equations, i.e.,

$$\begin{aligned} \mathbf{x}^*(j+1) - \mathbf{x}^*(j) &= \frac{\partial H}{\partial \mathbf{p}}(\mathbf{x}^*(j), \mathbf{p}^*(j), \mathbf{u}^*(j), p_0^*, j) \\ &= \mathbf{f}(\mathbf{x}^*(j), \mathbf{u}^*(j), j) \end{aligned} \tag{4.8}$$

$$\begin{aligned} \mathbf{p}^*(j+1) - \mathbf{p}^*(j) &= -\frac{\partial H}{\partial \mathbf{x}}(\mathbf{x}^*(j), \mathbf{p}^*(j), \mathbf{u}^*(j), p_0^*, j) \\ &= -p_0^* \frac{\partial L}{\partial \mathbf{x}}(\mathbf{x}^*(j), \mathbf{u}^*(j), j) \\ &\quad - \frac{\partial \mathbf{f}}{\partial \mathbf{x}}(\mathbf{x}^*(j), \mathbf{u}^*(j), j)' \, \mathbf{p}^*(j+1) \end{aligned} \tag{4.9}$$

for $j = 0, 1, \ldots, q-1$;

(c) $\mathbf{x}^*(\cdot)$ and $p_0^*, \mathbf{p}^*(\cdot)$ satisfy the boundary conditions

$$\mathbf{g}(\mathbf{x}^*(0)) = \mathbf{c}, \qquad \mathbf{p}^*(0) = -\frac{\partial \mathbf{g}}{\partial \mathbf{x}}(\mathbf{x}^*(0))\,\boldsymbol{\alpha} \tag{4.10}$$

$$\mathbf{h}(\mathbf{x}(q)) = \mathbf{d}, \qquad \mathbf{p}^*(q) = p_0^* \frac{\partial K}{\partial \mathbf{x}}(\mathbf{x}^*(q)) + \frac{\partial \mathbf{h}}{\partial \mathbf{x}}(\mathbf{x}^*(q))\,\boldsymbol{\beta} \tag{4.11}$$

where **g**, **h**, **c**, and **d** are vectors with components g_i, h_r, c_i, and d_r, respectively; and

(d) $\mathbf{u}^*(j)$ minimizes the Hamiltonian over Ω at j, i.e.,

$$H(\mathbf{x}^*(j), \mathbf{p}^*(j+1), \mathbf{u}^*(j), p_0^*, j) \leqslant H(\mathbf{x}^*(j), \mathbf{p}^*(j+1), \boldsymbol{\omega}, p_0^*, j) \tag{4.12}$$

for all $\boldsymbol{\omega}$ in Ω.

A proof of Theorem 4.7 is given by Canon *et al.* [C0].

If we call any triple $(\mathbf{x}(j), \mathbf{p}(j), \mathbf{u}(j))$ satisfying (a)–(d) of Theorem 4.7 an *extremal* of the control problem, then, just as in the continuous case, we attempt to determine all extremals. This leads to a TPBVP for a set of difference equations. More precisely, if the Hamiltonian is normal [A2], then the minimization equation (4.12) can be solved for $\mathbf{u}$ in terms of $\mathbf{x}$, $\mathbf{p}$, and j, i.e.,

$$\mathbf{u}(j) = \mathbf{u}^0(\mathbf{x}(j), \mathbf{p}(j+1), j). \tag{4.13}$$

Substitution of this expression into the canonical equations results in a system of difference equations of the form

$$\mathbf{x}(j+1) - \mathbf{x}(j) = \boldsymbol{\psi}(\mathbf{x}(j), \mathbf{p}(j+1), j) \tag{4.14}$$

$$\mathbf{p}(j+1) - \mathbf{p}(j) = \boldsymbol{\phi}(\mathbf{x}(j), \mathbf{p}(j+1), j) \tag{4.15}$$

with the boundary conditions (4.10) and (4.11). Since the sets S_0 and S_f are smooth manifolds, it is possible (at least in theory) to eliminate the unknown constants $\boldsymbol{\alpha}$ and $\boldsymbol{\beta}$ from the $n + k$ conditions (4.10) and the $n + l$ conditions (4.11), respectively. Assuming that this has been done and letting

$$y = [\mathbf{x}, \mathbf{p}] \tag{4.16}$$

$$F = [\boldsymbol{\psi}, \boldsymbol{\phi}] \tag{4.17}$$

$$g = [\hat{\mathbf{g}}, \mathbf{0}] \tag{4.18}$$

$$h = [\mathbf{0}, \hat{\mathbf{h}}] \tag{4.19}$$

$$c = [\hat{\mathbf{c}}, \mathbf{d}] \tag{4.20}$$

where (4.10) and (4.11) are replaced by the conditions $\hat{\mathbf{g}}(\mathbf{x}(0), \mathbf{p}(0)) = \hat{\mathbf{c}}$

and $\hat{\mathbf{h}}(\mathbf{x}(q), \mathbf{p}(q)) = \mathbf{d}$, respectively, we can see that the TPBVP can be written in the standard form

$$y(j+1) - y(j) = F(y(j+1), y(j), j), \qquad g(y(0)) + h(y(q)) = c. \tag{4.21}$$

We apply the results of Chapters 2 and 3 to the TPBVP (4.21) in the sequel.

4.5. Application to Continuous Problems I: The Method of Contraction Mappings

We have seen that if the conditions of Theorem 4.1 of Chapter 3 are satisfied, then TPBVP's, such as (2.25), are equivalent to operator equations of the form (see Section 8.3 in Chapter 3)

$$\begin{aligned} y(t) = T^J(y)(t) = H^J(t)\{c - g(y(0)) - h(y(1)) + My(0) + Ny(1)\} \\ + \int_0^1 G^J(t, s)\{F(y(s), s) - V(s)\, y(s)\}\, ds \end{aligned} \tag{5.1}$$

where $J = \{V(t), M, N\}$ is a boundary-compatible set. We shall apply the iterative methods of Chapter 2 to (5.1).

Let us begin with the method of contraction mappings. Following the prescription (formally), we select an initial element $y_0(\cdot)$ in $\mathscr{C}([0, 1], R_p)$ and successively generate a CM sequence $\{y_n(\cdot)\}$ for T^J based on $y_0(\cdot)$ by means of the algorithm $y_{n+1} = T^J(y_n)$, or, equivalently, by

$$\begin{aligned} y_{n+1}(t) = H^J(t)\{c - g(y_n(0)) - h(y_n(1)) + My_n(0) + Ny_n(1)\} \\ + \int_0^1 G^J(t, s)\{F(y_n(s), s) - V(s)\, y_n(s)\}\, ds. \end{aligned} \tag{5.2}$$

Since we know $y_n(\cdot)$ at each successive step, we can write (5.2) in the form

$$y_{n+1}(t) = H^J(t)\, \tilde{c}_n + \int_0^1 G^J(t, s)\, \tilde{f}_n(s)\, ds \tag{5.3}$$

where

$$\tilde{c}_n = c - g(y_n(0)) - h(y_n(1)) + My_n(0) + Ny_n(1)$$

and

$$\tilde{f}_n(s) = F(y_n(s), s) - V(s)\, y_n(s).$$

But (5.3) is the solution of the linear TPBVP

$$\dot{y}_{n+1} = V(t)\, y_{n+1} + \tilde{f}_n(t), \qquad My_{n+1}(0) + Ny_{n+1}(1) = \tilde{c}_n \tag{5.4}$$

or, equivalently, of the linear TPBVP

$$\begin{gathered} \dot{y}_{n+1} = V(t)[y_{n+1} - y_n] + F(y_n(t), t) \\ M[y_{n+1}(0) - y_n(0)] + N[y_{n+1}(1) - y_n(1)] = c - g(y_n(0)) - h(y_n(1)). \end{gathered} \tag{5.5}$$

Thus, the method of contraction mappings when applied to (5.1) essentially amounts to the successive solution of the linear TPBVP's (5.5). This is frequently referred to as *Picard's method.*

We now have the following.

DEFINITION 5.6. The TPBVP

$$\dot{y} = F(y, t), \qquad g(y(0)) + h(y(1)) = c \tag{5.7}$$

is differentiable on a subset S of $\mathscr{C}([0, 1], R_p)$ if (i) there is a boundary-compatible set $J = \{V(t), M, N\}$ such that the function $K(t, y, s) = G^J(t, s)\{F(y, s) - V(s)y\}$ satisfies the conditions of Lemma 8.5 of Chapter 3 on an open set D in R_p with the range of S contained in D, and (ii) g and h are differentiable. Similarly, the TPBVP (5.7) is twice differentiable on S if both $K(t, y, s)$ and $(\partial K/\partial y)(t, y, s)$ satisfy the conditions of Lemma 8.5 of Chapter 3 and if g and h are twice differentiable.

THEOREM 5.8. Let $y_0(\cdot)$ be an element of $\mathscr{C}([0, 1], R_p)$ and let $\bar{S} = \bar{S}(y_0, r)$. Suppose that (i) $J = \{V(t), M, N\}$ is a boundary-compatible set for which (5.7) is differentiable on $\bar{S}$, and (ii) there are real numbers η and α with $\eta \geqslant 0$ and $0 \leqslant \alpha < 1$ such that

$$\| T^J(y_0) - y_0 \| = \sup_i \sup_{t\in[0,1]} \{| T^J(y_0)_i(t) - y_{0,i}(t)|\} \leqslant \eta \tag{5.9}$$

$$\sup_{y\in\bar{S}}\{\|(T_y{}^J)'\|_{(a)}\} \leqslant \alpha \tag{5.10*}$$

$$\frac{1}{1-\alpha}\eta \leqslant r. \tag{5.11}$$

* See Section 8 of Chapter 3 and note that the theorem remains true if $\| (T_y{}^J)' \|_{(a)}$ is replaced by $\| (T_y{}^J)' \|_{(b)}$ or $\| (T_y{}^J)' \|_{(c)}$.

Then the CM sequence $\{y_n(\cdot)\}$ for the TPBVP based on y_0 and J converges uniformly to the unique solution $y^*(\cdot)$ of (5.7) in $\bar{S}$ and the rate of convergence is given by

$$\| y^*(\cdot) - y_n(\cdot)\| \leqslant \frac{\alpha^n}{1-\alpha} \| y_1(\cdot) - y_0(\cdot)\| . \tag{5.12}$$

Proof. Simply apply Chapter 2, Corollary 2.10 and the estimates of Chapter 3, Section 8.

Similarly, we can translate Corollary 2.34 of Chapter 2 to obtain the following.

THEOREM 5.13. Suppose that (i) $J = \{V(t), M, N\}$ is a boundary-compatible set for which (5.7) is twice differentiable on $\bar{S}$, and (ii) there are real numbers η, δ, and K with $\eta \geqslant 0$, $0 \leqslant \delta < 1$, and $K \geqslant 0$ such that

(5.14)* $$\| T^J(y_0) - y_0 \| \leqslant \eta, \qquad \|(T^J_{y_0})'\|_{(a)} \leqslant \delta$$

(5.15)* $$\sup_{y \in \bar{S}}\{\|(T_y{}^J)''\|_{(a)}\} \leqslant K$$

and

$$\frac{1-\sqrt{1-2h}}{h}\,\frac{\eta}{1-\delta} \leqslant r < \frac{1+\sqrt{1-2h}}{h}\,\frac{\eta}{1-\delta} \tag{5.16}$$

where $h = [K\eta/(1-\delta)^2] \leqslant \frac{1}{2}$. Then the CM sequence $\{y_n(\cdot)\}$ for the TPBVP based on y_0 and J converges uniformly to the unique solution $y^*(\cdot)$ of (5.7) in $\bar{S}$ and the rate of convergence is given by

$$\| y^*(\cdot) - y_n(\cdot)\| \leqslant [1-(1-\delta)\sqrt{1-2h}]^n \left[\frac{1-\sqrt{1-2h}}{h(1-\delta)}\right] \times \| y_1(\cdot) - y_0(\cdot)\| . \tag{5.17}$$

From Theorems 5.8 and 5.13 we can deduce some guidelines for the choice of the initial guess $y_0(\cdot)$ and the set of boundary-compatible matrices $V(t)$, M, and N. Before we do so, however, we should sound a word of caution with respect to the interpretation of the conditions given by these two theorems. Both theorems only involve sufficient

* Again, the theorem remains true if $\|(T^J_{y_0})'\|_{(a)}$ is replaced by $\|(T^J_{y_0})'\|_{(b)}$ or $\|(T^J_{y_0})'\|_{(c)}$ or if $\|(T_y{}^J)''\|_{(a)}$ is replaced by $\|(T_y{}^J)''\|_{(b)}$ or $\|(T_y{}^J)''\|_{(c)}$.

conditions. If the conditions are satisfied, then the convergence of the corresponding CM sequence is guaranteed. In many practical cases, however, the CM sequences will converge while the conditions are not satisfied. Therefore, our conclusions as regards convergence drawn from these conditions should be viewed practically as guidelines rather than strict rules.

The only explicit requirement for the choice of the initial guess $y_0(\cdot)$ is the stipulation that $y_0(\cdot)$ be a continuous p-vector function defined on $[0, 1]$ (or: $y_0(\cdot) \in \mathscr{C}([0, 1], R^p)$). Implicitly, however, the conditions on the norm of the first step η, which is strongly dependent on the choice of $y_0(\cdot)$, limit the choice of $y_0(\cdot)$ considerably. Assuming that the second Frechet derivative of T^J does not vary much over the sphere $\bar{S}$, it follows that the convergence constants (or contraction factors) α and h are roughly proportional to η. Hence, the smaller η, the better (i.e., faster) the convergence. The best choice for the initial guess $y_0(\cdot)$ is therefore the trajectory which according to the available data is as close (in the sense of the norm) to the actual solution $y^*(\cdot)$ of the TPBVP as possible. The first approximate solution $y_1(\cdot)$ will then be close to $y^*(\cdot)$ and hence also close to the initial guess. The norm of the difference $\| y_1 - y_0 \|$ will then be small. If the initial guess $y_0(\cdot)$ is chosen farther away, then η will increase and so too will α and h. If $y_0(\cdot)$ is chosen too far from $y^*(\cdot)$, then a point may be reached where the convergence of the CM sequence is no longer guaranteed by the theorems.

The convergence conditions given in Theorems 5.8 and 5.13 are, when combined with the estimates (8.17) and (8.18) of Chapter 3, rather explicit with respect to the choice of J. For example, a small convergence factor α will be obtained if $\sup_{y \in \bar{S}} \{\|(\partial F/\partial y)(y(\cdot), \cdot) - V(\cdot)\|\}$ and $\sup_{y \in \bar{S}} \{[\| M - (\partial g/\partial y)(y(0))\| + \| N - (\partial h/\partial y)(y(1))\|]\}$ are small. In essence, conditions on the norm of the operator T^J are translated into conditions on the norms of F and its derivatives and on the norms of $V(t)$, M, and N.

If the boundary conditions are linear, then M and N should be chosen "close" to the constant matrices $\partial g/\partial y$ and $\partial h/\partial y$. In the control problem case, it may usually be assumed that $[\partial g/\partial y, \partial h/\partial y]$ has maximum rank and so, by Lemma 2.13 of Chapter 2, that a boundary-compatible set can be chosen of the form $\{V(t), \partial g/\partial y, \partial h/\partial y\}$. Under such circumstances, the estimates of derivatives involve only $V(t)$ and $F(y, t)$. In a similar vein, it is often effective to choose $V(t)$ close to $(\partial F/\partial y)(y_0(t), t)$.

We conclude this section with two simple illustrative examples.

EXAMPLE 5.18 (Picard). Consider [P2] the TPBVP $\ddot{x} = f(x, \dot{x}, t)$, $x(0) = a$, $x(1) = b$ which can be written in the standard form

$$\begin{bmatrix} \dot{y}_1 \\ \dot{y}_2 \end{bmatrix} = \begin{bmatrix} y_2 \\ f(y_1, y_2, t) \end{bmatrix},$$

(5.19)

$$\begin{bmatrix} 1 & 0 \\ 0 & 0 \end{bmatrix} \begin{bmatrix} y_1(0) \\ y_2(0) \end{bmatrix} + \begin{bmatrix} 0 & 0 \\ 1 & 0 \end{bmatrix} \begin{bmatrix} y_1(1) \\ y_2(1) \end{bmatrix} = \begin{bmatrix} a \\ b \end{bmatrix}$$

We use the boundary-compatible set

$$V(t) = \begin{bmatrix} 0 & 1 \\ 0 & 0 \end{bmatrix}, \qquad M = \begin{bmatrix} 1 & 0 \\ 0 & 0 \end{bmatrix}, \qquad N = \begin{bmatrix} 0 & 0 \\ 1 & 0 \end{bmatrix} \tag{5.20}$$

and we choose as initial guess

$$y_0(t) = \begin{bmatrix} a + (b - a)t \\ b - a \end{bmatrix}$$

We further assume that there are two real numbers $\mu_1 \geqslant 0$ and $\mu_2 \geqslant 0$ such that

$$|f(y_1, y_2, t) - f(\tilde{y}_1, \tilde{y}_2, t)| \leqslant \mu_1 |y_1 - \tilde{y}_1| + \mu_2 |y_2 - \tilde{y}_2| \tag{5.21}$$

for y, $\tilde{y}$ in some sphere $\bar{S}(y_0, r)$ around $y_0(t)$. Thus, we have enough data to determine the convergence conditions for Picard's method.

In order to determine a value for α as defined in Theorem 5.8, we let $\mathbf{P}(t) = (p_{ij}(t))$ be a matrix with entries

$$p_{ij}(t) = \int_0^1 |g_{ij}^V(t, s)| \, ds \tag{5.22}$$

and $\mathbf{z} = (z_j)$ be a vector with entries

$$z_j = \sup_{t \in [0,1]} \sup_{y \in \bar{S}} \left\{ \sum_{k=1}^{2} \left| \frac{\partial f_j}{\partial y_k} (y(t), t) - V_{jk}(t) \right| \right\} \tag{5.23}$$

where $\bar{S} = \bar{S}(y_0, r)$. Then,

$$\|(T^J_{(y)})'\|_{(c)} = \sup_{t\in[0,1]} \|\mathbf{P}(t)\mathbf{z}\| = \sup_{t\in[0,1]} \sup_{i\in P} \left\{\sum_j p_{ij}(t)\, z_j\right\}.$$

Now the Green's matrix is given by

$$G^V(t,s) = \begin{cases} \begin{bmatrix} 1-t & -(1-t)s \\ -1 & s \end{bmatrix}, & 0 \leqslant s < t \\ \begin{bmatrix} -t & -(1-s)t \\ -1 & -(1-s) \end{bmatrix}, & t < s \leqslant 1 \end{cases} \tag{5.24}$$

and so

$$\mathbf{P}(t) = \begin{bmatrix} 2(t-t^2) & \frac{1}{2}(t-t^2) \\ 1 & \frac{1}{2}-(t-t^2) \end{bmatrix} \tag{5.25}$$

Assuming that f is differentiable and using the mean value theorem and (5.21), we deduce that

$$\mathbf{z} = \begin{bmatrix} 0 \\ \mu_1 + \mu_2 \end{bmatrix} \tag{5.26}$$

and hence that $\|(T^J_{(y)})'\|_{(c)} = \frac{1}{2}\mu_1 + \frac{1}{2}\mu_2 \leqslant \alpha$. Thus, the convergence condition $\alpha < 1$ becomes

$$\tfrac{1}{2}\mu_1 + \tfrac{1}{2}\mu_2 < 1. \tag{5.27}$$

Condition (5.27) is more stringent than the condition given by Picard [P2]

$$\tfrac{1}{8}\mu_1 + \tfrac{1}{2}\mu_2 < 1. \tag{5.28}$$

The reason for the difference between (5.27) and (5.28) lies in the choice of the norm. We investigate this in some detail: both convergence conditions (5.27) and (5.28) are expressions of the requirement that for convergence of the contraction mapping method the contraction factor should be smaller than 1. To determine this contraction factor the norm of the difference of two images of arbitrary elements in the sphere $\bar{S}(y_0, r)$ is compared with the norm of the difference between the elements. Calling

$$T^J(y) = u \qquad \text{and} \qquad T^J(\bar{y}) = \bar{u} \qquad (y, \bar{y} \in \bar{S}(y_0, r)),$$

this amounts to a comparison of the norms of the differences

$$u(t) - \bar{u}(t) = \int_0^1 g_{1,2}^V(t, s)[f(y, \dot{y}, s) - f(\bar{y}, \dot{\bar{y}}, s)]\, ds$$

$$\dot{u}(t) - \dot{\bar{u}}(t) = \int_0^1 g_{2,2}^V(t, s)[f(y, \dot{y}, s) - f(\bar{y}, \dot{\bar{y}}, s)]\, ds$$

For the suprema (over $t \in [0, 1]$) of the absolute values of these differences we have, in view of (5.21) and (5.25),

$$\sup_t | u(t) - \bar{u}(t)|$$

$$\leqslant \sup_t \int_0^1 | g_{1,2}(t, s)| \{\mu_1 \sup_s | y(s) - \bar{y}(s)| + | \mu_2 \sup_s | \dot{y}(s) - \dot{\bar{y}}(s)|\}\, ds$$

$$\leqslant \tfrac{1}{8} \{\mu_1 \sup_s | y(s) - \bar{y}(s)| + \mu_2 \sup_s | \dot{y}(s) - \dot{\bar{y}}(s)|\}$$

and

$$\sup | \dot{u}(t) - \dot{\bar{u}}(t)|$$

$$\leqslant \sup_t \int_0^1 | g_{2,2}(t, s)| \{\mu_1 \sup_s | y(s) - \bar{y}(s)| + \mu_2 \sup_s | \dot{y}(s) - \dot{\bar{y}}(s)|\}\, ds$$

$$\leqslant \tfrac{1}{2} \{\mu_1 \sup_s | y(s) - \bar{y}(s)| + \mu_2 \sup_s | \dot{y}(s) - \dot{\bar{y}}(s)|\}.$$

If we choose the uniform norm defined by

$$\| w(\cdot)\| = \sup_{t \in [0,1]} \sup_{i \in P} \{| w_i(t)|\} = \sup\{\sup_t | w(t)| , \sup_t | \dot{w}(t)|\}$$

then, the Lipschitz norm $\square\, T^J \,\square_S$ is given by

$$\square\, T^J \,\square_S = \sup_{y, \bar{y} \in \bar{S}} \{\| T^J(y) - T^J(\bar{y})\| / \| y - \bar{y} \|\}$$

and we obtain our earlier result (5.27)

$$\Box\, T^J \Box_{\bar{S}} = \sup_{y,\bar{y}\in\bar{S}} \left\{ \frac{\frac{1}{2}\{\mu_1 \sup_s |y(s)-\bar{y}(s)| + \mu_2 \sup_s |\dot{y}(s)-\dot{\bar{y}}(s)|\}}{\sup\{\sup_s |y(s)-\bar{y}(s)|,\ \sup_s |\dot{y}(s)-\dot{\bar{y}}(s)|\}} \right\}$$

$$\leqslant \tfrac{1}{2}\mu_1 + \tfrac{1}{2}\mu_2 \leqslant \alpha < 1.$$

On the other hand, if we use the special problem oriented norm

$$\| w \| = \mu_1 \sup_{t\in[0,1]} |w(t)| + \mu_2 \sup_{t\in[0,1]} |\dot{w}(t)| \tag{5.29}$$

then

$$\Box\, T^J \Box_{\bar{S}} = \sup_{y\in\bar{S}} \left\{ \frac{\frac{1}{8}\mu_1 \| y-\bar{y} \| + \frac{1}{2}\mu_2 \| y-\bar{y} \|}{\| y-\bar{y} \|} \right\} = \tfrac{1}{8}\mu_1 + \tfrac{1}{2}\mu_2$$

which is precisely the result of Picard (5.28). It should be noted that a problem oriented norm of the type (5.29) is feasible, in case the TPBVP is given in the form of an nth order ordinary differential equation. In cases where the TPBVP is given by a general set of first-order differential equations, this type of norm will seldom be feasible.

EXAMPLE 5.30. In this rather long example we discuss in detail the application of Picard's method to the nonlinear TPBVP considered in Section 3. First, we formally apply Picard's method to the problem and evaluate the first three approximate solutions. We compare these approximations with each other and with the exact solution (3.12) determined in Section 3. Next, having found indications of possible convergence, we determine the convergence conditions as given by both Theorems 5.8 and 5.13 in full detail for an assumed set of numerical data. Finally, we compare these convergence conditions.

In standard form, the TPBVP considered here has the form

$$\begin{bmatrix} \dot{y}_1 \\ \dot{y}_2 \end{bmatrix} = \begin{bmatrix} -\epsilon\sqrt{y_1} - b^2 y_2 \\ +\epsilon \dfrac{1}{2\sqrt{y_1}} y_2 \end{bmatrix}, \tag{5.31}$$

$$\begin{bmatrix}1 & 0\\0 & 0\end{bmatrix}\begin{bmatrix}y_1(0)\\y_2(0)\end{bmatrix}+\begin{bmatrix}0 & 0\\1 & 0\end{bmatrix}\begin{bmatrix}y_1(1)\\y_2(1)\end{bmatrix}=\begin{bmatrix}x_0\\x_1\end{bmatrix}.$$

Now we can write (5.31) in the form

$$\begin{bmatrix}\dot{y}_1\\\dot{y}_2\end{bmatrix}=\begin{bmatrix}0 & -b^2\\0 & 0\end{bmatrix}\begin{bmatrix}y_1\\y_2\end{bmatrix}+\epsilon\begin{bmatrix}-\sqrt{y_1}\\\dfrac{1}{2\sqrt{y_1}}y_2\end{bmatrix},$$

(5.32)

$$\begin{bmatrix}1 & 0\\0 & 0\end{bmatrix}\begin{bmatrix}y_1(0)\\y_2(0)\end{bmatrix}+\begin{bmatrix}0 & 0\\1 & 0\end{bmatrix}\begin{bmatrix}y_1(1)\\y_2(1)\end{bmatrix}=\begin{bmatrix}x_0\\x_1\end{bmatrix}.$$

We deduce that a good choice for a boundary-compatible set is given by

$$V(t)=\begin{bmatrix}0 & -b^2\\0 & 0\end{bmatrix},\qquad M=\begin{bmatrix}1 & 0\\0 & 0\end{bmatrix},\qquad N=\begin{bmatrix}0 & 0\\1 & 0\end{bmatrix}. \tag{5.33}$$

In view of the relation (see Section 6 of Chapter 3)

$$\Phi^V(t,s)=\begin{bmatrix}1 & -b^2(t-s)\\0 & 1\end{bmatrix}$$

we have

$$\det[M+N\Phi^V(1,0)]=\det\left\{\begin{bmatrix}1 & 0\\0 & 0\end{bmatrix}+\begin{bmatrix}0 & 0\\1 & 0\end{bmatrix}\begin{bmatrix}1 & -b^2\\0 & 1\end{bmatrix}\right\}$$

$$=\det\left\{\begin{bmatrix}1 & 0\\1 & -b^2\end{bmatrix}\right\}$$

$$=-b^2\neq 0.$$

Hence, these matrices satisfy the conditions for boundary compatibility. A good choice for the initial guess is given by the solution of the linear problem

$$\begin{bmatrix} \dot{y}_1 \\ \dot{y}_2 \end{bmatrix} = \begin{bmatrix} 0 & -b^2 \\ 0 & 0 \end{bmatrix} \begin{bmatrix} y_1 \\ y_1 \end{bmatrix},$$

(5.34)

$$\begin{bmatrix} 1 & 0 \\ 0 & 0 \end{bmatrix} \begin{bmatrix} y_1(0) \\ y_2(0) \end{bmatrix} + \begin{bmatrix} 0 & 0 \\ 1 & 0 \end{bmatrix} \begin{bmatrix} y_1(1) \\ y_2(1) \end{bmatrix} = \begin{bmatrix} x_0 \\ x_1 \end{bmatrix}$$

which corresponds to $\{V(t), M, N\}$. The solution of this TPBVP is easily found to be

$$y_1(t) = x_0 + (x_1 - x_0)t, \qquad y_2(t) = -\frac{1}{b^2}(x_1 - x_0) \tag{5.35}$$

Defining $d = x_0$, $e = x_1 - x_0$ and using superscripts (in parentheses) to indicate the number of the iteration, we write $y_{0,1}^{(0)}(t) = d + et$, $y_{0,2}^{(0)} = -(1/b^2)e$ and so, we have found our initial guess.

To determine the first approximate solution $y^{(1)}(t)$, we use the algorithm (5.5), i.e.,

$$\dot{y}^{(1)} - V(t)\,y^{(1)} = F[y^{(0)}(t), t] - V(t)\,y^{(0)}(t),$$
$$My^{(1)}(0) + Ny^{(1)}(1) = c$$

In view of (5.32) and (5.33), this becomes

$$\dot{y}_1^{(1)} + b^2 y_2^{(1)} = -\epsilon\sqrt{y^{(0)}} = -\epsilon\sqrt{d + et},$$

(5.36)

$$y_1^{(1)}(0) = d$$

$$\dot{y}_2^{(1)} = +\epsilon\frac{1}{2\sqrt{y_1^{(0)}}}\,y_2^{(0)} = -\frac{\epsilon}{2b^2}\frac{e}{\sqrt{d + et}},$$

$$y_1^{(1)}(1) = d + e.$$

The solution of this linear TPBVP can be found by straightforward integration followed by determination of the integration constants from the boundary conditions. The solution obtained in this way has the form

$$y^{(1)}(t) = d + et, \qquad y_2^{(1)}(t) = -\frac{1}{b^2}e - \frac{\epsilon}{b^2}\sqrt{d + et}\,. \tag{5.37}$$

Following the same procedure, i.e., by solving the linear TPBVP

$$\dot{y}_1^{(2)} + b^2 y_2^{(2)} = -\epsilon \sqrt{y_1^{(1)}} = -\epsilon \sqrt{d + et}$$

$$(5.38) \qquad \begin{aligned} y_1^{(2)}(0) &= d \\ \dot{y}_2^{(2)} &= +\epsilon \frac{1}{2\sqrt{y_1^{(1)}}} y_2^{(1)} = -\frac{\epsilon}{2b^2} \frac{e}{\sqrt{d + et}} - \frac{\epsilon^2}{2b^2}, \\ y_1^{(2)}(1) &= d + e \end{aligned}$$

we find as second approximate solution $y^{(2)}(t)$

$$(5.39) \qquad \begin{aligned} y_1^{(2)}(t) &= d + et + \frac{\epsilon^2}{4}(t^2 - t), \\ y_2^{(2)}(t) &= -\frac{1}{b^2}\sqrt{d + et} - \frac{\epsilon^2}{4b^2}(2t - 1). \end{aligned}$$

It is of interest to compare the differences between the successive approximate solutions. It follows immediately that

$$y_1^{(1)}(t) - y_1^{(0)}(t) = 0$$

$$y_2^{(1)}(t) - y_2^{(0)}(t) = \frac{\epsilon}{b^2}\sqrt{d + et}$$

$$y_1^{(2)}(t) - y_1^{(1)}(t) = \frac{\epsilon^2}{4}(t^2 - t)$$

$$y_2^{(2)}(t) - y_2^{(1)}(t) = \frac{\epsilon^2}{4b^2}(2t - 1)$$

and hence for the uniform norms of the differences between the successive approximations, that

$$(5.40) \qquad \begin{aligned} \| y^{(1)} - y^{(0)} \| &= \frac{\epsilon}{b^2}\sqrt{d + e} \\ \| y^{(2)} - y^{(1)} \| &= \frac{\epsilon^2}{4} \qquad \text{if } \; b \geqslant 1 \\ &= \frac{\epsilon^2}{4b^2} \qquad \text{if } \; b \leqslant 1 \end{aligned}$$

Comparison of these norms shows that if

$$(5.41)\qquad \begin{aligned} &\epsilon < \frac{4\sqrt{d+e}}{b^2} && \text{if}\quad b \geqslant 1\\ &\epsilon < 4\sqrt{d+e} && \text{if}\quad b \leqslant 1 \end{aligned}$$

then the norms of the differences between the successive approximations decrease (for the first three approximations). Convergence of Picard's method becomes a distinct possibility in that case.

We can also compare our approximate solutions with the exact solution determined in Section 3. This solution is given by

$$y_1{}^*(t) = d + et + \frac{\epsilon^2}{4}(t^2 - t),$$

$$y_2{}^*(t) = -\frac{1}{b^2}e - \frac{\epsilon^2}{4b^2}(2t-1) - \frac{\epsilon}{b^2}\sqrt{d + et + \frac{\epsilon^2}{4}(t^2 - t)}\,.$$

Such a comparison yields

$$\begin{aligned} y_1{}^*(t) - y_1^{(0)}(t) &= \frac{\epsilon^2}{4}(t^2 - t),\\ y_2{}^*(t) - y_2^{(0)}(t) &= -\frac{\epsilon^2}{4b^2}(2t-1) - \frac{\epsilon}{b^2}\sqrt{d + et + \frac{\epsilon^2}{4}(t^2 - t)}\\ y_1{}^*(t) - y_1^{(1)}(t) &= \frac{\epsilon^2}{4}(t^2 - t),\\ y_2{}^*(t) - y_2^{(1)}(t) &= -\frac{\epsilon^2}{4b^2}(2t-1)\\ &\qquad - \frac{\epsilon}{b^2}\left(\sqrt{d + et + \frac{\epsilon^2}{4}(t^2 - t)} - \sqrt{d+et}\right)\\ y_1{}^*(t) - y_1^{(2)}(t) &= 0,\\ y_2{}^*(t) - y_2^{(2)}(t) &= -\frac{\epsilon}{b^2}\left(\sqrt{d + et + \frac{\epsilon^2}{4}(t^2 - t)} - \sqrt{d+et}\right). \end{aligned} \qquad (5.42)$$

Without determining the uniform norms corresponding to these differences, it is already evident from inspection that (the absolute values of) the differences between the exact solution and the three first approximate solutions decrease. This points definitely towards convergence of this particular application of Picard's method. We investigate this convergence in the light of Theorems 5.8 and 5.13.

Since the application of Theorems 5.8 and 5.13 is almost impossible without specific numerical values, we assume the following data:

$$\epsilon = \tfrac{1}{4}, \qquad d = x_0 = 10$$

$$b = \tfrac{1}{2}\sqrt{2}, \qquad e = x_1 - x_0 = 15.$$

For these numerical values, we find from (5.40) and (5.41) that $\| y^{(1)} - y^{(0)} \| = 2.5$, $\| y^{(2)} - y^{(1)} \| = 3.12 \times 10^{-2}$ and similarly that

$$\| y^* - y^{(0)} \| = 2.531, \qquad \| y^* - y^{(1)} \| = 3.12 \times 10^{-2},$$

$$\| y^* - y^{(2)} \| = 2.32 \times 10^{-4}.$$

These numbers show that, at least, the first three approximations exhibit a rather rapid convergence.

In applying Theorems 5.8 and 5.13, we are most interested in the determination of the numbers α, δ, and K. Instead of trying to evaluate the defining expressions for α, δ, and K directly, we use the same indirect procedure as in the preceding example. That is, we define a matrix $\mathbf{P}(t)$ and vectors $\mathbf{z}$, $\mathbf{z}_0$, and $\mathbf{x}$ with elements (components) $p_{ij}(t)$, z_j, $z_{0,j}$, and x_j given by

$$p_{ij}(t) = \sup_{t\in[0,1]} \int_0^1 | g_{ij}^V(t, s) | \, ds$$

$$z_j = \sup_{y\in\bar{S}} \sup_{t\in[0,1]} \left\{ \sum_{k=1}^{p} \left| \frac{\partial F_j}{\partial y_k} (y(t), t) - v_{jk}(t) \right| \right\}$$

$$z_{0,j} = \sup_{t\in[0,1]} \left\{ \sum_{k=1}^{p} \left| \frac{\partial F_j}{\partial y_k} (y_0(t), t) - v_{jk}(t) \right| \right\}$$

$$x_j = \sup_{y\in\bar{S}} \sup_{t\in[0,1]} \left\{ \sum_{k=1}^{p} \sum_{l=1}^{p} \left| \frac{\partial^2 F_j}{\partial y_k \, \partial y_l} (y(t), t) \right| \right\}.$$

It follows that conservative values of α, δ, and K are given by

$$\| \mathbf{P}(\cdot)\, \mathbf{z} \| = \sup_i \sup_t \left\{ \sum_{j=1}^{p} p_{ij}(t)\, z_j \right\} \leqslant \alpha$$

$$\| \mathbf{P}(\cdot)\, \mathbf{z}_0 \| = \sup_i \sup_t \left\{ \sum_{j=1}^{p} p_{ij}(t)\, z_{0,j} \right\} \leqslant \delta$$

$$\| \mathbf{P}(\cdot)\, \mathbf{x} \| = \sup_i \sup_t \left\{ \sum_{j=1}^{p} p_{ij}(t)\, x_j \right\} \leqslant K.$$

We can readily deduce that

$$G^V(t, s) = \begin{bmatrix} 1 - t & b^2(1 - t)s \\ \dfrac{1}{b^2} & s \end{bmatrix} \qquad \text{for} \quad 0 \leqslant s < t$$

$$= \begin{bmatrix} -t & b^2 t(1 - s) \\ \dfrac{1}{b^2} & -(1 - s) \end{bmatrix} \qquad \text{for} \quad t < s \leqslant 1.$$

Integration of the absolute values yields

$$\mathbf{P}(t) = \left[\int_0^1 | g_{ij}^V(t, s)|\, ds \right] = \begin{bmatrix} 2(t - t^2) & \dfrac{b^2}{2}(t - t^2) \\ \dfrac{1}{b^2} & \tfrac{1}{2} - (t - t^2) \end{bmatrix}.$$

Next, we deduce formally from (5.31) and (5.33) that

$$\text{(5.43)} \qquad \frac{\partial F}{\partial y}(y(t), t) - V(t) = \begin{bmatrix} -\epsilon \dfrac{1}{2\sqrt{y_1(t)}} & 0 \\ -\epsilon \dfrac{y_2(t)}{4y_1(t)\sqrt{y_1(t)}} & \epsilon \dfrac{1}{2\sqrt{y_1(t)}} \end{bmatrix}.$$

It follows immediately that

$$\left[\sum_{k=1}^{p}\left|\frac{\partial F_j}{\partial y_k}(y(t), t) - v_{jk}(t)\right|\right] = \begin{bmatrix} \epsilon \dfrac{1}{2\sqrt{y_1(t)}} \\ \epsilon \dfrac{|y_2(t)|}{4\,|y_1(t)|\sqrt{y_1(t)}} + \epsilon \dfrac{1}{2\sqrt{y_1(t)}} \end{bmatrix}.$$

In order to determine the supremum over $t \in [0, 1]$ and $y(t) \in \bar{S}(y_0, r)$, we must specify the sphere $\bar{S}(y_0, r)$. With the initial guess $y^{(0)}(t)$ given by

$$y_1^{(0)}(t) = d + et = 10 + 15t, \qquad y_2^{(0)}(t) = -\frac{1}{b^2} e = -30,$$

we must assume a value for the radius r to completely specify $\bar{S}(y_0, r)$. Now, following Theorem 5.8, this radius must satisfy the condition $[1/(1-\alpha)]\eta \leqslant r$ where α is implicitly dependent on r. The usual procedure to determine r for given η is to assume a value of r, evaluate α for this r, and then adjust the guess for r depending on the difference $[1/(1-\alpha)]\eta - r$.

As a first guess for r in the present case, we assume that $r = 4$. This implies that the sphere $\bar{S}(y_0, r)$ contains all continuous two-vector functions such that

$$6 + 15t \leqslant y_1(t) \leqslant 14 + 15t, \qquad -34 \leqslant y_2(t) \leqslant -26.$$

Hence

$$\inf_{y\in\bar{S}} \inf_{t\in[0,1]} |y_1(t)| = 6 \qquad \sup_{y\in\bar{S}} \sup_{t\in[0,1]} |y_2(t)| = 34.$$

Using these extreme values, we find that

$$\begin{bmatrix} z_1 \\ z_2 \end{bmatrix} = \sup_{y\in\bar{S}} \sup_{t\in[0,1]} \begin{bmatrix} \epsilon \dfrac{1}{2\sqrt{y_1(t)}} \\ \epsilon \dfrac{|y_2(t)|}{4\,|y_1(t)|\sqrt{y_1(t)}} + \epsilon \dfrac{1}{2\sqrt{y_1(t)}} \end{bmatrix}$$

$$= \begin{bmatrix} \dfrac{1}{8\sqrt{6}} \\ \dfrac{34}{96\sqrt{6}} + \dfrac{1}{8\sqrt{6}} \end{bmatrix} = \begin{bmatrix} 0.0510 \\ 0.1955 \end{bmatrix}$$

and hence that

$$\| \mathbf{P}(\cdot)\mathbf{z} \| = \sup_{t \in [0,1]} \left\{ \begin{bmatrix} 2(t - t^2) & \frac{1}{4}(t - t^2) \\ 2 & \frac{1}{2} - (t - t^2) \end{bmatrix} \begin{bmatrix} 0.0510 \\ 0.1955 \end{bmatrix} \right\} = 0.1998.$$

Hence, we may take

$$\alpha = 0.1998 < 1.$$

Next, we check our estimate for r. We had $\| y^{(1)} - y^{(0)} \| = \eta = 2.5$ so that $[1/(1 - \alpha)]\eta = 1/(1 - 0.1998) \cdot (2.5) = 3.12 < 4$. Thus, we find that the α and η which we determined satisfy the main convergence conditions of Theorem 5.8 by an ample margin.

If our objective is limited to a proof of convergence of the CM sequence under consideration, then we might stop at this point. (It is easily verified that the other conditions of the theorem hold.) In case we are interested in convergence rates or error bounds, however, we might try to make α smaller by making r smaller and vice versa. For example, in the present case we might have assumed for r the value $r = 3.05$. This leads to a sphere $\bar{S}(y_0, r)$ which contains all continuous 2-vector functions, such that

$$6.95 + 15t \leqslant y_1(t) \leqslant 13.05 + 15t, \qquad -33.05 \leqslant y_2(t) \leqslant -26.05.$$

The extreme values of $y_1(t)$ and $y_2(t)$ now become

$$\inf_{y \in \bar{S}} \inf_{t \in [0,1]} | y_1(t)| = 6.95, \qquad \sup_{y \in \bar{S}} \sup_{t \in [0,1]} | y_2(t)| = 33.95.$$

Using these extreme values, we find for the vector $\mathbf{z}$

$$\begin{bmatrix} z_1 \\ z_2 \end{bmatrix} = \sup_{y \in \bar{S}} \sup_{t \in [0,1]} \begin{bmatrix} \epsilon \dfrac{1}{2\sqrt{y_1(t)}} \\ \epsilon \dfrac{| y_2(t)|}{4 | y_1(t)| \sqrt{y_1(t)}} + \epsilon \dfrac{1}{2\sqrt{y_1(t)}} \end{bmatrix}$$

$$= \begin{bmatrix} \dfrac{1}{8\sqrt{6.95}} \\ \dfrac{33.05}{16(6.95\sqrt{6.95})} + \dfrac{1}{8\sqrt{6.95}} \end{bmatrix} = \begin{bmatrix} 0.0474 \\ 0.1604 \end{bmatrix}$$

and hence, that

$$\| \mathbf{P}(\cdot)\mathbf{z} \| = \sup_t \left\| \begin{bmatrix} 2(t - t^2) & \frac{1}{4}(t - t^2) \\ 2 & \frac{1}{2} - (t - t^2) \end{bmatrix} \begin{bmatrix} .0474 \\ .1604 \end{bmatrix} \right\| = 0.1750.$$

Therefore, we may take $\alpha = 0.1750 < 1$. A check on the radius r now yields $[1/(1 - \alpha)]\eta = 1/(1 - 0.1750) \cdot (2.5) = 3.03 < 3.05$. Hence, this second choice for r indeed leads to a different value of α which together with η satisfies the conditions of Theorem 5.9. The last value of α is considerably lower than the one obtained previously and therefore leads to faster convergence rates and sharper error bounds.

In order to compare the application of Theorem 5.8 with the application of Theorem 5.13, we next determine δ and K. In view of the definition of $y^{(0)}(\cdot)$, we immediately find that

$$\inf_{t \in [0,1]} | y_1^{(0)}(t)| = 10, \qquad \sup_{t \in [0,1]} | y_2^{(0)}(t)| = 30.$$

Using this estimate, we deduce that

$$\begin{bmatrix} z_{0,1} \\ z_{0,2} \end{bmatrix} = \sup_{t \in [0,1]} \begin{bmatrix} \epsilon \dfrac{1}{2\sqrt{y_1^{(0)}(t)}} \\ \epsilon \dfrac{| y_2^{(0)}(t)|}{4\, | y_1^{(0)}(t)| \sqrt{y_1^{(0)}(t)}} + \epsilon \dfrac{1}{2\sqrt{y_1^{(0)}(t)}} \end{bmatrix}$$

$$= \begin{bmatrix} \dfrac{1}{8\sqrt{10}} \\ \dfrac{30}{16(10\sqrt{10})} + \dfrac{1}{8\sqrt{10}} \end{bmatrix} = \begin{bmatrix} 0.0396 \\ 0.0990 \end{bmatrix}$$

and

$$\| \mathbf{P}(\cdot)\, \mathbf{z}_0 \| = \sup_t \left\| \begin{bmatrix} 2(t - t^2) & \frac{1}{4}(t - t^2) \\ 2 & \frac{1}{2} - (t - t^2) \end{bmatrix} \begin{bmatrix} .0396 \\ .0990 \end{bmatrix} \right\| = 0.1287.$$

Hence, we may take $\delta = 0.1287 < 1$. To determine K, we must again guess a value for the radius r. We take $r = 3.0$. From (5.43) we derive the matrices of second derivatives as

$$\left[\frac{\partial^2 F_1}{\partial y_k\, \partial y_l}\right] = \begin{bmatrix} \dfrac{\epsilon}{4[y_1(t)]^{3/2}} & 0 \\ 0 & 0 \end{bmatrix},$$

$$\left[\frac{\partial^2 F_2}{\partial y_k\, \partial y_l}\right] = \begin{bmatrix} \epsilon \dfrac{3}{8} \dfrac{y_2(t)}{[y_1(t)]^{5/2}} & -\epsilon \dfrac{1}{4[y_1(t)]^{3/2}} \\ -\epsilon \dfrac{1}{4[y_1(t)]^{3/2}} & 0 \end{bmatrix}.$$

Using the extreme values of $|y_1(t)|$ and $|y_2(t)|$, we find that

$$\begin{bmatrix} x_1 \\ x_2 \end{bmatrix} = \sup_{y \in \bar{S}} \sup_{t \in [0,1]} \begin{bmatrix} \dfrac{\epsilon}{4[y_1(t)]^{3/2}} \\ \epsilon \dfrac{3}{8} \dfrac{|y_2(t)|}{[y_1(t)]^{5/2}} + \epsilon \dfrac{1}{2[y_1(t)]^{3/2}} \end{bmatrix}$$

$$= \begin{bmatrix} \dfrac{1}{16(7\sqrt{7})} \\ \dfrac{3(33)}{32(49\sqrt{7})} + \dfrac{1}{8(7\sqrt{7})} \end{bmatrix} = \begin{bmatrix} 0.00337 \\ 0.03060 \end{bmatrix}$$

and hence

$$\| \mathbf{P}(\cdot)\mathbf{x} \| = \sup_t \left\| \begin{bmatrix} 2(t - t^2) & \frac{1}{4}(t - t^2) \\ 2 & \frac{1}{2} - (t - t^2) \end{bmatrix} \begin{bmatrix} 0.00337 \\ 0.03060 \end{bmatrix} \right\| = 0.02205.$$

Thus, we may take $K = 0.02205$. The main convergence factor in theorem (5.13) is the number h defined by $h = K\eta/(1 - \delta)^2$. In view of our estimates, we see that

$$h = \frac{K\eta}{(1-\delta)^2} = \frac{(0.02205)(2.5)}{(1 - 0.1287)^2} = 0.0727 < \tfrac{1}{2}. \tag{5.44}$$

Evidently, (5.44) implies that the convergence condition on h of

Theorem 5.13 is satisfied. To check the radius r, we evaluate the expressions

$$\frac{1-\sqrt{1-2h}}{h}\cdot\frac{\eta}{1-\delta}=\frac{1-\sqrt{1-0.0727}}{0.0727}\cdot\frac{2.5}{(1-0.1287)}=2.98<3$$

and

$$\frac{1+\sqrt{1-2h}}{h}\cdot\frac{\eta}{1-\delta}=\frac{1+\sqrt{1-0.0727}}{0.0727}\cdot\frac{2.5}{(1-0.1287)}=76.0.$$

Since

$$2.98<r=3<76.0,$$

it follows that condition (5.16) is also satisfied for our values for δ, η, and h.

Thus, the conditions of Theorem 5.13 as regards the numbers η, δ, K, and h are satisfied. Since, in addition, the vector functions $F[y(t), t]$, $g[y(0)] = My(0)$, and $h[y(0)] = Ny(0)$ satisfy the existence and differentiability conditions on the sphere $\bar{S}(y^{(0)}, r)$, it follows that Theorem 5.13 applies. The CM sequence based on $y^{(0)}(t)$, $V(t)$, M, and N therefore converges to the unique solution $y^*(t)$ of the TPBVP. A guaranteed convergence rate for this CM sequence is given by the inequality

$$\begin{aligned}
&\sup_{i\in\mathscr{P}}\ \sup_{t\in[0,1]} |y_i^*(t)-y_i^{(n)}(t)| \\
&\quad\leqslant [1-(1-\delta)\sqrt{1-2h}]^n\,\frac{1-\sqrt{1-2h}}{h(1-\delta)}\sup_{i\in\mathscr{P}}\ \sup_{t\in[0,1]} |y_i^{(1)}(t)-y_i^{(0)}(t)| \\
&\quad\leqslant [1-(1-0.1287)\sqrt{1-2(0.0727)}]^n\,\frac{1-\sqrt{1-2(0.0727)}}{(0.0727)(1-0.1287)}(2.5) \\
&\quad\leqslant (0.1945)^n\,(2.98).
\end{aligned}$$

This convergence rate is conservative when compared to the actual convergence of the first three approximate solutions.

4.6. Application to Continuous Problems II: The Modified Contraction Mapping Method

We now examine the modified contraction mapping method as applied to operator equations of the form (5.1). We recall from Section 3 of Chapter 2 that the modified contraction mapping method coincides with the contraction mapping method applied to the operator $P = [I - V]^{-1}[T - V]$ for a suitably chosen V. We limit our discussion here to operators $V = U_{KL}^{J}$ of the form given by (10.2) of Chapter 3. Therefore, let $J = \{V(t), M, N\}$ and $\tilde{J} = \{U(t), K, L\}$ be boundary-compatible sets. Then, it follows from Lemma 10.1 that the modified contraction mapping method when applied to the equation $T^{J}(y) = y$ with modifying operator $V = U_{KL}^{J}$, is equivalent to the contraction mapping method applied to the equation $T^{\tilde{J}}(y) = y$. Having derived convergence conditions for the direct application of the contraction mapping method in Section 5, we focus our attention on the translation of Corollary 3.8 and Proposition 3.10 of Chapter 2.

With the aid of Lemma 10.1 of Chapter 3, the translation of the relevant results of Chapter 2 poses no real problems. However, before carrying out this translation, let us consider the advantages and disadvantages of the modified contraction mapping approach. The crucial convergence inequality is given by

$$\sup_{y \in \bar{S}}\{\|(I - U_{KL}^{J})^{-1}\,[(T_y^{\,J})' - U_{KL}^{J}]\|\} \leqslant \alpha < 1. \tag{6.1}$$

The first approach to this inequality is to simply note that

$$(I - U_{KL}^{J})^{-1}\,[(T_y^{\,J})' - U_{KL}^{J}] = (T_y^{\,\tilde{J}})'$$

so that (6.1) becomes

$$\sup_{y \in \bar{S}}\{\|(T_y^{\,\tilde{J}})'\|\} \leqslant \alpha < 1. \tag{6.2}$$

Since this is essentially the condition (5.10), nothing new has been developed. A second approach to (6.1) is to replace the single norm by a product of two norms so that

$$\sup_{y \in \bar{S}}\{\|(I - U_{KL}^{J})^{-1}\| \cdot \|(T_y^{\,J})' - U_{KL}^{J}\|\} \leqslant \alpha < 1 \tag{6.3}$$

becomes the relevant condition. This involves a majorization which results in less sharp convergence conditions. However, there may be offsetting advantages. One such advantage which is often important enough to warrant the loss of accuracy is the simplicity of evaluation of the estimates. As estimates of the form (6.3) rely on maximization over Green's matrices corresponding to boundary-compatible sets, we try to choose boundary-compatible sets for which this estimation is easy.

Now suppose that J is a boundary-compatible set for which the corresponding Green's matrices are easy to evaluate and estimate. Then, if $\| U^J_{KL} \| \leqslant q < 1$ so that $\|[I - U^J_{KL}]^{-1}\| \leqslant 1/(1-q)$, we can obtain an estimate of (6.3) which involves only the Green's matrices corresponding to J. This advantage may well offset the loss of accuracy resulting from using (6.3). We now have the following.

THEOREM 6.4. Let $y_0(\cdot)$ be an element of $\mathscr{C}([0, 1], R_p)$ and let $\bar{S} = \bar{S}(y_0, r)$. Suppose that (i) $J = \{V(t), M, N\}$ is a boundary-compatible set for which (5.7) is differentiable on $\bar{S}$; (ii) $\tilde{J} = \{U(t), K, L\}$ is a boundary-compatible set; and (iii) there are real numbers η, q, β, and α with $\eta \geqslant 0$, $0 \leqslant q < 1$, $\beta \geqslant 0$, and $\alpha = \beta/(1-q) < 1$ such that

$$(6.5) \qquad \| T^{\tilde{J}}(y_0) - y_0 \| = \sup_i \sup_t \{| T^{\tilde{J}}(y_0)_i(t) - y_{0,i}(t)|\} \leqslant \eta$$

$$(6.6) \qquad \| U^J_{KL} \|_{(a)} \leqslant q$$

$$(6.7) \qquad \sup_{y \in \bar{S}} \{\|(T_y{}^J)' - U^J_{KL}\|_{(a)}\} \leqslant \beta$$

$$(6.8) \qquad \frac{1}{1-\alpha}\eta \leqslant r$$

where

$$(6.9)^* \qquad \| U^J_{KL} \|_{(a)} = \sup_{\|v\| \leqslant 1} \sup_i \sup_t \left\{ \left| \sum_{k=1}^p \sum_{j=1}^p H^J_{ij}(t)\{[m_{jk} - k_{jk}]\, v_k(0) + [n_{jk} - l_{jk}]\, v_k(1)\} + \int_0^1 G^J_{ij}(t, s)[U_{jk}(s) - V_{jk}(s)]\, v_k(s)\, ds \right| \right\}$$

* Compare Section 8 of Chapter 3 and note that the theorem remains true if the analogous estimates $\| U^J_{KL} \|_{(b)}$ or $\| U^J_{KL} \|_{(c)}$, or $\| (T_y{}^J)' - U^J_{KL} \|_{(b)}$ or $\| (T_y{}^J)' - U^J_{KL} \|_{(c)}$ are used.

and

(6.10)* $$\|(T_y^J)' - U_{KL}^J\|_{(a)}$$

$$= \sup_{\|v\|\leqslant 1} \sup_i \sup_t \left\{ \left| \sum_{k=1}^{p} \sum_{j=1}^{p} H_{ij}^J(t) \left\{ \left[k_{jk} - \frac{\partial g_i}{\partial y_k}(y(0)) \right] v_k(0) \right. \right. \right.$$

$$\left. + \left[l_{jk} - \frac{\partial h_i}{\partial y_k}(y(1)) \right] v_k(1) \right\}$$

$$\left. \left. + \int_0^1 G_{ij}^J(t, s) \left[\frac{\partial F_j}{\partial y_k}(y(s), s) - U_{jk}(s) \right] v_k(s)\, ds \right| \right\}.$$

Then the MCM sequence $\{y_n(\cdot)\}$ for T^J based on $y_0(\cdot)$ and U_{KL}^J converges uniformly to the unique solution $y^*(\cdot)$ of (5.7) in $\bar{S}$ and the rate of convergence is given by

(6.11) $$\| y^*(\cdot) - y_n(\cdot)\| \leqslant \frac{\alpha^n}{1-\alpha} \| y_1(\cdot) - y_0(\cdot)\| .$$

Proof. Simply apply Corollary 3.8 of Chapter 2.

Similarly, we can translate Corollary 3.14 of Chapter 2 to obtain the following.

THEOREM 6.12. Suppose that (i) $J = \{V(t), M, N\}$ is a boundary-compatible set for which (5.7) is twice differentiable on $\bar{S}$; (ii) $\tilde{J} = \{U(t), K, L\}$ is a boundary-compatible set; and (iii) there are real numbers η, q, γ, κ, δ, and K with $\eta \geqslant 0$, $0 \leqslant q < 1$, $\gamma \geqslant 0$, $\kappa \geqslant 0$, $\delta = \gamma/(1-q) < 1$, and $K = \kappa/(1-q)$ such that

(6.13) $$\| T^{\tilde{J}}(y_0) - y_0 \| \leqslant \eta$$

(6.14)* $$\| U_{KL}^J \|_{(a)} \leqslant q$$

(6.15)* $$\|(T_{y_0}^J)' - U_{KL}^J \|_{(a)} \leqslant \gamma$$

(6.16)* $$\sup_{y\in\bar{S}}\{\|(T_y^J)''\|_{(a)}\} \leqslant \kappa$$

* Again, the theorem remains true if $\| U_{KL}^J \|_{(a)}$ or $\| (T_{y_0}^J)' - U_{KL}^J \|_{(a)}$ or $\| (T_y^J)'' \|_{(a)}$ are replaced by $\| U_{KL}^J \|_{(b)}$ or $\| U_{KL}^J \|_{(c)}$, or $\| (T_{y_0}^J)' - U_{KL}^J \|_{(b)}$ or $\| (T_{y_0}^J)' - U_{KL}^J \|_{(c)}$, or $\| (T_y^J)'' \|_{(b)}$ or $\| (T_y^J)'' \|_{(c)}$, respectively.

and

$$\frac{1-\sqrt{1-2h}}{h}\frac{\eta}{1-\delta} \leqslant r < \frac{1+\sqrt{1-2h}}{h}\frac{\eta}{1-\delta} \tag{6.17}$$

where $h = K\eta/(1-\delta)^2 \leqslant \frac{1}{2}$. Then the MCM sequence $\{y_n(\cdot)\}$ for T^J based on $y_0(\cdot)$ and U_{KL}^J converges uniformly to the unique solution $y^*(\cdot)$ of (5.7) in $\bar{S}$ and the rate of convergence is given by

$$\|y^*(\cdot)-y_n(\cdot)\| \leqslant [1-(1-\delta)\sqrt{1-2h}]^n \left[\frac{1-\sqrt{1-2h}}{h(1-\delta)}\right] \times \|y_1(\cdot)-y_0(\cdot)\| . \tag{6.18}$$

Proof. Simply apply Corollary 3.14 of Chapter 2.

4.7. Application to Continuous Problems III: Newton's Method

We now examine the application of Newton's method to the integral equation representation of TPBVP's. We begin our discussion with a formal application of Newton's method to the integral equation

$$y = T^J(y) \tag{7.1}$$

where $J = \{V(t), M, N\}$ is a boundary-compatible set. We find that the corresponding algorithm is equivalent to the solution of successive linearizations of the original TPBVP. Next, we consider the translation of the results of Chapter 2, Section 4. We can follow two approaches: namely, (1) an approach based on the direct application of Lemma 10.1 of Chapter 3; or (2) an approach based on the application of Banach's theorem on the inverse of an operator. We find that application of the first approach to Proposition 4.8 and Theorem 4.27 of Chapter 2 leads to impractical results since the translated convergence conditions involve the determination of suprema for integral expressions in which the Green's matrices are variable. As such evaluations are, in general, impossible, we do not apply the first approach. Instead, we only translate Theorem 4.27 using the second approach. We do not encounter such difficulties in applying the first approach to Theorem 4.38 of Chapter 2 and so obtain a practical convergence theorem for Newton's method, which is an improvement over similar theorems in the literature [B3, M2]. For the sake of completeness, we conclude with a translation of Theorem 4.38 based on the second approach.

Now, formally applying Newton's method to (7.1), we guess an initial $y_0(\cdot)$ and generate the NM sequence based on $y_0(\cdot)$ by the algorithm

$$y_{n+1} = T^J(y_n) + (T^J_{y_n})'(y_{n+1} - y_n) \tag{7.2}$$

or, equivalently, by the algorithm

$$y_{n+1} = [I - (T^J_{y_n})']^{-1}[T^J(y_n) - (T^J_{y_n})'y_n] \tag{7.3}$$

(provided that the indicated inverse exists). Equation (7.2) is equivalent to the linear TPBVP

$$\begin{aligned} \dot{y}_{n+1} - V(t)\,y_{n+1} &= F(y_n(t), t) - V(t)\,y_n(t) \\ &\quad + \left\{\frac{\partial F}{\partial y}(y_n(t), t) - V(t)\right\}(y_{n+1}(t) - y_n(t)) \\ My_{n+1}(0) + Ny_{n+1}(1) &= c - g(y_n(0)) - h(y_n(1)) + My_n(0) + Ny_n(1) \\ &\quad + \left[M - \frac{\partial g}{\partial y}(y_n(0))\right](y_{n+1}(0) - y_n(0)) \\ &\quad + \left[N - \frac{\partial h}{\partial y}(y_n(1))\right](y_{n+1}(1) - y_n(1)). \end{aligned} \tag{7.4}$$

If (7.4) has a solution $y_{n+1}(\cdot)$, then $y_{n+1}(\cdot)$ is also a solution of the TPBVP

$$\begin{aligned} \dot{y}_{n+1} &= F(y_n, t) + \frac{\partial F}{\partial y}(y_n, t)[y_{n+1} - y_n] \\ g(y_n(0)) + h(y_n(1)) &+ \frac{\partial g}{\partial y}(y_n(0))[y_{n+1}(0) - y_n(0)] \\ &+ \frac{\partial h}{\partial y}(y_n(1))[y_{n+1}(1) - y_n(1)] = c \end{aligned} \tag{7.5}$$

and conversely.

The iterative method for solving TPBVP's by replacing the TPBVP be a sequence of linear TPBVP's of the form (7.4) or (7.5) is called *Newton's method* (*or quasilinearization*) for TPBVP's. The sequence of iterates is called the NM *sequence for the* TPBVP *based on* $y_0(\cdot)$. This sequence coincides with the NM sequence for T^J based on $y_0(\cdot)$. The use of Newton's method in the solution of TPBVP's of the type arising in control problems has received much attention as the result of the work of Bellman and Kalaba [B3, K1], who use the name *quasilinearization*, and the work of McGill and Kenneth [K7, K8, K10, M1, M2, M3], who call the method, the *generalized Newton–Raphson method.*

As in most other applications of Newton's method, the convergence of Newton's method for TPBVP's is rapid if there is convergence at all. In order to increase the chance of convergence of the method in practical applications, it is most important that the initial approximate solution be chosen as close (in the sense of the norm) to the actual solution as feasible with the available data. It can be shown that basically any NM sequence converges if the initial approximate solution is chosen close enough to the actual solution (see Collatz [C4]). In case of linear boundary conditions, the algorithm insures that all successive solutions, except possibly the initial one, satisfy the boundary conditions. As a consequence of the requirement for closeness of the initial guess, it is good practice in the case of linear boundary conditions to select the initial approximation so as to satisfy the boundary conditions.

A well-known drawback of any Newton's method approach is that at each step of the iteration the inverse of an operator must be determined. In the case of Newton's method for TPBVP's this amounts to the requirement that at each stage a *different* linear TPBVP has to be solved. A considerable simplification can usually be achieved if the operator is inverted only at the first step and the same inverse is used for all succeeding steps. This procedure, which is generally known as the modified Newton's method, amounts, in the case of TPBVP's, to using a single boundary-compatible set J_0 for all iterations. Instead of having to solve a different linear TPBVP at each stage, we are only required to solve the same linear problem for different forcing functions.

Now, let us rewrite (7.5) in the form

$$
\begin{aligned}
&\dot{y}_{n+1} - \frac{\partial F}{\partial y}(y_n, t)\, y_{n+1} \\
&\qquad = F(y_n, t) - \frac{\partial F}{\partial y}(y_n, t)\, y_n \\
&\frac{\partial g}{\partial y}(y_n(0))\, y_{n+1}(0) + \frac{\partial h}{\partial y}(y_n(1))\, y_{n+1}(1) \\
&\qquad = c - g(y_n(0)) - h(y_n(1)) + \frac{\partial g}{\partial y}(y_n(0))\, y_n(0) + \frac{\partial h}{\partial y}(y_n(1))\, y_n(1).
\end{aligned}
\tag{7.6}
$$

It is then clear that (7.6) corresponds to a linear TPBVP with a set of matrices $Y_n = \{(\partial F/\partial y)(y_n, t), (\partial g/\partial y)(y_n(0)), (\partial h/\partial y)(y_n(1))\}$. If Y_n is a boundary-compatible set, then (7.6) is equivalent to the integral equation $y_{n+1} = T^{Y_n}(y_n)$. However, in general, Y_n need not be a boundary-compatible set and so we seek conditions on the sequence of iterates which insure the solvability of (7.6) for the *particular* elements of the sequence.

Proposition 4.8 of Chapter 2 followed from a consideration of Newton's method as a special case of the contraction mapping method. The key convergence condition (4.10) here takes the following form:

$$\sup_{y \in \bar{S}} \{[\| I - (T_y{}^J)']^{-1} (T_y{}^J)'' [I - (T_y{}^J)']^{-1} [T^J(y) - y]\|\} \leqslant \alpha < 1. \tag{7.7}$$

Letting $Y = \{(\partial F/\partial y)(y, t), (\partial g/\partial y)(y(0)), (\partial h/\partial y)(y(1))\}$ and assuming that Y is boundary compatible, we can use (10.4) and (10.6) of Chapter 3 to write (7.7) in the form

$$\sup_{y \in \bar{S}} \{\|(T_y{}^Y)'' [T^Y(y) - y]\|\} \leqslant \alpha < 1 \tag{7.8}$$

in view of (10.4) and (10.6) of Chapter 3. But (7.8) involves the evaluation of the Green's matrices $H^Y(t)$ and $G^Y(t, s)$ for *all* y in $\bar{S}$. Clearly, this is not very practical. A second approach to (7.7) is to try and majorize by a product of norms. If J is chosen so that $\sup_{y \in \bar{S}}\{\|(T_y{}^J)'\|\} \leqslant q < 1$, then $\sup_{y \in \bar{S}}\{\|[I - (T_y{}^J)']\|\} \leqslant 1/(1 - q)$ and we need only estimate $\|(T_y{}^J)''\|$, $\| T^J(y) - y \|$ for all y in $\bar{S}$. While this can be done, it is clear that the resulting convergence conditions will not be sharp because of the many majorizations involved. Thus, we omit the translation of Proposition 4.8.

Now let us consider theorem 4.27 of Chapter 2. Here, the main convergence condition is

$$\sup_{y \in \bar{S}} \{\|[I - (T_y{}^J)']^{-1} (T_y{}^J)'' \|\} \leqslant K. \tag{7.9}$$

Again, letting $Y = \{(\partial F/\partial y)(y, t), (\partial g/\partial y)(y(0)), (\partial h/\partial y)(y(1))\}$ and applying Lemma 10.1 of Chapter 3, we can write (7.9) as

$$\sup_{y \in \bar{S}} \{\|(T_y{}^Y)'' \|\} \leqslant K. \tag{7.10}$$

Clearly, (7.10) is not easily evaluated. The second approach, which is based on Banach's theorem, does not lead to such difficulties and, in particular, we have the following.

THEOREM 7.11. Let $y_0(\cdot)$ be an element of $\mathscr{C}([0, 1], R_p)$ and let $\bar{S} = \bar{S}(y_0, r)$. Suppose that (i) $J = \{V(t), M, N\}$ is a boundary-compatible set for which (5.7) is twice differentiable on S, and (ii) there are real numbers η, q, κ, K, and h with $\eta \geqslant 0$, $0 \leqslant q < 1$, $\kappa \geqslant 0$, $K = \kappa/(1 - q)$, and $h = K\eta$ such that

$$\|[I - (T_{y_0}^J)']^{-1}[T^J(y_0) - (T_{y_0}^J)' y_0] - y_0\| \leqslant \eta \tag{7.12}$$

$$\sup_{y \in \bar{S}}\{\|(T_y{}^J)'\|_{(a)}\} \leqslant q \tag{7.13)*$$

$$\sup_{y \in \bar{S}}\{\|(T_y{}^J)''\|_{(a)}\} \leqslant \kappa \tag{7.14)*$$

$$h < 2 \tag{7.15}$$

$$\sum_{k=0}^{\infty} \left(\frac{h}{2}\right)^{2^k - 1} \eta < r. \tag{7.16}$$

Then the NM sequence $\{y_n(\cdot)\}$ based on $y_0(\cdot)$ converges uniformly to a solution $y^*(\cdot)$ of (5.7) in $\bar{S}$ and the rate of convergence is given by

$$\|y^*(\cdot) - y_n(\cdot)\| \leqslant \frac{(h/2)^{2^n - 1}}{[1 - h/2]^{2^n}} \|y_1(\cdot) - y_0(\cdot)\|. \tag{7.17}$$

Proof. Simply check that the hypotheses of Theorem 4.27 of Chapter 2 are satisfied.

The Kantorovich theorem (Theorem 4.38 of Chapter 2) can be readily translated into practical terms with the aid of Chapter 3, Lemma 10.1. We have the following.

THEOREM 7.18. Let $y_0(\cdot)$ be an element of $\mathscr{C}([0, 1], R_p)$ and let $\bar{S} = \bar{S}(y_0, r)$. Suppose that (i) $J = \{V(t), M, N\}$ is a boundary-compatible set for which (5.7) is twice differentiable on $\bar{S}$; (ii) $Y_0 = \{(\partial F/\partial y)(y_0(t), t), (\partial g/\partial y)(y_0(0)), (\partial h/\partial y)(y_0(1))\}$ is a boundary-

* Again, the theorem holds for the coarser estimates $\|(T_y{}^J)'\|_{(b)}$, $\|(T_y{}^J)'\|_{(c)}$, $\|(T_y{}^J)''\|_{(b)}$, or $\|(T_y{}^J)''\|_{(c)}$.

compatible set; and (iii) there are real numbers η, K, and h with $\eta \geqslant 0$, $K \geqslant 0$, and $h = K\eta$ such that

$$\|[I - (T^J_{y_0})']^{-1} [T^J(y_0) - y_0]\| \leqslant \eta \tag{7.19}$$

$$\sup_{y \in \bar{S}} \{\|(T^{Y_0}_y)'' \|_{(a)}\} \leqslant K \tag{7.20*}$$

$$h \leqslant \tfrac{1}{2} \tag{7.21}$$

$$\frac{1 - \sqrt{1 - 2h}}{h} \eta \leqslant r < \frac{1 + \sqrt{1 - 2h}}{h} \eta. \tag{7.22}$$

Then the NM sequence $\{y_n(\cdot)\}$ for (5.7) based on $y_0(\cdot)$ converges uniformly to the unique solution $y^*(\cdot)$ of (5.7) in $\bar{S}$ and the rate of convergence is given by

$$\| y^*(\cdot) - y_n(\cdot)\| \leqslant \frac{1}{2^{n-1}} [2h]^{2^n - 1} \| y_1(\cdot) - y_0(\cdot)\| \tag{7.23}$$

and $\| y^*(\cdot) - y_1(\cdot)\| \leqslant [h/(1 - h)]\| y_1(\cdot) - y_0(\cdot)\|$.

Proof. Simply verify the assumptions of Theorem 4.38, Chapter 2. Note that since Y_0 is boundary compatible, $[I - (T^J_{y_0})']^{-1}$ exists by virtue of Lemma 10.1, Chapter 3, and that

$$\sup_{y \in \bar{S}} \{\|(T^{Y_0}_y)''\|\} = \sup_{y \in \bar{S}} \{\|[I - (T^J_{y_0})']^{-1} (T_y{}^J)'' \|\}$$

by virtue of (10.6), Chapter 3.

We can also use the approach based on Banach's theorem to obtain the following.

THEOREM 7.24. Let $y_0(\cdot)$ be an element of $\mathscr{C}([0, 1], R_p)$ and let $\bar{S} = \bar{S}(y_0, r)$. Suppose that (i) $J = \{V(t), M, N\}$ is a boundary-compatible set for which (5.7) is twice differentiable on $\bar{S}$, and (ii) there are real numbers η, q, κ, K, and h with $\eta \geqslant 0$, $0 \leqslant q < 1$, $\kappa \geqslant 0$, $K = \kappa/(1 - q)$, and $h = K\eta$ such that

$$\|[I - (T^J_{y_0})']^{-1} [T^J(y_0) - y_0]\| \leqslant \eta \tag{7.25}$$

* Again, $\| (T^{Y_0}_y)'' \|_{(b)}$ or $\| (T^{Y_0}_y)'' \|_{(c)}$ may be used.

(7.26)* $$\|(T^J_{y_0})'\|_{(a)} \leqslant q$$

(7.27)* $$\sup_{y \in \bar{S}}\{\|(T_y{}^J)''\|_{(a)}\} \leqslant \kappa$$

(7.28) $$h = K\eta \leqslant \tfrac{1}{2}$$

(7.29) $$\frac{1-\sqrt{1-2h}}{h}\,\eta \leqslant r < \frac{1+\sqrt{1-2h}}{h}\,\eta.$$

Then the NM sequence $\{y_n(\cdot)\}$ based on $y_0(\cdot)$ converges uniformly to the unique solution $y^*(\cdot)$ of (5.7) in $\bar{S}$ and the rate of convergence is given by

$$\|y^*(\cdot) - y_n(\cdot)\| \leqslant \frac{1}{2^{n-1}}(2h)^{2^n-1}\|y_1(\cdot) - y_0(\cdot)\|$$

and $\|y^*(\cdot) - y_1(\cdot)\| \leqslant [h/(1-h)]\,\|y_1(\cdot) - y_0(\cdot)\|$.

We note that these theorems are, from a practical standpoint, somewhat better than the results by McGill and Kenneth [M2] and Bellman and Kalaba [B3] since our theorems apply to general TPBVP's.

EXAMPLE 7.30. We consider the simple second-order problem

(7.31) $$\ddot{y} = -\tfrac{1}{2}\dot{y}^2 + \tfrac{1}{2}t^2 - \tfrac{1}{2}t - \tfrac{7}{8}, \qquad y(0) = y(1) = 0$$

or in standard form

(7.32) $$\begin{bmatrix}\dot{y}_1\\ \dot{y}_2\end{bmatrix} = \begin{bmatrix} y_2 \\ -\tfrac{1}{2}y_2{}^2 + \tfrac{1}{2}t^2 - \tfrac{1}{2}t - \tfrac{7}{8}\end{bmatrix},$$

$$\begin{bmatrix}1 & 0\\ 0 & 0\end{bmatrix}\begin{bmatrix}y_1(0)\\ y_2(0)\end{bmatrix} + \begin{bmatrix}0 & 0\\ 1 & 0\end{bmatrix}\begin{bmatrix}y_1(1)\\ y_2(1)\end{bmatrix} = \begin{bmatrix}0\\ 0\end{bmatrix}.$$

It is easily verified (by substitution) that a solution of this TPBVP is given by

(7.33) $$y_1{}^*(t) = \tfrac{1}{2}(t - t^2), \qquad y_2{}^*(t) = \tfrac{1}{2} - t.$$

* Again, $\|(T^J_{y_0})'\|_{(b)}$ or $\|(T^J_{y_0})'\|_{(b)}$, or $\|(T_y{}^J)''\|_{(b)}$ or $\|(T_y{}^J)''\|_{(c)}$ may be used.

From (7.32), we have

$$\left[\frac{\partial F}{\partial y}\right] = \begin{bmatrix} 0 & 1 \\ 0 & -y_2 \end{bmatrix}, \qquad \left[\frac{\partial g}{\partial y}\right] = \begin{bmatrix} 1 & 0 \\ 0 & 0 \end{bmatrix}, \qquad \left[\frac{\partial h}{\partial y}\right] = \begin{bmatrix} 0 & 0 \\ 1 & 0 \end{bmatrix}.$$

Using superscripts for the iteration number, the algorithm becomes

$$\text{(7.34)} \qquad \begin{bmatrix} \dot{y}_1^{(n+1)} \\ \dot{y}_2^{(n+1)} \end{bmatrix} = \begin{bmatrix} y_2^{(n)} \\ -\frac{1}{2}(y_2^{(n)})^2 + \frac{1}{2}t^2 - \frac{1}{2}t - \frac{7}{8} \end{bmatrix} + \begin{bmatrix} 0 & 1 \\ 0 & -y_2^{(n)} \end{bmatrix} \begin{bmatrix} y_1^{(n+1)} - y_1^{(n)} \\ y_2^{(n+1)} - y_2^{(n)} \end{bmatrix},$$

$$\begin{bmatrix} y_1^{(n+1)}(0) \\ y_1^{(n+1)}(1) \end{bmatrix} = \begin{bmatrix} 0 \\ 0 \end{bmatrix}.$$

As initial guess, we select the simplest function satisfying the (linear) boundary conditions, namely,

$$\text{(7.35)} \qquad y_1^{(0)}(t) \equiv 0, \qquad y_2^{(0)}(t) \equiv 0.$$

In view of (7.34) and (7.35) the first approximate solution $y^{(1)}(t)$ is the solution of the linear TPBVP

$$\begin{bmatrix} \dot{y}_1^{(1)} \\ \dot{y}_2^{(1)} \end{bmatrix} = \begin{bmatrix} y_2^{(1)} \\ \frac{1}{2}t^2 - \frac{1}{2}t - \frac{7}{8} \end{bmatrix}, \qquad \begin{bmatrix} y_1^{(1)}(0) \\ y_1^{(1)}(1) \end{bmatrix} = \begin{bmatrix} 0 \\ 0 \end{bmatrix}.$$

By straightforward integration, we find that

$$\text{(7.36)} \qquad \begin{aligned} y_1^{(1)}(t) &= \tfrac{1}{24}t^4 - \tfrac{1}{12}t^3 - \tfrac{7}{16}t^2 + \tfrac{23}{48}t, \\ y_2^{(1)}(t) &= \tfrac{1}{6}t^3 - \tfrac{1}{4}t^2 + \tfrac{7}{8}t + \tfrac{23}{48} \end{aligned}$$

The second approximate solution is then the solution of

$$\begin{bmatrix} \dot{y}_1^{(2)} \\ \dot{y}_2^{(2)} \end{bmatrix} = \begin{bmatrix} y_2^{(2)} \\ -(\frac{1}{6}t^3 - \frac{1}{4}t^2 + \frac{7}{8}t + \frac{23}{48})y_2^{(2)} + \frac{1}{2}(\frac{1}{6}t^3 - \frac{1}{4}t^2 + \frac{7}{8}t + \frac{23}{48})^2 \\ + \frac{1}{2}t^2 - \frac{1}{2}t - \frac{7}{8} \end{bmatrix},$$

$$\begin{bmatrix} y_1^{(2)}(0) \\ y_1^{(2)}(1) \end{bmatrix} = \begin{bmatrix} 0 \\ 0 \end{bmatrix}.$$

The solution of this TPBVP is no longer a simple analytic expression.

In order to investigate the convergence, we evaluate the differences between the successive solutions $y^{(0)}(t)$ and $y^{(1)}(t)$ as well as the difference between these approximate solutions and the exact solution. We thus obtain

$$y_1^{(1)} - y_0^{(0)} = \frac{1}{24}t^4 - \frac{1}{12}t^3 - \frac{7}{16}t^2 + \frac{23}{48}t,$$

$$y_1{}^* - y_1^{(0)} = +\frac{1}{2}(t - t^2),$$

$$y_1{}^* - y_1^{(1)} = -\frac{1}{24}t^4 + \frac{1}{12}t^3 - \frac{1}{16}t^2 + \frac{1}{48}t,$$

$$y_2^{(1)} - y_2^{(0)} = \frac{1}{6}t^3 - \frac{1}{4}t^2 - \frac{7}{8}t + \frac{23}{48}$$

$$y_2{}^* - y_2^{(0)} = +\frac{1}{2} - t,$$

$$y_2{}^* - y_2^{(1)} = -\frac{1}{6}t^3 + \frac{1}{4}t^2 - \frac{1}{8}t + \frac{1}{48}.$$

The norms of these differences are

$$\| y^{(1)} - y^{(0)} \| = \eta = \frac{23}{48} = 0.4792$$

$$\| y^* - y^{(0)} \| = \frac{1}{2} = 0.500$$

$$\| y^* - y^{(1)} \| = \frac{1}{48} = 0.0208.$$

The first approximate solution $y^{(1)}(t)$ is considerably closer to the exact solution than the initial guess $y^{(0)}(t)$. This points towards convergence of Newton's method.

We next consider the application of Theorem 7.11 to check the convergence of the NM sequence. To do so, we select as boundary-compatible matrices $V(t)$, M, and N, the set

$$V(t) = \left[\frac{\partial F}{\partial y}\right]_{(y^{(0)}(t))} = \begin{bmatrix} 0 & 1 \\ 0 & 0 \end{bmatrix} \tag{7.38}$$

$$M = \left[\frac{\partial g}{\partial y}\right]_{(y^{(0)})} = \begin{bmatrix} 1 & 0 \\ 0 & 0 \end{bmatrix}$$

$$N = \left[\frac{\partial h}{\partial y}\right]_{(y^{(0)})} = \begin{bmatrix} 0 & 0 \\ 1 & 0 \end{bmatrix}.$$

To evaluate q and κ, we define a matrix $\mathbf{P}(t)$ and vectors $\mathbf{z}$ and $\mathbf{x}$ with elements $p_{ij}(t)$, z_j, and x_j given by

$$p_{ij}(t) = \int_0^1 |\, g_{ij}^V(t, s)|\, ds$$

$$z_j = \sup_{t\in[0,1]} \sup_{y\in\bar{S}} \left\{ \sum_{k=1}^{p} \left| \frac{\partial F_j}{\partial y_k}(y(t), t) - v_{jk}(t) \right| \right\}$$

$$x_j = \sup_{t\in[0,1]} \sup_{y\in\bar{S}} \left\{ \sum_{k=1}^{p} \sum_{l=1}^{p} \left| \frac{\partial^2 F_j}{\partial y_k\, \partial y_l}(y(t), t) \right| \right\}.$$

We now have the following simple expressions for (conservative values of) the numbers q and κ:

$$\| \mathbf{P}(\cdot)\mathbf{z} \| = \sup_i \sup_t \left\{ \sum_{j=1}^{p} p_{ij}(t)\, z_j \right\} \leqslant q \tag{7.39}$$

$$\| \mathbf{P}(\cdot)\mathbf{x} \| = \sup_i \sup_t \left\{ \sum_{j=1}^{p} p_{ij}(t)\, x_j \right\} \leqslant \kappa. \tag{7.40}$$

In Example 5.18 we derived the relation (see Eq. (5.25) of this chapter)

$$\mathbf{P}(t) = \begin{bmatrix} 2(t - t^2) & \tfrac{1}{2}(t - t^2) \\ 1 & \tfrac{1}{2} - (t - t^2) \end{bmatrix}.$$

We have

$$\left[\frac{\partial F_j}{\partial y_k}(y(t), t) - v_{jk}(t)\right] = \begin{bmatrix} 0 & 0 \\ 0 & y_2(t) \end{bmatrix}.$$

Hence, in order to determine the vector $\mathbf{z}$, we need to select a radius r for the sphere $\bar{S}(y^{(0)}, r)$. A good choice in this respect is

$$r = 0.58.$$

With $y_2^{(0)} \equiv 0$, we then have

$$\mathbf{z} = \begin{bmatrix} 0 \\ 0.58 \end{bmatrix}$$

and, in view of (7.39),

$$\| \mathbf{P}(\cdot)\mathbf{z} \| = \sup_t \left\| \begin{bmatrix} 2(t - t^2) & \tfrac{1}{2}(t - t^2) \\ 1 & \tfrac{1}{2} - (t - t^2) \end{bmatrix} \begin{bmatrix} 0 \\ .58 \end{bmatrix} \right\| = 0.29.$$

Hence, we may select as a conservative value for q, $q = 0.29$. Since

$$\left[\frac{\partial^2 F_1}{\partial y_k\, \partial y_l}\right] = \begin{bmatrix} 0 & 0 \\ 0 & 0 \end{bmatrix}, \qquad \left[\frac{\partial^2 F_2}{\partial y_k\, \partial y_l}\right] = \begin{bmatrix} 0 & 0 \\ 0 & -1 \end{bmatrix}$$

it follows that

$$\mathbf{x} = \begin{bmatrix} 0 \\ 1 \end{bmatrix}$$

and that

$$\| \mathbf{P}(\cdot)\mathbf{x} \| = \sup_t \left\{ \left\| \begin{bmatrix} 2(t-t^2) & \frac{1}{2}(t-t^2) \\ 1 & \frac{1}{2}-(t-t^2) \end{bmatrix} \begin{bmatrix} 0 \\ 1 \end{bmatrix} \right\| \right\} = 0.5.$$

Thus, we may select as a conservative value for κ, $\kappa = 0.5$. With these values for η, q, and κ we calculate that

$$h = K\eta = \frac{\kappa}{1-q}\eta = \frac{0.5}{1-0.29}(0.4792) = 0.337 < 2.$$

Hence, we conclude that the main convergence condition (7.15) of Theorem 7.11 is satisfied. To check the last condition (7.16) of the theorem, we note that for $h/2 < 1$, we have

$$\sum_{k=0}^{\infty} \left(\frac{h}{2}\right)^{2^k-1} < \sum_{l=0}^{\infty} \left(\frac{h}{2}\right)^{l} = \frac{1}{1-(h/2)}.$$

It follows then that

$$\sum_{k=0}^{\infty} \left(\frac{h}{2}\right)^{2^k-1} \eta < \frac{1}{1-(h/2)}\eta = \frac{0.4792}{1-\frac{1}{2}(0.337)} = 0.576 = 0.58 = r.$$

Thus, noting that the differentiability assumptions are clearly satisfied, we find that all conditions of Theorem 7.11 are fulfilled. Therefore, the conclusions of the theorem hold. First, this implies that the NM sequence is convergent to a (not necessarily unique) solution $y^*(\cdot)$ of the TPBVP in $\bar{S}(y^{(0)}, r)$. Secondly, this means that a guaranteed convergence rate is given by the expression

$$\| y^*(\cdot) - y^{(n)}(\cdot) \| \leqslant \frac{(h/2)^{2^n-1}}{1-(h/2)^{2^n}} \| y^{(1)}(\cdot) - y^{(0)}(\cdot) \|$$

$$\leqslant \frac{(0.169)^{2^n-1}}{1-(0.169)^{2^n}}(0.479).$$

Besides showing that the convergence is rapid, this expression also implies that the solution $y^*(\cdot)$ is close to the first approximate solution $y^{(1)}(\cdot)$. For, for $n = 1$, we have

$$\| y^*(\cdot) - y^{(1)}(\cdot) \| \leqslant \frac{(h/2)}{1-(h/2)^2} \| y^{(1)}(\cdot) - y^{(0)}(\cdot) \|$$

$$\leqslant \frac{(0.169)}{1-(0.169)^2} (0.479)$$

$$\leqslant 0.0832.$$

To evaluate the convergence conditions given by Theorem 7.18 we define, in addition to the matrix $\mathbf{P}(t)$ and the vectors $\mathbf{z}$ and $\mathbf{x}$ another matrix $\mathbf{P}^{Y_0}(t)$ with elements $p_{ij}^{Y_0}(t)$ given by

$$p_{ij}^{Y_0}(t) = \left\{ \int_0^1 | G_{ij}^{Y_0}(t, s) | \, ds \right\}.$$

We then find that a conservative value for the number K is given by the expression

$$\| \mathbf{P}^{Y_0}(\cdot)\mathbf{x} \| = \sup_i \sup_t \left\{ \sum_{j=1}^{p} p_{ij}^{Y_0}(t) \, x_j \right\} \leqslant K.$$

Since the set of matrices Y_0 coincides with the set $V(t)$, M, and N considered in the earlier part of this example, it follows that

$$\mathbf{P}^{Y_0}(t) = \mathbf{P}(t) = \begin{bmatrix} 2(t-t^2) & \frac{1}{2}(t-t^2) \\ 1 & \frac{1}{2}-(t-t^2) \end{bmatrix}$$

and hence

$$\| \mathbf{P}^{Y_0}(\cdot)\mathbf{x} \| = \sup_t \left\{ \left\| \begin{bmatrix} 2(t-t^2) & \frac{1}{2}(t-t^2) \\ 1 & \frac{1}{2}-(t-t^2) \end{bmatrix} \begin{bmatrix} 0 \\ 1 \end{bmatrix} \right\| \right\} = 0.5.$$

Thus, we deduce that a conservative value for K is $K = 0.5$. With the value of η given by 0.4792 we find that

$$h = K\eta = (0.5)(0.4792) = 0.2396 \leqslant \tfrac{1}{2}.$$

Thus, we find that the main convergence condition (7.21) of

Theorem 7.18 is satisfied. To determine a radius r for the sphere $\bar{S}(y^{(0)}, r)$ (since the second derivative is independent of y, we did not have to assume a value for r beforehand to evaluate $\mathbf{x}$), we evaluate the expressions

$$\frac{1 - \sqrt{1 - 2h}}{h}\eta = \frac{1 - \sqrt{1 - 2(0.2396)}}{0.2396}(0.4792) = 0.5566$$

and

$$\frac{1 + \sqrt{1 - 2h}}{h}\eta = \frac{1 + \sqrt{1 - 2(0.2396)}}{0.2396}(0.4792) = 3.443.$$

Hence, we may select r as any number satisfying $0.557 \leqslant r < 3.44$. Since the differentiability assumptions are clearly satisfied, it follows that all conditions of Theorem 7.18 hold. This insures that the NM sequence converges to the unique solution $y^*(\cdot)$ in $\bar{S}(y^{(0)}, r)$. In addition, Theorem 7.18 guarantees a convergence rate given by (7.23) and an estimate on $\| y^{(1)}(\cdot) - y^*(\cdot)\|$ given by

$$\| y^{(1)}(\cdot) - y^*(\cdot)\| \leqslant \frac{0.14}{0.76}(0.4792).$$

4.8. Application to Continuous Problems IV: Multipoint Methods*

We now turn our attention to the application of the multipoint algorithms of Section 5, Chapter 2, to TPBVP's of the form (5.7). Our main result is the following theorem which represents the translation of Theorem 5.48 of Chapter 2 into the TPBVP context.

THEOREM 8.1. Let $y_{0,\alpha}(\cdot)$ be an element of $\mathscr{C}([0, 1], R_p)$ and let $\bar{S}_\alpha = \bar{S}(y_{0,\alpha}, r_\alpha)$. Suppose that (i) $J = \{V(t), M, N\}$ is a boundary-compatible set for which (5.7) is twice differentiable on $\bar{S}_\alpha$, and (ii) there are real numbers δ_α, $B_{0,\alpha}$, $d_{0,\alpha}$, K_α, and $\eta_{0,\alpha}$ with $0 \leqslant \delta_\alpha < 1$ such that

$$\|(T^J_{y_{0,\alpha}})'\|_{(a)} \leqslant \delta_\alpha \tag{8.2}$$

* See Bosarge and Falb [B7].

(8.3) $$\|y_{0,\alpha} - T^J(y_{0,\alpha})\| \leqslant (1 - \delta_\alpha)\, d_{0,\alpha}$$

(8.4) $$\sup_{y \in \bar{S}_\alpha} \{\|(T_y{}^J)''\|_{(a)}\} \leqslant K_\alpha$$

(8.5) $$\eta_{0,\alpha} = \gamma_{0,\alpha}^{(\alpha)}\, d_{0,\alpha}$$

(where $\gamma_{0,\alpha}^{(\alpha)}$ is given by (5.50), Chapter 2),

(8.6) $$B_{0,\alpha} = \frac{1}{1 - \delta_\alpha}$$

(8.7) $$h_{0,\alpha} = K_\alpha B_{0,\alpha} \eta_{0,\alpha} \leqslant \tfrac{1}{2}$$

(8.8) $$r_\alpha = \tfrac{16}{11}\, \eta_{0,\alpha}$$

(8.9) $$\gamma_{0,\alpha}^{(\alpha)} \leqslant 2$$

for $\alpha = 1, 2, \ldots$. Then the M sequence $\{\psi_\alpha(y_{n,\alpha})(\cdot)\}$ converges uniformly to a solution $y_0{}^*(\cdot)$ of (5.7) in $\bar{S}_\alpha$ and the rate of convergence is given by

(8.10) $$\|y_\alpha{}^*(\cdot) - y_{n,\alpha}(\cdot)\| \leqslant \tfrac{16}{11}\, (\tfrac{5}{16})^n\, (2h_{0,\alpha})^{(\alpha+1)^n - 1}\, \eta_{0,\alpha}$$

for $\alpha = 1, 2, \ldots$.

Proof. We simply verify that the hypotheses of Theorem 5.48, Chapter 2, are satisfied by the mapping $F^J = I - T^J$. In view of (i), F^J is twice differentiable on $\bar{S}_\alpha$. Moreover, from (8.2) and the fact that $\delta_\alpha < 1$, we deduce that $(F^J_{y_{0,\alpha}})'^{-1} = [I - (T^J_{y_{0,\alpha}})']^{-1}$ exists and that $\|(F^J_{y_{0,\alpha}})'^{-1}\| \leqslant 1/(1 - \delta_\alpha)$. Combining this with (8.3), we find that $\|(F^J_{y_{0,\alpha}})'^{-1}\|\,\|F^J(y_{0,\alpha})\| \leqslant d_{0,\alpha}$. In view of our other assumptions, we see immediately that the hypotheses of Theorem 5.48 hold.

The basic strength of Theorem 8.1 lies in the possibility of replacing the sequence of operator iterations $y_{n+1,\alpha} = \psi_\alpha(y_{n,\alpha})$ by an equivalent sequence of linear TPBVP's. To illustrate what is involved, let us consider the third-order method generated by ψ_2. Beginning with an initial guess $y_0(\cdot) = y_0$ and proceeding formally, we have

(8.11) $$y_{n+1} = \{[I - (T^J_{y_n})']^{-1}\, [T^J - (T^J_{y_n})']\}^2\, (y_n)$$

where $J = \{V(t), M, N\}$ is a boundary-compatible set. However, (8.11) is equivalent to the pair of equations

$$z_n = (T^J_{y_n})' z_n + [T^J - (T^J_{y_n})'] (y_n) \tag{8.12a}$$

$$y_{n+1} = (T^J_{y_n})' y_{n+1} + [T^J - (T^J_{y_n})'] (z_n). \tag{8.12b}$$

But these equations are both linear and of exactly the same form. Now, let

$$A_n(t) = \frac{\partial F}{\partial y} (y_n(t), t), \qquad B_n = \frac{\partial g}{\partial y} (y_n(0)), \qquad C_n = \frac{\partial h}{\partial y} (y_n(1)).$$

Then it follows from the results of Chapter 3, Section 8, that (8.12a) and (8.12b) are equivalent to the pair of integral equations

$$\begin{aligned} z_n(t) = {} & H^J(t)\{c - g(y_n(0)) - h(y_n(1)) + B_n y_n(0) + C_n y_n(1) \\ & + [M - B_n]\, z_n(0) + [N - C_n]\, z_n(1)\} \\ & + \int_0^1 G^J(t, s)\{[F(y_n(s), s) \\ & - A_n(s)\, y_n(s)] + [A_n(s) - V(s)]\, z_n(s)\}\, ds \end{aligned} \tag{8.13a}$$

$$\begin{aligned} y_{n+1}(t) = {} & H^J(t)\{c - g(z_n(0)) - h(z_n(1)) + B_n z_n(0) + C_n z_n(1) \\ & + [M - B_n]\, y_{n+1}(0) + [N - C_n]\, y_{n+1}(1)\} \\ & + \int_0^1 G^J(t, s)\{[F(z_n(s), s) - A_n(s)\, z_n(s)] \\ & + [A_n(s) - V(s)]\, y_{n+1}(s)\}\, ds. \end{aligned} \tag{8.13b}$$

However, these integral equations are equivalent to the linear TPBVP's

$$\begin{aligned} \dot{z}_n &= A_n(t)\, z_n + [F(y_n(t), t) - A_n(t)\, y_n] \\ & B_n z_n(0) + C_n z_n(1) = c_n \end{aligned} \tag{8.14a}$$

$$\begin{aligned} \dot{y}_{n+1} &= A_n(t)\, y_{n+1} + [F(z_n(t), t) - A_n(t)\, z_n] \\ & B_n y_{n+1}(0) + C_n y_{n+1}(1) = d_n \end{aligned} \tag{8.14b}$$

where $c_n = c - g(y_n(0)) - h(y_n(1)) + B_n y_n(0) + C_n y_n(1)$ and $d_n = c - g(z_n(0)) - h(z_n(1)) + B_n z_n(0) + C_n z_n(1)$. Now, assuming that the conditions of Theorem 8.1 are satisfied, we deduce that (8.11) has a solution and hence that all the pairs (8.12)–(8.14) have solutions. Thus, under the assumptions of the theorem, the multipoint algorithm $y_{n+1} = \psi_2(y_n)$ is equivalent to the successive solution of the linear TPBVP's (8.14). Since the Jacobian $A_n(s)$ is the same in (8.14a) and (8.14b), we actually are only required to solve the same linear TPBVP at each stage for different forcing functions and so only one integration of the homogeneous equation is needed at each step. Thus, the extra computation required to obtain higher-order convergence is small. This represents the major advantage of the multipoint methods when applied to TPBVP's.

4.9. Application to Discrete Problems I: The Method of Contraction Mappings

We have seen that if the conditions of Theorem 5.1 of Chapter 3 are satisfied, then TPBVP's [such as (4.21)] of the form

$$(9.1)\qquad \begin{aligned} &y(j+1) - y(j) = F(y(j+1), y(j), j),\\ &g(y(0)) + h(y(q)) = c \end{aligned}$$

are equivalent to summation equations of the form

$$(9.2)\qquad \begin{aligned} y(j) &= T^J(y)(j)\\ &= H^J(j)\{c - g(y(0)) - h(y(q)) + My(0) + Ny(q)\}\\ &\quad + \sum_{k=0}^{q-1} G^J(j,k)\{F(y(k+1), y(k), k) - A(k)\, y(k+1)\\ &\quad - B(k)\, y(k)\} \end{aligned}$$

where $J = \{A(j), B(j), M, N\}$ is a boundary-compatible set. Now, just as in the continuous case, we view the summation equation as an operator equation and apply the methods of Chapter 2. As the results and ideas are entirely analogous to those of the continuous case, we are more succinct in out treatment of the discrete case.

We begin with the method of contraction mappings. Proceeding formally, we first select an initial element $y_0(\cdot)$ in $\mathscr{S}(\mathbf{Q}, R_p)$. Next we generate the CM sequence $\{y_n(\cdot)\}$ for T^J based on y_0 by means of the algorithm $y_{n+1} = T^J(y_n)$ or, equivalently, by

$$(9.3)\quad y_{n+1}(j) = H^J(j)\{c - g(y_n(0)) - h(y_n(q)) + My_n(0) + Ny_n(q)\} + \sum_{k=0}^{q-1} G^J(j, k)\{F(y_n(k+1), y_n(k), k) - A(k)\, y_n(k+1) - B(k)\, y_n(k)\}.$$

Since the function $y_n(\cdot)$ is known, we can write (9.3) in the form

$$(9.4)\qquad y_{n+1}(j) = H^J(j)\, \tilde{c}_n + \sum_{k=0}^{q-1} G^J(j, k)\, \tilde{f}_n(k)$$

where $\tilde{c}_n = c - g(y_n(0)) - h(y_n(q)) + My_n(0) + Ny_n(q)$ and $\tilde{f}_n(k) = F(y_n(k+1), y_n(k), k) - A(k) y_n(k+1) - B(k) y_n(k)$. However, (9.4) is the solution of the linear TPBVP

$$(9.5)\qquad \begin{aligned} &y_{n+1}(j+1) - y_{n+1}(j) = A(j)\, y_{n+1}(j+1) + B(j)\, y_{n+1}(j) + \tilde{f}_n(j) \\ &My_{n+1}(0) + Ny_{n+1}(q) = \tilde{c}_n \end{aligned}$$

and so it follows that the method of contraction mappings essentially amounts to the successive solution of linear TPBVP's. This is often referred to as *Picard's method*.

We now have the following.

DEFINITION 9.6. The TPBVP (9.1) is differentiable on a subset S of $\mathscr{S}(\mathbf{Q}, R_p)$ is (i) there is a boundary-compatible set $J = \{A(j), B(j), M, N\}$ such that the function $K(j, x, y, k) = G^J(j, k)\{F(x, y, k) - A(k)\, x - B(k) y\}$ satisfies the conditions of Lemma 9.5 of Chapter 3 for an open D in R_p with the range of S contained in D, and (ii) g and h are differentiable. Similarly, the TPBVP (9.1) is twice differentiable on S if $K(j, x, y, k)$, $(\partial K/\partial x)(j, x, y, k)$ and $(\partial K/\partial y)(j, x, y, k)$ satisfy the conditions of Lemma 9.5 of Chapter 3 and if g and h are twice differentiable.

THEOREM 9.7. Let y_0 be an element of $\mathscr{S}(\mathbf{Q}, R_p)$ and let $\bar{S} = \bar{S}(y_0, r)$. Suppose that (i) $J = \{A(j), B(j), M, N\}$ is a boundary-compatible set for which (9.1) is differentiable on $\bar{S}$, and, (ii) there are real numbers η and α with $\eta \geqslant 0$ and $0 \leqslant \alpha < 1$ such that

$$\| T^J(y_0) - y_0 \| \leqslant \eta \tag{9.8}$$

$$\sup_{y \in \bar{S}} \{ \| (T_y{}^J)' \|_{(a)} \} \leqslant \alpha \tag{9.9}$$

$$\frac{1}{1-\alpha} \eta \leqslant r. \tag{9.10}$$

Then the CM sequence $\{y_n(\cdot)\}$ for (9.1) based on y_0 and J converges uniformly to the unique solution $y^*(\cdot)$ of (9.1) in $\bar{S}$ and the rate of convergence is given by

$$\| y^*(\cdot) - y_n(\cdot) \| \leqslant \frac{\alpha^n}{1-\alpha} \| y_1(\cdot) - y_0(\cdot) \| . \tag{9.11}$$

We note that $\|(T_y{}^J)'\|_{(a)}$ in (9.9) can be replaced by either $\|(T_y{}^J)'\|_{(b)}$ or $\|(T_y{}^J)'\|_{(c)}$. As this type of replacement can be done in general, we shall not call attention to it again.

We can also translate Corollary 2.34, Chapter 2, to obtain the following.

THEOREM 9.12. Suppose that (i) $J = \{A(j), B(j), M, N\}$ is a boundary-compatible set for which (9.1) is twice differentiable on $\bar{S}$, and (ii) there are real numbers η, δ, and K with $\eta \geqslant 0$, $0 \leqslant \delta < 1$, and $K \geqslant 0$ such that

$$\| T^J(y_0) - y_0 \| \leqslant \eta, \qquad \|(T^J_{y_0})'\|_{(a)} \leqslant \delta \tag{9.13}$$

$$\sup_{y \in \bar{S}} \{ \| (T_y{}^J)'' \|_{(a)} \} \leqslant K \tag{9.14}$$

and

$$\frac{1-\sqrt{1-2h}}{h} \frac{\eta}{1-\delta} \leqslant r < \frac{1+\sqrt{1-2h}}{h} \frac{\eta}{1-\delta} \tag{9.15}$$

where $h = K\eta/(1-\delta)^2 \leqslant \frac{1}{2}$. Then the CM sequence $\{y_n(\cdot)\}$ for the TPBVP (9.1) based on y_0 and J converges uniformly to the unique solution $y^*(\cdot)$ of (9.1) in $\bar{S}$ and the rate of convergence is given by

$$\| y^*(\cdot) - y_n(\cdot) \| \leqslant [1-(1-\delta)\sqrt{1-2h}]^n \left[\frac{1-\sqrt{1-2h}}{h(1-\delta)} \right] \times \| y_1(\cdot) - y_0(\cdot) \| . \tag{9.16}$$

We conclude this section with a simple illustrative example. We apply Picard's method twice to the discrete TPBVP considered in Section 7 of Chapter 3. We will see that the first application does not result in convergence no matter how close the initial guess is to the actual solution. The second application is convergent. We check the results against the theory by evaluating the relevant estimates. These estimates turn out to be inconclusive and we then discuss the situation in some detail.

EXAMPLE 9.17. Consider the TPBVP

$$\begin{bmatrix} y_1(j+1) \\ y_2(j+1) \end{bmatrix} - \begin{bmatrix} y_1(j) \\ y_2(j) \end{bmatrix} = \begin{bmatrix} -y_2(j+1) \\ -y_1^3(j) \end{bmatrix}$$
$$\begin{bmatrix} y_1(0) \\ 0 \end{bmatrix} + \begin{bmatrix} 0 \\ y_1(4) \end{bmatrix} = \begin{bmatrix} -3 \\ 3 \end{bmatrix} \tag{9.18}$$

where $j = 0, 1, 2, 3$. In order to apply Picard's method we must select a set of boundary-compatible matrices $\{A(j), B(j), M, N\}$. As a first choice, the set

$$A(j) = \begin{bmatrix} 0 & -1 \\ 0 & 0 \end{bmatrix}, \qquad B(j) = \begin{bmatrix} 0 & 0 \\ 0 & 0 \end{bmatrix}$$
$$M = \begin{bmatrix} 1 & 0 \\ 0 & 0 \end{bmatrix}, \qquad N = \begin{bmatrix} 0 & 0 \\ 1 & 0 \end{bmatrix} \tag{9.19}$$

is selected. With this choice, the application of Picard's method turns out to be unsuccessful. Next, as a second set of boundary compatible matrices, we take

$$A(j) = \begin{bmatrix} 0 & -1 \\ 0 & 0 \end{bmatrix}, \qquad B(j) = \begin{bmatrix} 0 & 0 \\ -3 & 0 \end{bmatrix}$$
$$M = \begin{bmatrix} 1 & 0 \\ 0 & 0 \end{bmatrix}, \qquad N = \begin{bmatrix} 0 & 0 \\ 1 & 0 \end{bmatrix}. \tag{9.20}$$

This choice produces a successful application of Picard's method.

Considering Picard's method with the boundary compatible set (9.19), we easily verify that this amounts to the successive solution of the linear problems

$$(9.21)\quad y_1^{(n+1)}(j+1) - y_1^{(n+1)}(j) = -\,y_2^{(n+1)}(j+1), \qquad y_1^{(n+1)}(0) = -\,3$$

$$y_2^{(n+1)}(j+1) - y_2^{(n+1)}(j) = -\,[y_1^{(n)}(j)]^3, \qquad y_1^{(n+1)}(4) = +\,3.$$

Taking as a first guess for the solution the sequences

$$y_1^{(0)}(j) = \{-\,3,\ -\,1.5, 0,\ +\,1.5,\ +\,3.0\}$$

$$y_1^{(0)}(j) = \{-\,28.5,\ -\,1.5,\ -\,1.5,\ -\,1.5,\ -\,1.5\}$$

TABLE I

Number of iterations \ j	0	1	2	3	4
0	−3.000	−1.5000	0.0	+1.5000	+3.000
1	−3.000	+0.1875	0.0	−0.1875	+3.000
2	−3.000	−1.5033	0.0	+1.5033	+3.000
3	−3.000	+0.1986	0.0	−0.1986	+3.000
4	−3.000	−1.5039	0.0	+1.5039	+3.000
5	−3.000	+0.2008	0.0	−0.2008	+3.000
6	−3.000	−1.5040	0.0	+1.5040	+3.000
7	−3.000	+0.2012	0.0	−0.2012	+3.000
8	−3.000	−1.5041	0.0	+1.5041	+3.000
9	−3.000	+0.2013	0.0	−0.2013	+3.000
10	−3.000	−1.5041	0.0	+1.5041	+3.000

we obtain the divergent sequence of iterates given in Table I.* For an initial guess given by $y_1^{(0)}(j) = \{-3.0, -1.01, 0, +1.01, +3.0\}$, $y_2^{(0)}(j) = \{-28.99, -1.99, -1.01, -1.01, -1.99\}$, which is very close to the exact solution $y_1{}^*(j) = \{-3.0, -1.0, 0, +1.0, +3.0\}$, $y_2{}^*(j) = \{-29.0, -2.0, -1.0, -1.0, -2.0\}$, we again obtain a divergent sequence of iterates (Table II).

After this unsuccessful application of Picard's method, we try the method once more but using the boundary-compatible set (9.20).

* All tables in this section involve only $y_1(j)$.

TABLE II

Number of iterations \ j	0	1	2	3	4
0	−3.000	−1.0100	0.0	+1.0100	+3.000
1	−3.000	−0.9848	0.0	+0.9848	+3.000
2	−3.000	−1.0223	0.0	+1.0223	+3.000
3	−3.000	−0.9657	0.0	+0.9657	+3.000
4	−3.000	−1.0497	0.0	+1.0497	+3.000
5	−3.000	−0.9216	0.0	+0.9216	+3.000
6	−3.000	−1.1086	0.0	+1.1086	+3.000
7	−3.000	−0.8187	0.0	+0.8187	+3.000
8	−3.000	−1.2256	0.0	+1.2256	+3.000
9	−3.000	−0.5795	0.0	+0.5795	+3.000
10	−3.000	−1.4027	0.0	+1.4027	+3.000

The algorithm then reduces to the successive solution of the TPBVP's

$$
\begin{aligned}
y_1^{(n+1)}(j+1) - y_1^{(n+1)}(j+1) &= -\, y_2^{(n+1)}(j+1), \\
y_1^{(n+1)}(0) &= -\,3 \\
y_2^{(n+1)}(j+1) - y_2^{(n+1)}(j+1) &= -\,3[y_1^{(n+1)}(j) - y_1^{(n)}(j)] - [y_1^{(n)}(j)]^3 \\
y_1^{(n+1)}(4) &= +\,3.
\end{aligned}
\tag{9.22}
$$

The sequence of solutions obtained with this algorithm is given in Table III.

TABLE III

Number of iterations \ j	0	1	2	3	4
0	−3.000	−1.500	0.0	+1.5000	+3.000
1	−3.000	−0.8250	0.0	+0.8250	+3.000
2	−3.000	−0.9827	0.0	+0.9827	+3.000
3	−3.000	−0.9998	0.0	+0.998	+3.000
4	−3.000	−1.0000	0.0	+1.0000	+3.000
5	−3.000	−1.000	0.0	+1.0000	+3.000

This application of Picard's method is quite successful as the fourth iterate agrees with the exact solution to four significant digits. The reason for this fast convergence lies in the fact that the matrix $B(j)$ equals the matrix of partial derivatives $(\partial F/\partial y)(j)$, evaluated at the exact solution at the important points of the interval ($j = 1$, $j = 3$). This will become clearer in the sequel when the determination of the convergence conditions is discussed.

In order to investigate the practicality of the conditions given in Theorems 9.7 and 9.12 on the convergence of Picard's method, we must estimate the norms $\|(T^J_{(\varphi)})'\|$ and $\|(T^J_{(\varphi)})''\|$. In view of the fact that the original TPBVP (9.18) is linear in the boundary conditions, it follows immediately from (9.15) of Chapter 3, that the norm $\|(T^J_{(\varphi)})'\|$ is given by

$$\text{(9.23)} \qquad \|(T^J_{(\varphi)})'\|_{(a)} = \sup_{\|u\|\leqslant 1} \sup_{i} \sup_{\alpha} \left\{ \left| \sum_{\mu=1}^{p} \sum_{\beta=0}^{q-1} \sum_{k=1}^{p} G^V_{ik}(\alpha, \beta) \right.\right. \times \left[\frac{\partial F_k}{\partial y_\mu}(\beta) - b_{k\mu}(\beta) \right] u_\mu(\beta) \left.\left.\right| \right\}$$

while the norm $\|(T^J_{(\varphi)})''\|$ is given by

$$\text{(9.24)} \qquad \|(T^J_{(\varphi)})''\|_{(a)} = \sup_{\substack{\|u\|\leqslant 1 \\ \|v\|\leqslant 1}} \sup_{i} \sup_{\alpha} \left\{ \left| \sum_{\mu=1}^{p} \sum_{\nu=1}^{p} \sum_{\beta=0}^{q-1} \sum_{k=1}^{p} G^V_{ik}(\alpha, \beta) \right.\right. \times \frac{\partial^2 F_k}{\partial y_\mu \, \partial y_\nu}(\beta)\, u_\mu(\beta)\, v_\nu(\beta) \left.\left.\right| \right\}.$$

The simplicity of the TPBVP under consideration makes it possible to efficiently evaluate a number of increasingly simpler, though coarser, estimates for the norm:

$$\text{(9.25)} \quad \|(T^J_{(\varphi)})'\|_{(b)} = \sup_{\alpha} \sup_{i} \left\{ \sum_{\beta=0}^{q-1} \sum_{\mu=1}^{p} \left| \sum_{k=1}^{p} G^V_{ik}(\alpha, \beta) \left[\frac{\partial F_k}{\partial y_\mu}(\beta) - b_{k\mu}(\beta) \right] \right| \right\}$$

$$\text{(9.26)} \quad \|(T^J_{(\varphi)})'\|_{(b')} = \sup_{\alpha} \sup_{i} \left\{ \sum_{\beta=0}^{q-1} \sum_{\mu=1}^{p} \sum_{k=1}^{p} \left| G^V_{ik}(\alpha, \beta) \right| \left| \left[\frac{\partial F_k}{\partial y_\mu}(\beta) - b_{k\mu}(\beta) \right] \right| \right\}$$

$$\|(T^J_{(\varphi)})'\|_{(c)} = \sup_\alpha \sup_i \left\{ \sum_{k=1}^{p} \left(\sum_{\beta=0}^{q-1} | G^V_{ik}(\alpha, \beta)| \right) \times \left(\sup_{\beta \in Q'} \left\{ \sum_{\mu=1}^{p} \left| \left[\frac{\partial F_k}{\partial y_\mu}(\beta) - b_{k\mu}(\beta) \right] \right| \right\} \right) \right\} \tag{9.27}$$

and

$$\begin{aligned} \|(T^J_{(\varphi)})'\|_{(d)} &= \sup_\alpha \sup_i \left\{ \sum_{k=1}^{p} \sum_{\beta=0}^{q-1} | G^V_{ik}(\alpha, \beta)| \right\} \\ &\quad \times \sup_{\beta \in Q'} \sup_{k \in P} \left\{ \sum_{\mu=1}^{p} \left| \frac{\partial F_k}{\partial y_\mu}(\beta) - b_{k\mu}(\beta) \right| \right\} \\ &= \left\| \sum_{\beta=0}^{q-1} | G^V(\alpha, \beta)| \right\| \cdot \left\| \left[\frac{\partial F}{\partial y}(\beta) - B(\beta) \right] \right\| . \end{aligned} \tag{9.28}$$

It is simple to show that

$$\begin{aligned} \|(T^J_{(\varphi)})'\|_{(a)} &\leqslant \|(T^J_{(\varphi)})'\|_{(b)} \leqslant \|(T^J_{(\varphi)})'\|_{(b')} \\ &\leqslant \|(T^J_{(\varphi)})'\|_{(c)} \leqslant \|(T^J_{(\varphi)})'\|_{(d)} . \end{aligned} \tag{9.29}$$

Estimates for $\|(T^J_{(\varphi)})''\|$ similar to (9.25)–(9.28) are given by

$$\|(T^J_{(\varphi)})''\|_{(b)} = \sup_\alpha \sup_i \left\{ \sum_{\beta=0}^{q-1} \sum_{\mu=1}^{p} \sum_{\nu=1}^{p} \left| \sum_{k=1}^{p} G^V_{ik}(\alpha, \beta) \frac{\partial^2 F_k}{\partial y_\mu \, \partial y_\nu}(\beta) \right| \right\} \tag{9.30}$$

$$\|(T^J_{(\varphi)})''\|_{(b')} = \sup_\alpha \sup_i \left\{ \sum_{\beta=0}^{q-1} \sum_{\mu=1}^{p} \sum_{\nu=1}^{p} \sum_{k=1}^{p} | G^V_{ik}(\alpha, \beta)| \left| \frac{\partial^2 F_k}{\partial y_\mu \, \partial y_\nu}(\beta) \right| \right\} \tag{9.31}$$

$$\|(T^J_{(\varphi)})''\|_{(c)} = \sup_\alpha \sup_i \left\{ \sum_{k=1}^{p} \left(\sum_{\beta=0}^{q-1} | G^V_{ik}(\alpha, \beta)| \right) \times \left(\sup_{\beta \in Q'} \left\{ \sum_{\mu=1}^{p} \sum_{\nu=1}^{p} \left| \frac{\partial^2 F_k}{\partial y_\mu \, \partial y_\nu}(\beta) \right| \right\} \right) \right\} \tag{9.32}$$

and

$$\text{(9.33)} \quad \|(T^J_{(\varphi)})''\|_{(d)} = \sup_\alpha \sup_i \left\{ \sum_{k=1}^{p} \sum_{\beta=0}^{q-1} | G^V_{ik}(\alpha, \beta)| \right\}$$

$$\times \sup_{k \in P} \sup_{\beta \in Q'} \left\{ \sum_{\mu=1}^{p} \sum_{\nu=1}^{p} \left| \frac{\partial^2 F_k}{\partial y_\mu \, \partial y_\nu} (\beta) \right| \right\}$$

$$= \left\| \sum_{\beta=0}^{q-1} | G^V(\alpha, \beta)| \right\| \cdot \left\| \frac{\partial^2 F}{\partial y^2} (\beta) \right\| .$$

For the first application, the Green's matrix $G^V(\alpha, \beta)$ and the matrices of partial derivatives $[\partial F/\partial y - B]$ and $[\partial^2 F/\partial y^2]$ are given by

$$G^V(\alpha, \beta) = \begin{bmatrix} 1 - \frac{1}{4}\alpha & \beta - \frac{1}{4}\alpha\beta \\ \frac{1}{4} & \frac{1}{4}\beta \end{bmatrix}, \qquad 0 \leqslant \beta \leqslant \alpha - 1$$

$$= \begin{bmatrix} -\frac{1}{4}\alpha & \alpha - \frac{1}{4}\alpha\beta \\ \frac{1}{4} & \frac{1}{4}\beta - 1 \end{bmatrix}, \qquad \alpha \leqslant \beta \leqslant 4$$

$$\left[\frac{\partial F}{\partial y} - B\right] = \begin{bmatrix} 0 & 0 \\ -3y_1{}^2(\beta) & 0 \end{bmatrix}$$

and

$$\frac{\partial^2 F}{\partial y_1 \, \partial y} = \begin{bmatrix} 0 & 0 \\ -6y_1(\beta) & 0 \end{bmatrix}, \qquad \frac{\partial^2 F}{\partial y_2 \, \partial y} = \begin{bmatrix} 0 & 0 \\ 0 & 0 \end{bmatrix}.$$

Evaluation of the estimates (9.25)–(9.28) and (9.30)–(9.33) corresponding to the exact solution y^* results in

$$\text{(9.34)} \quad \begin{aligned} \|(T^J_{(y^*)})'\|_{(b)} &= 30, & \|(T^J_{(y^*)})'\|_{(b')} &= 30 \\ \|(T^J_{(y^*)})'\|_{(c)} &= 67.5, & \|(T^J_{(y^*)})'\|_{(d)} &= 108 \end{aligned}$$

and

$$\text{(9.35)} \quad \begin{aligned} \|(T^J_{(y^*)})''\|_{(b)} &= 24, & \|(T^J_{(y^*)})''\|_{(b')} &= 24 \\ \|(T^J_{(y^*)})''\|_{(c)} &= 45, & \|(T^J_{(y^*)})''\|_{(d)} &= 72. \end{aligned}$$

From Theorem 9.7, it follows that convergence can only be guaranteed when the norm $\|(T^J_{(y^*)})'\|$ is smaller than 1.0 on $\bar{S}$. Given (9.34), it is not possible to guarantee convergence for the application of Picard's method by means of the algorithm (9.21). This result seems to be in line with the observed divergence of this application of Picard's method (Tables I and II). However, it should be remarked in this context that the Theorem 9.7 provides only a sufficient condition for convergence. It is quite possible, as we will see, that Picard's method converges even though the norm $\|(T^J_{(y^*)})'\|$ is much larger than 1.0.

For the evaluation of the norms (9.25)–(9.28) and (9.30)–(9.33) which correspond to the application of the algorithm (9.22), we again need the Green's matrix $G^V(\alpha, \beta)$. Having no simple analytic expression for this matrix, we can generate the matrix by solving the linear TPBVP's.

$$\begin{aligned} y_1(j+1) - y_1(j) &= -y_2(j+1) + \delta(j-\beta), && y_1(0) = 0 \\ y_2(j+1) - y_2(j) &= -3y_1(j), && y_1(4) = 0 \end{aligned} \tag{9.36}$$

and

$$\begin{aligned} y_1(j+1) - y_1(j) &= -y_2(j+1), && y_1(0) = 0 \\ y_2(j+1) - y_1(j) &= -3y_1(j) + \delta(j-\beta), && y_1(4) = 0 \end{aligned} \tag{9.37}$$

for all β in $\mathbf{Q}'$ where $\delta(j)$ is the equivalent of the δ function in the continuous case, i.e., $\delta(j) = 0$ if $j \neq 0$, $\delta(0) = 1$. The solution of the TPBVP's (9.36) gives the first columns of the matrix $G^V(\alpha, \beta)$, and those of (9.37) the second columns.

The matrices of partial derivatives required for the norm determination are almost the same as before and are given by

$$\frac{\partial F}{\partial y} - B = \begin{bmatrix} 0 & 0 \\ 3 - 3y_1^2(\beta) & 0 \end{bmatrix}$$

and

$$\frac{\partial^2 F}{\partial y_1\, \partial y} = \begin{bmatrix} 0 & 0 \\ -6y_1(\beta) & 0 \end{bmatrix}, \qquad \frac{\partial^2 F}{\partial y_2\, \partial y} = \begin{bmatrix} 0 & 0 \\ 0 & 0 \end{bmatrix}.$$

Evaluating these derivatives along the exact solution y^* and carrying out the required numerical computations, we obtain the following estimates of the norms, namely,

$$\begin{aligned} &\|(T^J_{(y^*)})'\|_{(b)} = 24.1304, \qquad \|(T^J_{(y^*)})'\|_{(b')} = 24.1304 \\ &\|(T^J_{(y^*)})'\|_{(c)} = 30.2609, \qquad \|(T^J_{(y^*)})'\|_{(d)} = 54.2609 \end{aligned} \tag{9.38}$$

and

$$\begin{aligned} &\|(T^J_{(y^*)})''\|_{(b)} = 19.3043, \qquad \|(T^J_{(y^*)})''\|_{(b')} = 19.3043 \\ &\|(T^J_{(y^*)})''\|_{(c)} = 22.6957, \qquad \|(T^J_{(y^*)})''\|_{(d)} = 40.6957. \end{aligned} \tag{9.39}$$

The numerical values obtained for these norms are all larger than 1.0. This result is at first sight somewhat surprising since the corresponding Picard's method sequence was found to be convergent (see Table III). The reason for this behavior of the convergence condition norm lies in the large contribution to this norm by the derivative $\partial F_2/\partial y_1 = 3y_1^2(\beta)$ at the initial point $y_1(0) = -3.0$. The same derivative does not contribute to the ratio

$$\| T^J(y_{n+1}) - T^J(y_n)\|/\| y_{n+1} - y_n \|,$$

which provides the actual contraction factor of Picard's method. The reason for the derivative not contributing to this ratio lies in the fact that the initial value of $y_1(0)$ is kept at its fixed value for all successive iterates. For, if we write out the norm $\| T^J(y_{n+1}) - T^J(y_n)\|$, we find

$$\begin{aligned} &\| T^J(y_{n+1}) - T^J(y_n)\| \\ &\quad \leqslant \| (T^J_{(\tilde{y})})' (y_{n+1} - y_n)\| \\ &\quad \leqslant \sup_\alpha \left\| \sum_{\beta=0}^{3} G^V(\alpha, \beta) \left[\frac{\partial F}{\partial y} (\tilde{y}(\beta), \beta) - B(\beta) \right] [y_{n+1}(\beta) - y_n(\beta)] \right\| \end{aligned} \tag{9.40}$$

where according to the mean value theorem $\tilde{y} = y_n + \theta(y_{n+1} - y_n)$, $0 < \theta < 1$. As $y_1^{(n+1)}(0) - y_1^{(n)}(0) = 0$ and $\partial F_1/\partial y_2 - b_{12} = \partial F_2/\partial y_2 - b_{22} = 0$ for all successive iterates, it follows that there is indeed no contribution to the sum in (9.40) for $\beta = 0$. In the determination of the convergence condition by evaluating the norm

$\|(T^J_{(y)})'\| = \sup_\alpha \| \sum_{\beta=0}^{3} G^V(\alpha, \beta)[(\partial F/\partial y)(y^*(\beta), \beta) - B(\beta)]\|$ this fact was not taken into account. Had it been taken into account, then the norms $\|(T^J_{(y^*)})'\|$ for both Picard's method applications would have had the values

$$\|(T^J_{(y^*)})'\|^0 = 3$$

and

$$\|(T^J_{(y^*)})'\|^0 = 0.652$$

respectively.

It is clear that these numbers are consistent with the observed divergence and convergence, respectively.

Since the norm $\|(T^J_{(y^*)})'\|$ for the second application of Picard's method is too large for verification of the convergence by means of Theorems 9.7 and 9.12, there is little point in evaluating the remaining convergence conditions given by these theorems. In view of this, the example given here seems to be of limited value. However, it serves to illustrate several important points. First, the choice of a boundary-compatible set is often of critical significance in obtaining convergence. Second, the theorems are only sufficient conditions and are often quite conservative in practice. Third, a theorem analogous to Theorem 4.71 of Chapter 2 would be quite useful for the contraction mapping method.

4.10. Application to Discrete Problems II: The Modified Contraction Mapping Method

Just as in the continuous case, we can view the application of the modified contraction mapping method to (9.1) as equivalent to the contraction mapping method applied to the operator $P = [I - V]^{-1}[T^J - V]$ for a suitably chosen V. We again limit our discussion to operators $V = U^J_{KL}$ of the form given by (11.2) of Chapter 3. So, we let $J = \{A(j), B(j), M, N\}$ and $\tilde{J} = \{C(j), D(j), K, L\}$ be boundary-compatible sets. We then note that, by virtue of Lemma 11.1, the modified contraction mapping method when applied to the equation $T^J(y) = y$ with modifying operator $V = U^J_{KL}$, is equivalent to the contraction mapping method applied to the equation $T^{\tilde{J}}(y) = y$.

Now, with the aid of Lemma 11.1 of Chapter 3, we can translate the relevant results of Chapter 2 with no difficulty. However, as we noted in detail in Section 6, the choice of different approaches did not, in general, lead to simpler or better convergence conditions. Only in those cases where we could use boundary-compatible sets for which the corresponding Green's matrices were easy to evaluate was there any practical advantage to using the modified contraction method. Precisely the same considerations apply in the discrete case. Thus, we do not repeat the discussion here but rather simply state the convergence theorems analogous to Theorems 6.4 and 6.12.

THEOREM 10.1. Let y_0 be an element of $\mathscr{S}(\mathbf{Q}, R_p)$ and let $\bar{S} = \bar{S}(y_0, r)$. Suppose that (i) $J = \{A(j), B(j), M, N\}$ is a boundary-compatible set for which (9.1) is differentiable on $\bar{S}$; (ii) $\tilde{J} = \{C(j), D(j), K, L\}$ is a boundary-compatible set; and (iii) there are real numbers η, q, β, and α with $\eta \geqslant 0$, $0 \leqslant q < 1$, $\beta \geqslant 0$, and $\alpha = \beta/(1-q) < 1$ such that

$$\| T^{\tilde{J}}(y_0) - y_0 \| \leqslant \eta \tag{10.2}$$

$$\| U_{KL}^{J} \|_{(a)} \leqslant q \tag{10.3}$$

$$\sup_{y \in \bar{S}} \{\| (T_y^{J})' - U_{KL}^{J} \|_{(a)}\} \leqslant \beta \tag{10.4}$$

$$\frac{1}{1-\alpha} \eta \leqslant r \tag{10.5}$$

where

$$\begin{aligned} \| U_{KL}^{J} \|_{(a)} = \sup_{\|u\| \leqslant 1} \sup_{i} \sup_{\alpha} \Bigg\{ \Bigg| \sum_{\mu=1}^{p} \sum_{k=1}^{p} & H_{ik}^{J}(\alpha)\{[m_{k\mu} - k_{k\mu}]\, u_\mu(0) \\ & + [n_{k\mu} - l_{k\mu}]\, u_\mu(q)\} \\ & + \sum_{\nu=0}^{q-1} G_{ik}^{J}(\alpha, \nu)\{[c_{k\mu}(\nu) - a_{k\mu}(\nu)]\, u_\mu(\nu+1) \\ & + [d_{k\mu}(\nu) - b_{k\mu}(\nu)]\, u_\mu(\nu)\} \end{aligned} \tag{10.6}$$

and

$$(10.7)\quad \|(T_y^J)' - U_{KL}^J\|_{(a)} = \sup_{\|u\|\leqslant 1} \sup_i \sup_\alpha \Bigg\{ \Bigg| \sum_{\mu=1}^{p} \sum_{k=1}^{p} H_{ik}^J(\alpha) \times \Bigg\{ \Bigg[k_{k\mu} - \frac{\partial g_k}{\partial y_\mu}(y(0)) \Bigg] u_\mu(0) + \Bigg[l_{k\mu} - \frac{\partial h_k}{\partial y_\mu}(y(q)) \Bigg] u_\mu(q) \Bigg\} + \sum_{\nu=0}^{q-1} G_{ik}^J(\alpha, \nu) \Bigg\{ \Bigg[\frac{\partial F_k}{\partial x_\mu}(y(\nu+1), y(\nu), \nu) - c_{k\mu}(\nu) \Bigg] u_\mu(\nu+1) + \Bigg[\frac{\partial F_k}{\partial y_\mu}(y(\nu+1), y(\nu), \nu) - d_{k\mu}(\nu) \Bigg] u_\mu(\nu) \Bigg\} .$$

Then the MCM sequence $\{y_n(\cdot)\}$ for T^J based on y_0 and U_{KL}^J converges uniformly to the unique solution $y^*(\cdot)$ of (9.1) in $\bar{S}$ and the rate of convergence is given by

$$(10.8)\qquad \|y^*(\cdot) - y_n(\cdot)\| \leqslant \frac{\alpha^n}{1-\alpha} \|y_1(\cdot) - y_0(\cdot)\| .$$

Proof. Simply check that the hypotheses of Corollary 3.8, Chapter 2, are satisfied.

THEOREM 10.9. Suppose that (i) $J = \{A(j), B(j), M, N\}$ is a boundary-compatible set for which (9.1) is twice differentiable on $\bar{S}$; (ii) $\tilde{J} = \{C(j), D(j), K, L\}$ is a boundary-compatible set; and (iii) there are real numbers η, q, γ, κ, δ, and K with $\eta \geqslant 0$, $0 \leqslant q < 1$, $\gamma \geqslant 0$, $\kappa \geqslant 0$, $\delta = \gamma/(1-q) < 1$, and $K = \kappa/(1-q)$ such that

$$(10.10)\qquad \| T^{\tilde{J}}(y_0) - y_0 \| \leqslant \eta$$

$$(10.11)\qquad \| U_{KL}^J \|_{(a)} \leqslant q$$

$$(10.12)\qquad \|(T_{y_0}^J)' - U_{KL}^J\|_{(a)} \leqslant \gamma$$

$$(10.13)\qquad \sup_{y\in\bar{S}} \{\|(T_y^J)''\|_{(a)}\} \leqslant \kappa$$

and

$$\frac{1-\sqrt{1-2h}}{h}\,\frac{\eta}{1-\delta}\leqslant r<\frac{1+\sqrt{1-2h}}{h}\,\frac{\eta}{1-\delta} \tag{10.14}$$

where $h = K\eta/(1-\delta)^2 \leqslant \frac{1}{2}$. Then the MCM sequence $\{y_n(\cdot)\}$ for T^J based on y_0 and U^J_{KL} converges uniformly to the unique solution $y^*(\cdot)$ of (9.1) in $\bar{S}$ and the rate of convergence is given by

$$\begin{aligned}\|y^*(\cdot)-y_n(\cdot)\| \leqslant [1-(1-\delta)\sqrt{1-2h}]^n\left[\frac{1-\sqrt{1-2h}}{h(1-\delta)}\right]\\ \times\|y_1(\cdot)-y_0(\cdot)\|.\end{aligned} \tag{10.15}$$

4.11. Application to Discrete Problems III: Newton's Method

Just as was the case in previous sections, the remarks made with regard to Newton's method for continuous problems apply almost verbatim in the discrete case. Therefore, we limit ourselves to a brief discussion of a few details of the application of Newton's method and to the translation of Theorems 4.27 and 4.38 of Chapter 2.

The point of departure for our discussion is again the operator equation $y = T^J(y)$. To apply Newton's method, we guess an initial solution y_0 and generate an NM sequence by means of the algorithm

$$y_{n+1} = T^J(y_n) + (T^J_{y_n})'(y_{n+1} - y_n) \tag{11.1}$$

or, equivalently, by

$$y_{n+1} = [I - (T^J_{y_n})']^{-1}[T^J(y_n) - (T^J_{y_n})' y_n] \tag{11.2}$$

(provided that the indicated inverse exists). Now, (11.2) is equivalent to the linear TPBVP

$$\begin{aligned}
y_{n+1}(j+1) - y_{n+1}(j) - A(j)\,y_{n+1}(j+1) - B(j)\,y_{n+1}(j)\\
= F(y_n(j+1), y_n(j), j) - A(j)\,y_n(j+1) - B(j)\,y_n(j)\\
+\left\{\frac{\partial F}{\partial x}(y_n(j+1), y_n(j), j) - A(j)\right\}(y_{n+1}(j+1) - y_n(j+1))\\
+\left\{\frac{\partial F}{\partial y}(y_n(j+1), y_n(j), j) - B(j)\right\}(y_{n+1}(j) - y_n(j)),
\end{aligned}$$

$$
\begin{aligned}
&My_{n+1}(0) + Ny_{n+1}(q) \\
&\quad = c - g(y_n(0)) - h(y_n(q)) + My_n(0) + Ny_n(q) \\
&\qquad + \left[M - \frac{\partial g}{\partial y}(y_n(0))\right](y_{n+1}(0) - y_n(0)) \\
&\qquad + \left[N - \frac{\partial h}{\partial y}(y_n(q))\right](y_{n+1}(q) - y_n(q))
\end{aligned}
$$

which can be written as

$$
\begin{aligned}
(11.3) \quad & y_{n+1}(j+1) - y_{n+1}(j) \\
&\quad - \frac{\partial F}{\partial x}(y_n(j+1), y_n(j), j)\, y_{n+1}(j+1) \\
&\quad - \frac{\partial F}{\partial y}(y_n(j+1), y_n(j), j)\, y_{n+1}(j) \\
&\qquad = F(y_n(j+1), y_n(j), j) \\
&\qquad\quad - \frac{\partial F}{\partial x}(y_n(j+1), y_n(j), j)\, y_n(j+1) \\
&\qquad\quad - \frac{\partial F}{\partial y}(y_n(j+1), y_n(j), j)\, y_n(j)\, \frac{\partial g}{\partial y}(y_n(0))\, y_{n+1}(0) \\
&\qquad\quad + \frac{\partial h}{\partial y}(y_n(q))\, y_{n+1}(q) \\
&\qquad = c - g(y_n(0)) - h(y_n(q)) + \frac{\partial g}{\partial y}(y_n(0))\, y_n(0) \\
&\qquad\quad + \frac{\partial h}{\partial y}(y_n(q))\, y_n(q).
\end{aligned}
$$

The iterative method for solving TPBVP's by replacing the TPBVP by a sequence of linear TPBVP's of the form (11.3) is called *Newton's method* (*or quasilinearization*) for TPBVP's. The sequence of iterates is called the NM *sequence for the* TPBVP *based on* y_0 (*and* J). This sequence coincides with the NM sequence for T^J based on y_0.

Now, it is clear that (11.3) corresponds to a linear TPBVP with a set of matrices

$$Y_n = \left\{ \frac{\partial F}{\partial x}(y_n(j+1), y_n(j), j), \frac{\partial F}{\partial y}(y_n(j+1), y_n(j), j), \right.$$

$$\left. \frac{\partial g}{\partial y}(y_n(0)), \frac{\partial h}{\partial y}(y_n(q)) \right\}.$$

If Y_n is a boundary-compatible set, then (11.3) is equivalent to the integral equation $y_{n+1} = T^{Y_n}(y_n)$. However, in general, Y_n need not be a boundary-compatible set and so, we seek conditions on the sequence of iterates which insure the solvability of (11.3) for the *particular* elements of the sequence.

Again, there are two approaches to the translation of the results of Chapter 2; namely, (1) an approach based on the direct application of Lemma 11.1 of Chapter 3; or (2) an approach based on the application of Banach's theorem on the inverse of an operator. As before, two practical convergence theorems results. The first such theorem is the translation of Mysovskikh's theorem using the second approach and the second such theorem is the translation of Kantorovich's theorem using Lemma 11.1, Chapter 3. Thus, we have the following.

THEOREM 11.4. Let $y_0(\cdot)$ be an element of $\mathscr{S}(\mathbf{Q}, R_p)$ and let $\bar{S} = \bar{S}(y_0, r)$. Suppose that (i) $J = \{A(j), B(j), M, N\}$ is a boundary-compatible set for which (9.1) is twice differentiable, and (ii) there are real numbers η, q, κ, K, and h with $\eta \geqslant 0$, $0 \leqslant q < 1$, $\kappa \geqslant 0$, $K = \kappa/(1-q)$, and $h = K\eta$ such that

(11.5) $$\| [I - (T^J_{y_0})']^{-1} [T^J(y_0) - (T^J_{y_0})' y_0] - y_0 \| \leqslant \eta$$

(11.6) $$\sup_{y \in \bar{S}} \{ \| (T_y{}^J)' \|_{(a)} \} \leqslant q$$

(11.7) $$\sup_{y \in \bar{S}} \{ \| (T_y{}^J)'' \|_{(a)} \} \leqslant \kappa$$

(11.8) $$h < 2$$

(11.9) $$\sum_{k=0}^{\infty} \left(\frac{h}{2}\right)^{2^k - 1} \eta < r.$$

Then the NM sequence $\{y_n(\cdot)\}$ based on y_0 converges uniformly to a solution $y^*(\cdot)$ of (9.1) in $\bar{S}$ and the rate of convergence is given by

$$\|y^*(\cdot) - y_n(\cdot)\| \leqslant \frac{(h/2)^{2^n-1}}{[1 - h/2]^{2^n}} \|y_1(\cdot) - y_0(\cdot)\| . \tag{11.10}$$

THEOREM 11.11. Let $y_0(\cdot)$ be an element of $\mathscr{S}(\mathbf{Q}, R_p)$ and let $\bar{S} = \bar{S}(y_0, r)$. Suppose that (i) $J = \{A(j), B(j), M, N\}$ is a boundary-compatible set for which (9.1) is twice differentiable on $\bar{S}$; (ii)

$$Y_0 = \left\{\frac{\partial F}{\partial x}(y_0(j+1), y_0(j), j), \frac{\partial F}{\partial y}(y_0(j+1), y_0(j), j),\right.$$
$$\left.\frac{\partial g}{\partial y}(y_0(0)), \frac{\partial h}{\partial y}(y_0(q))\right\}$$

is a boundary-compatible set; and (iii) there are real numbers η, K, and h with $\eta \geqslant 0$, $K \geqslant 0$, and $h = K\eta$ such that

$$\|[I - (T_{y_0}^J)']^{-1}[T^J(y_0) - y_0]\| \leqslant \eta \tag{11.12}$$

$$\sup_{y \in \bar{S}}\{\|(T_y^{Y_0})''\|_{(a)}\} \leqslant K \tag{11.13}$$

$$h \leqslant \tfrac{1}{2} \tag{11.14}$$

$$\frac{1 - \sqrt{1 - 2h}}{h}\eta \leqslant r < \frac{1 + \sqrt{1 - 2h}}{h}\eta. \tag{11.15}$$

Then the NM sequence $\{y_n(\cdot)\}$ for (9.1) based on y_0 converges uniformly to the unique solution $y^*(\cdot)$ of (9.1) in $\bar{S}$ and the rate of convergence is given by

$$\|y^*(\cdot) - y_n(\cdot)\| \leqslant \frac{1}{2^{n-1}}[2h]^{2^n-1}\|y_1(\cdot) - y_0(\cdot)\| \tag{11.16}$$

and $\|y^*(\cdot) - y_1(\cdot)\| \leqslant [h/(1 - h)]\|y_1(\cdot) - y_0(\cdot)\|$.

Proof. Simply verify that the hypotheses of Theorem 4.38, Chapter 2, are satisfied. Note that since Y_0 is boundary compatible, $[I - (T_{y_0}^J)']^{-1}$ exists by virtue of Lemma 11.1, Chapter 3, and that

$\sup_{y \in \bar{S}}\{\|(T_J^{Y_0})''\|_{(a)}\} = \sup_{y \in \bar{S}}\{\|[I - (T_{y_0}^J)']^{-1}(T_y{}^J)''\|_{(a)}\}$ be virtue of (11.6), Chapter 3.

We omit treatment of the application of the multipoint methods to discrete problems as this would simply involve a verbatim repetition of Section 8.

4.12. Summary

We have combined the results on iterative methods for the solution of operator equations of Chapter 2 and the results on the representation of TPBVP's by operator equations of Chapter 3 to obtain convergence theorems and algorithms for the iterative solution of TPBVP's of the type that arise in optimal control problems. We briefly indicated the way in which TPBVP's arise in optimal control problems with both continuous and discrete time domains.

Our translation of the results of Chapter 2 relied heavily on the notion of boundary compatibility and on the estimates of derivatives obtained in Chapter 3. We treated some analytical examples to illustrate some of the ideas involved. In Chapter 6, we shall examine some numerical examples to indicate the role played by our results in some "practical" problems.

Considering TPBVP's of the form (5.7) or (9.1), and letting J be a boundary-compatible set, we noted that the TPBVP's could be rewritten as integral or summation equations which could be viewed as an operator equation of the form $y = T^J(y)$. Applying the method of contraction mappings to this operator equation was equivalent to the successive solution of a sequence of linear TPBVP's of the form (5.5) or (9.5). These linear TPBVP's formed the basis of the algorithm which we called Picard's method. Theorems 5.8, 5.13, 9.7, and 9.12 were the resulting convergence theorems for Picard's method.

Next, we considered the application of the modified contraction mapping method. As modifying operator V, we chose the linear operator U_{KL}^J given by (10.2) or (11.2) of Chapter 3. We found that this application of the modified contraction mapping method was equivalent to the application of Picard's method to the original TPBVP with the boundary-compatible set $\tilde{J}$ replacing J. In other words, the operators $T^{\tilde{J}}$ and $[I - U_{KL}^J]^{-1}[T^J - U_{KL}^J]$ were the same. For theoretical purposes, this is significant as it implies that we can consider Picard's method for $T^{\tilde{J}}$ as an application of the contraction mapping method or as an application of the modified contraction mapping method. For practical purposes, the distinction between these viewpoints was not too important since the operator $[I - U_{KL}^J]^{-1}$ made the determination of practical convergence conditions somewhat difficult. However, if $\| U_{KL}^J \| \leqslant q < 1$, then the use of Banach's theorem simplified our task and led to some useful results.

We then considered Newton's method. We found that the corresponding algorithm was equivalent to the successive solution of the linear TPBVP's (7.3) or (11.3). We used two approaches to the translation of the results of Chapter 2; the first approach was based on a direct application of Lemma 10.1 or Lemma 11.1 of Chapter 3, and the second approach was based on the use of Banach's theorem on the inverse of an operator. Theorems 7.11, 7.18, 7.24, 11.4, and 11.11 were the main convergence results.

Finally, we examined multipoint methods and translated Theorem 5.48, Chapter 2, into the TPBVP context. Theorem 8.1 represented this translation.

CHAPTER 5

APPLICATION TO OSCILLATION PROBLEMS

5.1. Introduction

We now consider the application of the results of Chapters 2 and 3 to several classes of TPBVP's arising in the study of oscillation problems. In particular, we examine "almost linear problems" and problems with boundary conditions of the form $y(0) = y(1)$ (so-called "periodic" boundary conditions). "Almost linear problems" occur in both control and oscillation problems and are particularly well suited to the use of the contraction mapping method. Problems with "periodic" boundary conditions are, in effect, problems involving periodic solutions.

We begin, in the next section, with a discussion of "almost linear problems," i.e., TPBVP's of the form

$$\begin{aligned} \dot{y} &= A(t)y + f(t) + \psi(\epsilon, y, t) \\ My(0) + Ny(1) &+ \theta(\epsilon, y(0)) + \gamma(\epsilon, y(1)) = c \end{aligned} \tag{1.1}$$

where ϵ is a parameter. Several convergence theorems are obtained for the application of the contraction mapping method (Picard's method) to (1.1). Several second-order examples are analyzed in Section 5.3.

Considerable research has been done on the application of successive approximation methods to oscillation problems and a good starting point for an account of this area is given by Hale [H1 or H2]. In this brief chapter, we only scratch the surface of a very large mountain.

5.2. Almost Linear Problems

Previously we discussed the application of various iterative methods to the solution of general TPBVP's. Here, we consider some aspects of the use of these methods in the important special case of almost linear TPBVP's. We begin with the following.

DEFINITION 2.1. The TPBVP $\dot{y} = F(y, t), g(y(0)) + h(y(1)) = c$ is an almost linear TPBVP if

$$F(y, t) = A(t)y + f(t) + \psi(\epsilon, y, t) \tag{2.2}$$

$$g(y) = My + \gamma(\epsilon, y), \qquad h(y) = Ny + \theta(\epsilon, y) \tag{2.3}$$

where ϵ is a "small" scalar and there is a constant m such that

$$\| \psi(\epsilon, y, t)\| \leqslant m\epsilon, \qquad \| \theta(\epsilon, y)\| \leqslant m\epsilon$$

for all y and t. If $\dot{y} = F(y, t)$, $g(y(0)) + h(y(1)) = c$ is an almost linear problem, then the linear TPBVP corresponding to it is $\dot{y} = A(t)y + f(t)$, $My(0) + Ny(1) = c$.

We observe that if $y_\epsilon(t)$ is a solution of the linear TPBVP corresponding to an almost linear problem, then $y_\epsilon(t)$ is an $m\epsilon$-approximate solution of the almost linear problem.

Almost linear problems occur frequently in connection with oscillations (or perturbations of periodic solutions). However, they are not uncommon in control theory. For example, suppose that we consider a control problem with system

$$\dot{x} = A(t)x + B(t)u + \epsilon e(x, u, t), \tag{2.4}$$

sets S_0 and S_f of initial and final states given by

$$\begin{aligned} S_0 &= \{x: Kx + \epsilon k(x) = d_1\} \\ S_f &= \{x: Lx + \epsilon l(x) = d_2\}, \end{aligned} \tag{2.5}$$

and a cost functional

$$J(u) = \tfrac{1}{2}\left\{\langle x(t_0), Cx(t_0)\rangle + \langle x(t_f), Dx(t_f)\rangle + \int_{t_0}^{t_f} [\langle x, Q(t)x\rangle + \langle u, R(t)u\rangle]\, dt\right\} \tag{2.6}$$

with C, D, and $Q(t)$ positive semidefinite and $R(t)$ positive definite. The Hamiltonian for this problem is given by

$$H(x, p, u, p_0, t) = \tfrac{1}{2} p_0 \{\langle x, Q(t)x\rangle + \langle u, R(t)u\rangle\} + \langle p(t), A(t)x\rangle + \langle p(t), B(t)u\rangle + \epsilon\langle p(t), e(x, u, t)\rangle$$

and the canonical equations are given by

$$\dot{x} = \frac{\partial H}{\partial p} = A(t)x + B(t)u + \epsilon e(x, u, t)$$

$$\dot{p} = -\frac{\partial H}{\partial x} = -p_0 Q(t)x - A'(t)p - \epsilon \left(\frac{\partial e}{\partial x}\right)' p.$$

The appropriate boundary conditions are

$$\sum_{j=1}^{n} k_{ij} x_j(t_0) + \epsilon k_i[x(t_0)] = c_i, \qquad i = 1, \ldots, k$$

$$\sum_{j=1}^{n} l_{ij} x_j(t_f) + \epsilon l_i[x(t_f)] = d_i, \qquad i = 1, \ldots, l$$

$$p_j(t_0) = -p_0 \left\{\sum_{i=1}^{n} (c_{ij} + c_{ji})\, x_i(t_0)\right\} + \sum_{i=1}^{k} \alpha_i k_{ij} + \epsilon \left\{\sum_{i=1}^{k} \alpha_i \frac{\partial k_i}{\partial x_i}(x(t_0))\right\}, \qquad j = 1, \ldots, n \tag{2.7}$$

$$p_j(t_f) = p_0 \left\{\sum_{i=1}^{n} (d_{ij} + d_{ji})\, x_i(t_f)\right\} + \sum_{i=1}^{l} \beta_i l_{ij} + \epsilon \left\{\sum_{i=1}^{l} \beta_i \frac{\partial l_i}{\partial x_j}(x(t_f))\right\}, \qquad j = 1, \ldots, n$$

where the α_i and β_i are constants. Assuming that the control is unconstrained and that the problem is regular [A2], we can, for $p_0 \neq 0$ and ϵ "small", write the H-minimal control $u^0(x, p, p_0, t)$ in the form

$$u^0(x, p, p_0, t) = -\frac{1}{p_0} R^{-1}(t)\, B'(t)p + \epsilon \hat{u}(x, p, p_0, t).$$

It follows that the extremals of the control problem are the solutions of the system

$$
\begin{aligned}
\dot{x} &= A(t)x - \frac{B(t)}{p_0} R^{-1}(t)\, B'(t) p + \epsilon[B(t)\, \hat{u}(x, p, p_0, t) + e(x, p, p_0, t, \epsilon)] \\
\dot{p} &= -p_0 Q(t)x - A'(t)p - \epsilon \left[\frac{\partial e}{\partial x}(x, p, p_0, t, \epsilon)\right]' p
\end{aligned}
\tag{2.8}
$$

with the boundary conditions (2.7). If we set $p_0 = 1$ and if we let

$$y(t) = [x(t), p(t)]$$

$$W(t) = \begin{bmatrix} A(t) & -B(t)\, R^{-1}(t)\, B'(t) \\ -Q(t) & -A'(t) \end{bmatrix}$$

and

$$E(y(t), t) = \begin{bmatrix} B(t)\, \hat{u}(x, p, t) + e(x, p, t, \epsilon) \\ -\left[\frac{\partial e}{\partial x}(x, p, t, \epsilon)\right]' p \end{bmatrix}$$

then we can write (2.8) in the form

$$\dot{y} = W(t)y + \epsilon E[y(t), t]. \tag{2.9}$$

Elimination of the constants α_i and β_i from the boundary conditions (2.7) will result in almost linear relations of the form

$$
\begin{aligned}
G_1 x(t_0) + H_1 p(t_0) + \epsilon g_1[x(t_0), p(t_0)] &= a_1 \\
G_2 x(t_f) + H_2 p(t_f) + \epsilon g_2[x(t_f), p(t_f)] &= a_2
\end{aligned}
$$

where G_1 and H_1 are $(n - k) \times n$ matrices, G_2 and H_2 are $(n - l) \times n$ matrices, g_1 and a_1 $(n - k)$ vectors and g_2 and a_2 $(n - l)$ vectors, with a_1 and a_2 known constant vectors. Defining $2n \times n$ matrices M and N, a $2n$ vector c and $2n$ vector functions $m(\cdot)$ and $n(\cdot)$ by

$$
M = \left[\begin{array}{c|c} K & 0 \\ G_1 & H_1 \\ \hline 0 & 0 \end{array}\right], \qquad
N = \left[\begin{array}{c|c} 0 & 0 \\ \hline L & 0 \\ G_2 & H_2 \end{array}\right], \qquad
c = \begin{bmatrix} d_1 \\ a_1 \\ d_2 \\ a_2 \end{bmatrix}
$$

$$m[x(t_0), p(t_0)] = \begin{bmatrix} k[x(t_0)] \\ g_1[x(t_0), p(t_0)] \end{bmatrix}$$

$$n[x(t_f), p(t_f)] = \begin{bmatrix} l[x(t_f)] \\ g_2[x(t_f), p(t_f)] \end{bmatrix}$$

we can write the boundary conditions (2.7) in the form

$$My(t_0) + Ny(t_f) + \epsilon m(y(t_0)) + \epsilon n(y(t_f)) = c. \tag{2.10}$$

The TPBVP (2.9), (2.10) is thus an almost linear problem. This is a typical way in which almost linear problems arise in control theory.

Now let us consider the almost linear TPBVP

$$\begin{aligned} \dot{y} &= A(t)y + f(t) + \psi(\epsilon, y, t) \\ My(0) &+ Ny(1) + \gamma(\epsilon, y(0)) + \theta(\epsilon, y(1)) = c. \end{aligned} \tag{2.11}$$

Application of the method of contraction mappings (Picard's method) to (2.11) can result in some important simplifications of the procedure. Suppose that $J = \{A(t), M, N\}$ is a boundary-compatible set. Then the operator T^J is given by

$$\begin{aligned} T^J(y)(t) = {} & H^J(t)[c - \gamma(\epsilon, y(0)) - \theta(\epsilon, y(1))] \\ & + \int_0^1 G^J(t, s)[f(s) + \psi(\epsilon, y(s), s)]\, ds \end{aligned} \tag{2.12}$$

and the corresponding algorithm of Picard's method can be written in the form

$$\begin{aligned} \dot{y}_{n+1} - A(t)y_{n+1} &= A(t)y_n + f(t) + \psi(\epsilon, y_n, t) - A(t)y_n \\ My_{n+1}(0) + Ny_{n+1}(1) &= c - \gamma(\epsilon, y_n(0)) - \theta(\epsilon, y_n(1)) \end{aligned} \tag{2.13}$$

or equivalently as

$$\begin{aligned} \dot{y}_{n+1} - A(t)y_{n+1} &= f(t) + \psi(\epsilon, y_n(t), t) \\ My_{n+1}(0) + Ny_{n+1}(1) &= c - \gamma(\epsilon, y_n(0)) - \theta(\epsilon, y_n(1)). \end{aligned} \tag{2.14}$$

Thus, only a single linear equation (with changing forcing term) needs to be solved. Moreover, it is not necessary to guess an initial approximate solution since an excellent candidate is the solution of the linear problem

$$\dot{y} = A(t)y + f(t), \qquad My(0) + Ny(1) = c \tag{2.15}$$

which corresponds to (2.11). The simplifications of the procedure are reflected in the corresponding convergence theorems. In view of the importance of almost linear problems, we give the two main convergence theorems on the contraction mapping method for this situation. We note that the theorems are essentially the same as Theorems 5.8 and 5.13 of Chapter 4 but that the form of the resulting convergence conditions is of interest. We have the following.

THEOREM 2.16. Consider the almost linear TPBVP (2.11). Suppose that $J = \{A(t), M, N\}$ is a boundary-compatible set and let $y_0(\cdot)$ be the solution of the linear problem (2.15) corresponding to (2.11). Let $\bar{S} = \bar{S}(y_0, r)$. Suppose further that (i) the function $G^J(t, s)[f(s) + \psi(\epsilon, y, s)]$ satisfies the conditions of Lemma 8.5 of Chapter 3; (ii) $\gamma(\epsilon, y)$ and $\theta(\epsilon, y)$ are differentiable with respect to y; and (iii) there are real numbers η and α with $\eta \geqslant 0$ and $0 \leqslant \alpha < 1$ such that

$$\| T^J(y_0) - y_0 \| = \Big\| H^J(\cdot)[-\gamma(\epsilon, y_0(0)) - \theta(\epsilon, y_0(1))] + \int_0^1 G^J(t, s)\, \psi(\epsilon, y_0(s), s)\, ds \Big\| \leqslant \eta \tag{2.17}$$

$$\sup_{y\in\bar{S}} \sup_i \sup_t \left\{ \sum_{k=1}^{p} \int_0^1 \left| \sum_{j=1}^{p} G^J_{ij}(t, s) \frac{\partial\psi_j}{\partial y_k}(\epsilon, y(s), s) \right| ds \right\} + \sup_{y\in\bar{S}} \sup_i \sup_t \left\{ \sum_{k=1}^{p} \left[\left| \sum_{j=1}^{p} \left\{ H^J_{ij}(t) \times \left[\frac{\partial\gamma_j}{\partial y_k}(\epsilon, y(0)) + \frac{\partial\theta_j}{\partial y_k}(\epsilon, y(1)) \right] \right\} \right| \right] \right\} \leqslant \alpha \tag{2.18}$$

$$\frac{1}{1-\alpha}\eta \leqslant r. \tag{2.19}$$

Then the CM sequence $\{y_n(\cdot)\}$ for the TPBVP based on $y_0(\cdot)$ and J

converges uniformly to the unique solution $y^*(\cdot)$ of (2.11) in $\bar{S}$ and the rate of convergence is given by

$$\|y^*(\cdot) - y_n(\cdot)\| \leqslant \frac{\alpha^n}{1-\alpha}\|y_1(\cdot) - y_0(\cdot)\|. \tag{2.20}$$

We note that if $\psi(\epsilon, y, s) = \epsilon\tilde{\psi}(y, s)$ and $\gamma(\epsilon, y) = \epsilon\tilde{\gamma}(y)$, $\theta(\epsilon, y) = \epsilon\tilde{\theta}(y)$, then (2.17) becomes

$$\eta \geqslant \epsilon \Big\| H^J(\cdot)[-\tilde{\gamma}(y_0(0)) - \tilde{\theta}(y_0(1))] + \int_0^1 G^J(t, s)\,\tilde{\psi}(y_0(s), s)\, ds \Big\| \tag{2.21}$$

and (2.18) becomes

$$\epsilon \sup_{y\in\bar{S}} \left\{ \Big\| H^J(\cdot)\left[\frac{\partial\tilde{\gamma}}{\partial y}(y(0)) + \frac{\partial\tilde{\theta}}{\partial y}(y(1))\right] + \int_0^1 G^J(\cdot, s)\frac{\partial\tilde{\psi}}{\partial y}(y(s), s)\, ds \Big\| \right\} \leqslant \alpha. \tag{2.22}$$

Thus, in this case the convergence estimates essentially depend upon ϵ. For example, if $\tilde{\psi}(y, s)$, $\tilde{\gamma}(y)$, and $\tilde{\theta}(y)$ are continuously differentiable with respect to y, then there is a nondecreasing function $M(r)$ such that

$$\sup_{y\in\bar{S}} \left\{ \Big\| H^J(\cdot)\left[\frac{\partial\tilde{\gamma}}{\partial y}(y(0)) + \frac{\partial\tilde{\theta}}{\partial y}(y(1))\right] + \int_0^1 G^J(\cdot, s)\frac{\partial\tilde{\psi}}{\partial y}(y(s), s)\, ds \Big\| \right\} \leqslant M(r). \tag{2.23}$$

The estimates then become

$$\epsilon\mu(y_0) \leqslant \eta \tag{2.24}$$

$$\epsilon M(r) < 1 \tag{2.25}$$

where

$$\mu(y_0) = \Big\| H^J(\cdot)[-\tilde{\gamma}(y_0(0)) - \tilde{\theta}(y_0(1))] + \int_0^1 G^J(t, s)\,\tilde{\psi}(y_0(s), s)\, ds \Big\|.$$

These estimates are frequently quite useful in particular problems.

We now have as the analog of Theorem 5.13 of Chapter 4, the following.

THEOREM 2.26. Consider the almost linear TPBVP (2.11). Suppose that $J = \{A(t), M, N\}$ is a boundary-compatible set and let $y_0(\cdot)$ be the solution of the linear problem (2.15) corresponding to (2.11). Let $\bar{S} = \bar{S}(y_0, r)$. Suppose further that (i) the functions $G^J(t, s)[f(s) + \psi(\epsilon, y, s)]$ and $G^J(t, s)[(\partial\psi/\partial y)(\epsilon, y, s)]$ satisfy the conditions of Lemma 8.5 of Chapter 3; (ii) $\gamma(\epsilon, y)$ and $\theta(\epsilon, y)$ are twice differentiable with respect to y; and (iii) there are real numbers η, δ, and K with $\eta \geqslant 0$, $0 \leqslant \delta < 1$, and $K \geqslant 0$ such that

$$\| T^J(y_0) - y_0 \| = \Big\| H^J(\cdot)[-\gamma(\epsilon, y_0(0)) - \theta(\epsilon, y_0(1))] + \int_0^1 G^J(t, s)\, \psi(\epsilon, y_0(s), s)\, ds \Big\| \leqslant \eta \tag{2.27}$$

$$\sup_i \sup_t \left\{ \sum_{k=1}^{p} \left[\left| \sum_{j=1}^{p} \left[H^J_{ij}(t) \left\{ \frac{\partial \gamma_j}{\partial y_k}(\epsilon, y_0(0)) + \frac{\partial \theta_j}{\partial y_k}(\epsilon, y_0(1)) \right]\right\}\right|\right]\right\} + \sup_i \sup_t \left\{ \sum_{k=1}^{p} \int_0^1 \left| \sum_{j=1}^{p} G^J_{ij}(t, s) \frac{\partial \psi_j}{\partial y_k}(\epsilon, y_0(s), s) \right| ds \right\} \leqslant \delta \tag{2.28}$$

$$\sup_{y \in \bar{S}} \sup_i \sup_t \left\{ \sum_{k=1}^{p} \sum_{l=1}^{p} \left(\left| \sum_{j=1}^{p} \left\{ H^J_{ij}(t) \times \left[\frac{\partial^2 \gamma_j}{\partial y_k\, \partial y_l}(\epsilon, y(0)) + \frac{\partial^2 \theta_j}{\partial y_k\, \partial y_l}(\epsilon, y(1)) \right]\right\}\right|\right) + \sum_{k=1}^{p} \sum_{l=1}^{p} \int_0^1 \left| \sum_{k=1}^{p} G^J_{ij}(t, s) \frac{\partial^2 \psi_j}{\partial y_k\, \partial y_l}(\epsilon, y(s), s) \right| ds \right\} \leqslant K \tag{2.29}$$

$$\frac{1 - \sqrt{1 - 2h}}{h} \frac{\eta}{1 - \delta} \leqslant r < \frac{1 + \sqrt{1 - 2h}}{h} \frac{\eta}{1 - \delta} \tag{2.30}$$

where $h = K\eta/(1 - \delta)^2 \leqslant \frac{1}{2}$. Then the *CM* sequence $\{y_n(\cdot)\}$ for the TPBVP based on $y_0(\cdot)$ and J converges uniformly to the unique solution $y^*(\cdot)$ of (2.11) in $\bar{S}$ and the rate of convergence is given by

$$\| y^*(\cdot) - y_n(\cdot) \| \leqslant [1 - (1 - \delta)\sqrt{1 - 2h}]^n \left[\frac{1 - \sqrt{1 - 2h}}{h(1 - \delta)} \right] \| y_1(\cdot) - y_0(\cdot) \|. \tag{2.31}$$

We again note that if $\psi(\epsilon, y, s) = \epsilon\tilde{\psi}(y, s)$, $\gamma(\epsilon, y) = \epsilon\tilde{\gamma}(y)$, and $\theta(\epsilon, y) = \epsilon\tilde{\theta}(y)$, then the convergence estimates will essentially depend upon ϵ.

Now let us turn our attention to almost linear problems with "periodic" boundary conditions. In other words, we consider TPBVP's of the form

$$\dot{y} = A(t)y + f(t) + \psi(\epsilon, y, t) \tag{2.32}$$

$$y(0) = y(1). \tag{2.33}$$

We note that (2.33) may be written in the form

$$Iy(0) - Iy(1) = \mathbf{0} \tag{2.34}$$

where I is the identity matrix. Let $J = \{A(t), I, -I\}$. If J is a boundary-compatible set, then it is quite natural to apply the contraction mapping method to the operator T^J given by

$$T^J(y)(t) = \int_0^1 G^J(t, s)\{f(s) + \psi(\epsilon, y(s), s)\}\, ds \tag{2.35}$$

in an effort to solve (2.32), (2.34). If the set $\{A(t), I, -I\}$ is not boundary compatible, then we may replace (2.32) by the equation $\dot{y} = \{A(t) - \epsilon B(t)\}\, y + f(t) + \{\psi(\epsilon, y, t) + \epsilon B(t)\}$ and use the boundary-compatible set $\{A(t) - \epsilon B(t), I, -I\}$. Thus, we shall assume from now on that the set $J = \{A(t), I, -I\}$ is boundary compatible and shall investigate Picard's method for (2.35).

Now natural choices for the initial guess y_0 are the solutions of the linear problems

$$\dot{y} = A(t)y + f(t), \qquad y(0) = y(1) \tag{2.36}$$

or

$$\dot{y} = A(t)y, \qquad y(0) = y(1). \tag{2.37}$$

Note that $y(t) \equiv 0$ is the solution of (2.37) and that use of (2.37) is particularly appropriate when $A(t)$ is constant, i.e., $A(t) \equiv A$. The operator T^J is given by (2.35) and the corresponding algorithm of Picard's method can be written in the form

$$\begin{aligned} \dot{y}_{n+1} - A(t)y_{n+1} &= f(t) + \psi(\epsilon, y_n, t) \\ Iy_{n+1}(0) - Iy_{n+1}(1) &= 0. \end{aligned} \tag{2.38}$$

We observe that all the iterates will be periodic, i.e., will satisfy the boundary conditions. This is, of course, an important aspect of the method. We now have the following.

THEOREM 2.39. Let $y_0(\cdot)$ be the solution of (2.36) and let $\bar{S} = \bar{S}(y_0, r)$. Suppose that (i) the function $G^J(t, s)[f(s) + \psi(\epsilon, y, s)]$ satisfies the conditions of Lemma 8.5, Chapter 3; and (ii) there are real numbers η and α with $\eta \geqslant 0$ and $0 \leqslant \alpha < 1$ such that

$$(2.40) \qquad \| T^J(y_0) - y_0 \| = \left\| \int_0^1 G^J(t, s)\, \psi(\epsilon, y_0(s), s)\, ds \right\| \leqslant \eta$$

$$(2.41) \qquad \sup_{y \in \bar{S}} \sup_i \sup_t \left\{ \sum_{k=1}^{p} \int_0^1 \left| \sum_{j=1}^{p} G^J_{ij}(t, s) \frac{\partial \psi_j}{\partial y_k}(\epsilon, y(s), s) \right| ds \right\} \leqslant \alpha$$

$$(2.42) \qquad \frac{1}{1-\alpha}\,\eta \leqslant r.$$

Then the CM sequence $\{y_n(\cdot)\}$ given by $y_{n+1}(\cdot) = T^J(y_n)(\cdot)$ converges uniformly to the unique solution $y^*(\cdot)$ of (2.32), (2.33), in $\bar{S}$ and the rate of convergence is given by $\| y^*(\cdot) - y_n(\cdot)\| \leqslant \alpha^n \| y_1(\cdot) - y_0(\cdot)\|/(1 - \alpha)$.

THEOREM 2.43. Let $y_0(\cdot)$ be the solution of (2.36) and let $\bar{S} = \bar{S}(y_0, r)$. Suppose that (i) the functions $G^J(t, s)\{f(s) + \psi(\epsilon, y, s)\}$ and $G^J(t, s)\{(\partial\psi/\partial y)(\epsilon, y, s)\}$ satisfy the conditions of Lemma 8.5, Chapter 3; and (ii) there are real numbers η, δ, and K with $\eta \geqslant 0$, $0 \leqslant \delta < 1$, and $K \geqslant 0$ such that

$$(2.44) \qquad \| T^J(y_0) - y_0 \| = \left\| \int_0^1 G^J(t, s)\, \psi(\epsilon, y_0(s), s)\, ds \right\| \leqslant \eta$$

$$(2.45) \qquad \sup_i \sup_t \left\{ \sum_{k=1}^{p} \int_0^1 \left| \sum_{j=1}^{p} G^J_{ij}(t, s) \frac{\partial \psi_j}{\partial y_k}(\epsilon, y_0(s), s) \right| ds \right\} \leqslant \delta$$

$$(2.46) \qquad \sup_{y \in \bar{S}} \sup_{\substack{\|u\| \leqslant 1 \\ \|v\| \leqslant 1}} \sup_i \sup_t \left\{ \left| \sum_{k=1}^{p} \sum_{j=1}^{p} \sum_{l=1}^{p} \int_0^1 G^J_{ij}(t, s) \times \frac{\partial^2 \psi_j}{\partial y_k\, \partial y_l}(\epsilon, y(s), s)\, u_l(s)\, v_k(s)\, ds \right| \right\} \leqslant K$$

and

$$\frac{1 - \sqrt{1 - 2h}}{h} \frac{\eta}{1 - \delta} \leqslant r < \frac{1 + \sqrt{1 - 2h}}{h} \frac{\eta}{1 - \delta} \tag{2.47}$$

where $h = K\eta/(1 - \delta)^2 \leqslant \frac{1}{2}$. Then the CM sequence $\{y_n(\cdot)\}$ given by $y_{n+1}(\cdot) = T^J(y_n)(\cdot)$ converges uniformly to the unique solution $y^*(\cdot)$ of (2.32), (2.33) in $\bar{S}$ and the rate of convergence is given by (2.31).

Now let us use the results of the appendix of Chapter 3 to obtain a convergence theorem in the case where $\psi(\epsilon, y, s)$ is Lipschitz in y. In particular, we have the following.

THEOREM 2.48. Let $y_0(\cdot)$ be the solution of (2.36) and let $\bar{S} = \bar{S}(y_0, r)$. Suppose that (i) $f(s)$ is integrable in s; (ii) $\psi(\epsilon, y, s)$ is measurable in s for each fixed y and continuous in y for each fixed s; (iii) $\| \psi(\epsilon, y_1, s) - \psi(\epsilon, y_2, s)\| \leqslant K(\epsilon, s)\| y_1 - y_2 \|$ for all y_1, y_2 in the range of $\bar{S}$ where $K(\epsilon, s)$ is an integrable function of s; (iv) $\| \psi(\epsilon, y, s)\| \leqslant m_\psi(s)$ where $\int_0^1 m_\psi(s)\, ds < \infty$; and (v) there are real numbers η and α with $\eta \geqslant 0$ and $0 \leqslant \alpha < 1$ such that

$$\| T^J(y_0) - y_0 \| = \left\| \int_0^1 G^J(t, s)\, \psi(\epsilon, y_0(s), s)\, ds \right\| \leqslant \eta \tag{2.49}$$

$$\sup_t \int_0^1 \| G^J(t, s)\|\, K(\epsilon, s)\, ds \leqslant \alpha \tag{2.50}$$

$$\frac{1}{1 - \alpha} \eta \leqslant r. \tag{2.51}$$

Then the CM sequence $\{y_n(\cdot)\}$ given by $y_{n+1}(\cdot) = T^J(y_n)(\cdot)$ converges uniformly to the unique solution $y^*(\cdot)$ of (2.32), (2.33) in $\bar{S}$ and the rate of convergence is given by

$$\| y^* - y_n \| \leqslant \alpha^n \| y_1 - y_n \|/(1 - \alpha).$$

Proof. All that we need show is that $\square\, T^J \,\square_S$ is majorized by the left-hand side of (2.50). Now, if $u(\cdot)$ and $v(\cdot)$ are in $\bar{S}$, then

$$\begin{aligned} \| T^J(u)(t) - T^J(v)(t)\| &\leqslant \int_0^1 \| G^J(t, s)\{\psi(\epsilon, u(s), s) - \psi(\epsilon, v(s), s)\}\| ds \\ &\leqslant \left(\int_0^1 \| G^J(t, s)\|\, K(\epsilon, s)\, ds\right) \| u(\cdot) - v(\cdot)\| \end{aligned}$$

and the result follows.

5.3. Some Second-Order Examples

Here we begin by considering the TPBVP

$$\ddot{x} + \lambda x + \epsilon f(x) = 0 \tag{3.1}$$

$$\begin{aligned} x(0) - x(\pi) &= 0, \\ \dot{x}(0) - \dot{x}(\pi) &= 0 \end{aligned} \tag{3.2}$$

where $\lambda > 0$ and $\epsilon > 0$ are parameters. We note that this is an almost linear type of problem with periodic boundary conditions. We shall use the convergence results of the previous sections to obtain conditions on $f(\cdot)$ which insure the existence of solutions of the TPBVP [i.e., of periodic solutions of (3.1)].

Now, letting

$$x_1 = x \qquad \text{and} \qquad x_2 = \dot{x}_1 = \dot{x},$$

we may write (3.1) and (3.2) in the vector form

$$\begin{bmatrix} \dot{x}_1 \\ \dot{x}_2 \end{bmatrix} = \begin{bmatrix} 0 & 1 \\ -\lambda & 0 \end{bmatrix} \begin{bmatrix} x_1 \\ x_2 \end{bmatrix} + \epsilon \begin{bmatrix} 0 \\ -f(x_1) \end{bmatrix} \tag{3.3}$$

$$\begin{bmatrix} 1 & 0 \\ 0 & 1 \end{bmatrix} \begin{bmatrix} x_1(0) \\ x_2(0) \end{bmatrix} + \begin{bmatrix} -1 & 0 \\ 0 & -1 \end{bmatrix} \begin{bmatrix} x_1(\pi) \\ x_2(\pi) \end{bmatrix} = \begin{bmatrix} 0 \\ 0 \end{bmatrix} \tag{3.4}$$

or, in the form

$$\dot{\mathbf{x}} = \mathbf{A}\mathbf{x} + \epsilon \mathbf{f}(\mathbf{x}),$$

$$\mathbf{I}\mathbf{x}(0) - \mathbf{I}\mathbf{x}(\pi) = \mathbf{0}$$

where

$$\mathbf{A} = \begin{bmatrix} 0 & 1 \\ -\lambda & 0 \end{bmatrix}, \qquad \mathbf{f}(\mathbf{x}) = \begin{bmatrix} 0 \\ -f(x_1) \end{bmatrix} \tag{3.5}$$

and $\mathbf{I}$ is the identity matrix. We let

$$J = \{\mathbf{A}, \mathbf{I}, -\mathbf{I}\} \qquad \text{and} \qquad \Phi^J(t, s) = e^{\mathbf{A}(t-s)}$$

be the fundamental matrix of the linear system $\dot{\mathbf{x}} = \mathbf{A}\mathbf{x}$. Then

$$(3.6)\qquad \Phi^J(t, s) = \begin{bmatrix} \cos \sqrt{\lambda}(t-s) & \dfrac{1}{\sqrt{\lambda}} \sin \sqrt{\lambda}(t-s) \\ -\sqrt{\lambda} \sin \sqrt{\lambda}(t-s) & \cos \sqrt{\lambda}(t-s) \end{bmatrix}.$$

For convenience, we let $\lambda = \nu^2$ with $\nu > 0$ so that $\Phi^J(t, s)$ can also be written as

$$(3.7)\qquad \Phi^J(t, s) = \begin{bmatrix} \cos \nu(t-s) & \nu^{-1} \sin \nu(t-s) \\ -\nu \sin \nu(t-s) & \cos \nu(t-s) \end{bmatrix}.$$

The set J will be a boundary–compatible set if and only if

$$\det(\mathbf{I} - \Phi^J(\pi, 0)) \neq 0,$$

i.e., if and only if

$$(3.8)\qquad \det\left(\begin{bmatrix} 1 - \cos \nu\pi & -\nu^{-1} \sin \nu\pi \\ \nu \sin \nu\pi & 1 - \cos \nu\pi \end{bmatrix}\right) = 2(1 - \cos \nu\pi) \neq 0$$

or, equivalently, if and only if $\nu \neq 2k$ or

$$(3.9)\qquad \lambda \neq 4k^2$$

for $k = 0, 1, \ldots$. If $\lambda = 4k^2$, then λ is an eigenvalue of the linear problem

$$\ddot{x} + \lambda x = 0, \qquad x(0) - x(\pi) = 0,$$
$$\dot{x}(0) - \dot{x}(\pi) = 0$$

which has the family of solutions $a \cos 2kt + b \sin 2kt$. If λ is an eigenvalue, then we can rewrite (3.1) in the form

$$\ddot{x} + (\lambda - \epsilon)x + \epsilon\{f(x) + x\} = 0$$

and apply the results which we shall soon derive for the case where λ is not an eigenvalue. We leave this to the reader and so, shall assume from now on that $\lambda(\neq 4k^2)$ is not an eigenvalue of the linear problem. In other words, J is a boundary-compatible set.

Assuming that $f(\cdot)$ is continuous, we deduce from Theorem 4.1 of Chapter 3 that the TPBVP (3.3), (3.4) has the equivalent integral representation

$$\mathbf{x}(t) = \int_0^\pi G^J(t, s)\{\epsilon\mathbf{f}(\mathbf{x}(s))\}\, ds \tag{3.10}$$

where $G^J(t, s)$ is the Green's matrix corresponding to the boundary-compatible set J. Writing (3.10) in component form, we have

$$\begin{aligned} x_1(t) &= \int_0^\pi G_{12}^J(t, s)\{-\epsilon f(x_1(s))\}\, ds \\ x_2(t) &= \int_0^\pi G_{22}^J(t, s)\{-\epsilon f(x_1(s))\}\, ds \end{aligned} \tag{3.11}$$

for t in $[0, \pi]$. Thus, we need only calculate $G_{12}^J(t, s)$ and $G_{22}^J(t, s)$ to obtain the estimates required by the convergence theorems.

We first note that $[\mathbf{I} - \Phi^J(\pi, 0)]^{-1}$ is given by

$$[\mathbf{I} - \Phi^J(\pi, 0)]^{-1} = \frac{1}{2}\begin{bmatrix} 1 & \dfrac{\nu^{-1}\sin\nu\pi}{1 - \cos\nu\pi} \\ -\dfrac{\nu\sin\nu\pi}{1-\cos\nu\pi} & 1 \end{bmatrix}. \tag{3.12}$$

It follows that $\Phi^J(t, 0)[\mathbf{I} - \Phi^J(\pi, 0)]^{-1}$ is given by

$$\frac{1}{2(1-\cos\nu\pi)}\begin{bmatrix} -2\sin\nu\left(t - \dfrac{\pi}{2}\right)\sin\dfrac{\nu\pi}{2} & 2\nu^{-1}\sin\nu\left(t-\dfrac{\pi}{2}\right)\cos\dfrac{\nu\pi}{2} \\ -2\nu\sin\nu\left(t-\dfrac{\pi}{2}\right)\cos\dfrac{\nu\pi}{2} & -2\sin\nu\left(t-\dfrac{\pi}{2}\right)\sin\dfrac{\nu\pi}{2} \end{bmatrix}. \tag{3.13}$$

Thus, in order to compute $G_{12}^J(t, s)$ and $G_{22}^J(t, s)$, we need only multiply the second columns of the matrices $\Phi^J(0, s)$ and $\Phi^J(\pi, s)$ by the matrix (3.13). We find that

$$\begin{aligned} G_{12}^J(t, s) &= \frac{\sin\nu(t - \pi/2)\cos\nu(s - \pi/2)}{\nu(1 - \cos\nu\pi)}, \qquad 0 \leqslant s < t \\ &= \frac{\sin\nu(t-\pi/2)\cos\nu(s - 3\pi/2)}{(1-\cos\nu\pi)}, \qquad t < s \leqslant \pi \end{aligned} \tag{3.14}$$

$$\text{(3.15)} \quad G_{22}^J(t, s) = -\frac{\sin \nu(t - \pi/2) \sin \nu(s - \pi/2)}{(1 - \cos \nu\pi)}, \qquad 0 \leqslant s < t$$

$$= -\frac{\sin \nu(t - \pi/2) \sin \nu(s - 3\pi/2)}{(1 - \cos \nu\pi)}, \qquad t < s \leqslant \pi$$

or equivalently that

$$\text{(3.16)} \quad G_{12}^J(t, s) = \frac{\sin \nu(t + s - \pi) + \sin \nu(t - s)}{2\nu(1 - \cos \nu\pi)}, \qquad 0 \leqslant s < t$$

$$= \frac{\sin \nu(t + s - 2\pi) + \sin \nu(t - s - \pi)}{2\nu(1 - \cos \nu\pi)}, \qquad t < s \leqslant \pi$$

$$\text{(3.17)} \quad G_{22}^J(t, s) = \frac{\cos \nu(t + s - \pi) - \cos \nu(t - s)}{2(1 - \cos \nu\pi)}, \qquad 0 \leqslant s < t$$

$$= \frac{\cos \nu(t + s - 2\pi) - \cos \nu(t - s - \pi)}{2(1 - \cos \nu\pi)}, \qquad t < s \leqslant \pi$$

where $\nu = \sqrt{\lambda}$. We are now ready to apply the convergence theorems.

To illustrate what is involved, let us first suppose that $0 < \lambda \leqslant 2$ and that we wish to apply the method of contraction mappings. The operator T^J is given by

$$\text{(3.18)} \qquad T^J(\mathbf{y})(t) = \begin{bmatrix} -\epsilon \int_0^\pi G_{12}^J(t, s) f(y_1(s))\, ds \\ \\ -\epsilon \int_0^\pi G_{22}^J(t, s) f(y_1(s))\, ds \end{bmatrix}$$

and its derivative is given by

$$\text{(3.19)} \qquad (T_y{}^J)'\, v(t) = \begin{bmatrix} -\epsilon \int_0^\pi G_{12}^J(t, s) \dfrac{\partial f}{\partial x}(y_1(s))\, v_1(s)\, ds \\ \\ -\epsilon \int_0^\pi G_{22}^J(t, s) \dfrac{\partial f}{\partial x}(y_1(s))\, v_1(s)\, ds \end{bmatrix}$$

if $\partial f/\partial x$ is defined and satisfies the conditions of Section 8 of Chapter 3. As our initial guess, we take $\mathbf{y}(t) \equiv \mathbf{0}$ and so the estimate for η becomes

$$\eta \geqslant \sup_i \| T^J(\mathbf{0})_i(t) \|. \tag{3.20}$$

But

$$T^J(0)_i(t) = -\epsilon \int_0^\pi G_{i2}^J(t, s)\, f(0)\, ds$$

and so, we may take

$$\eta = \epsilon\, |f(0)| \max\{|\, 1/\nu(1 - \cos \nu\pi)|, |\, 1/(1 - \cos \nu\pi)|\} \tag{3.21}$$

where $\nu = \sqrt{\lambda}$. Now, as a (somewhat coarse) estimate for α, we have

$$\epsilon m(\nu) \sup_{y_1(s)} \left\| \frac{\partial f}{\partial x}(y_1(s)) \right\| \leqslant \alpha \tag{3.22}$$

where

$$m(\nu) = \max\{|\, 1/\nu(1 - \cos \nu\pi)|, |\, 1/(1 - \cos \nu\pi)|\} \tag{3.23}$$

and $\mathbf{y}(\cdot)$ is an element of the sphere $\bar{S} = \bar{S}(\mathbf{0}, r)$. If $\partial f/\partial x$ is continuous, then, since the values $\mathbf{y}(t)$ of the elements $\mathbf{y}(\cdot)$ of $\bar{S}(\mathbf{0}, r)$ lie in a compact set, there is an $M(r)$ such that

$$\sup_{\mathbf{y} \in \bar{S}} \left\| \frac{\partial f}{\partial x}(y_1(s)) \right\| \leqslant M(r) \tag{3.24}$$

For example, if $f(x) = x^2/2$, then we may take $M(r) = r$. It follows that an estimate for α is given by

$$\alpha = \epsilon m(\nu)\, M(r) \tag{3.25}$$

and so, we have the following.

THEOREM 3.26. Suppose that $f(\cdot)$ is continuously differentiable and that

$$\epsilon m(\nu)\, M(r) < 1 \tag{3.27}$$

$$\epsilon\, |f(0)|\, m(\nu) \leqslant r(1 - \epsilon m(\nu)\, M(r)) \tag{3.28}$$

Then (3.1) has a unique periodic solution in $\bar{S} = \bar{S}(\mathbf{0}, r)$.

For example, if $\lambda = 1$ and $f(x) = x^2/2 + 1$, then we deduce that $\ddot{x} + x + \epsilon(x^2/2 + 1) = 0$ has a unique periodic solution in $\bar{S}(\mathbf{0}, r)$ if

$$\epsilon r < 2 \qquad \text{and} \qquad \epsilon \leqslant 2r[(1 - \epsilon r)/2]$$

or, equivalently, if

$$\epsilon \leqslant \epsilon_r = 2r/(1 + r^2).$$

Similarly, if $\lambda = 1$ and $f(x) = \cos x$, then $\ddot{x} + x + \epsilon \cos x = 0$ has a unique periodic solution in $\bar{S}(\mathbf{0}, r)$ if

$$\epsilon < 2 \qquad \text{and} \qquad r \geqslant \epsilon/(2 - \epsilon).$$

The main point here is not the explicit calculations or estimates but rather the use of the convergence theorems to obtain proofs of the existence of periodic solutions. A similar technique can be applied to obtain periodic solutions "near" any of the "eigensolutions" $a_k \cos 2kt + b_k \sin 2kt$. The various other convergence theorems (e.g., on Newton's method) can also be applied to obtain periodic solutions. These applications are left to the reader.

A general theorem analogous to Theorem 3.26 is the following.

THEOREM 3.29. Let $\mathbf{y}_0(\cdot)$ be an element of $\mathscr{C}([0, \pi], R_2)$ and let $\bar{S} = \bar{S}(\mathbf{y}_0, r)$. Suppose that $f(\cdot)$ is continuously differentiable so that $\sup_{\mathbf{y}\in\bar{S}} \|(\partial f/\partial x)(\mathbf{y}_1(s))\| \leqslant M$ for some $M > 0$. Let

$$\eta = \| \mathbf{y}_0(\cdot)\| + \epsilon m(\nu) \| f(\mathbf{y}_{0,1}(\cdot))\| \tag{3.30}$$

where $m(\nu)$ is given by (3.23). If

$$\epsilon m(\nu) M < 1 \tag{3.31}$$

and

$$\frac{\| \mathbf{y}_0(\cdot)\| + \epsilon m(\nu) \| f(\mathbf{y}_{0,1}(\cdot))\|}{1 - \epsilon m(\nu) M} \leqslant r \tag{3.32}$$

then (3.1), (3.2) has a unique solution $\mathbf{y}^*(\cdot)$ in $\bar{S}$ and the sequence $\mathbf{y}_n(\cdot) = T^J(\mathbf{y}_{n-1})(\cdot)$ converges uniformly to $\mathbf{y}^*(\cdot)$ (see Theorem 5.8 of Chapter 3).

We now turn our attention to the forced version of (3.1), (3.2), i.e., to the TPBVP

$$\ddot{x} + \lambda x + \epsilon f(x) = g(t) \tag{3.33}$$

$$x(0) - x(\pi) = 0, \qquad \dot{x}(0) - \dot{x}(\pi) = 0 \tag{3.34}$$

where $\lambda > 0$ and $\epsilon > 0$ are parameters. We have the following.

THEOREM 3.35. Let $\mathbf{y}_0(\cdot)$ be an element of $\mathscr{C}([0, \pi], R_2)$ and let $\bar{S} = \bar{S}(\mathbf{y}_0, r)$. Suppose that $g(\cdot)$ is continuous and that $f(\cdot)$ is continuously differentiable so that $\sup_{\mathbf{y}\in\bar{S}} \|(\partial f/\partial x)(\mathbf{y}_1(s))\| \leqslant M$ for some $M > 0$. If

$$\epsilon m(\nu) M < 1 \tag{3.36}$$

and

$$\frac{\| \mathbf{y}_0(\cdot)\| + m(\nu)\{\epsilon \,| f(\mathbf{y}_{0,1}(\cdot))\| + \| g(\cdot)\|\}}{1 - \epsilon m(\nu) M} \leqslant r \tag{3.37}$$

where $m(\nu)$ is given by (3.23), then (3.33), (3.34) has a unique solution $\mathbf{y}^*(\cdot)$ in $\bar{S}$.

Proof. This is simply a rephrasing of Theorem 5.8 of Chapter 4 with $\alpha = \epsilon m(\nu) M$ and $\eta = \| \mathbf{y}_0(\cdot)\| + m(\nu)\{\epsilon \,\| f(\mathbf{y}_{0,1}(\cdot))\| + \| g(\cdot)\|\}$. Note that $(T_y{}^J)'$ is still given by (3.19) but that T^J is given by

$$T^J(\mathbf{y})(t) = \begin{bmatrix} -\epsilon \int_0^\pi G_{12}^J(t, s) f(y_1(s))\, ds + \int_0^\pi G_{12}^J(t, s)\, g(s)\, ds \\ \\ -\epsilon \int_0^\pi G_{22}^J(t, s) f(y_1(s))\, ds + \int_0^\pi G_{22}^J(t, s)\, g(s)\, ds \end{bmatrix} \tag{3.38}$$

rather than by (3.18).

As an illustration of the theorem, we let $f(x) = x^3/x$ and $f(t) = \cos 2t$. Then $\partial f/\partial x = x^2$ and $M = M(r) = r^2$ for $\mathbf{y}_0 \equiv \mathbf{0}$. We deduce that if $\epsilon m(\nu) r^2 < 1$ and $m(\nu) \leqslant r(1 - \epsilon m(\nu) r^2)$, then (3.33) has a unique periodic solution in $\bar{S} = \bar{S}(\mathbf{0}, r)$. For example, if $\lambda = 9$ and $r = 1$, then $\ddot{x} + 9x + \epsilon x^3/3 = \cos 2t$ will have a unique periodic solution $x_\epsilon{}^*(t)$ with $| x_\epsilon{}^*(t)| \leqslant 1$ if $\epsilon \leqslant 1$. Moreover, $\lim_{\epsilon\to 0} x_\epsilon{}^*(t) = (\cos 2t)/5$ is the periodic solution of $\ddot{x} + 9x = \cos 2t$.

We again leave the task of interpreting the various other convergence theorems to the reader. Let us now turn our attention to problems of the form

$$\ddot{x} + \lambda x + \epsilon f(x, t) = g(t) \tag{3.39}$$

$$x(0) - x(\pi) = 0, \qquad \dot{x}(0) - \dot{x}(\pi) = 0 \tag{3.40}$$

where $\lambda > 0$ and ϵ are parameters. The basic convergence theorem becomes the following.

THEOREM 3.41. Let $\mathbf{y}_0(\cdot)$ be an element of $\mathscr{C}([0, \pi], R_2)$ and let $\bar{S} = \bar{S}(\mathbf{y}_0, r)$. Suppose that $g(\cdot)$ is continuous and that $\| f(x, s)\| \leqslant \mu_1(s)$, $\|(\partial f/\partial x)(x, s)\| \leqslant \mu(s)$ on the range of $\bar{S}$ where $\int_0^\pi \mu(s)\, ds = M < \infty$. If

$$\epsilon m(\nu) M < 1 \tag{3.42}$$

and

$$\| \mathbf{y}_0(\cdot)\| + M(\nu)\{\epsilon \| f(\mathbf{y}_{0,1}(\cdot), \cdot)\| + \| g(\cdot)\|\} \leqslant (1 - \epsilon m(\nu) M) r \tag{3.43}$$

where $m(\nu)$ is given by (3.23), then (3.39), (3.40) has a unique solution $\mathbf{y}^*(\cdot)$ in $\bar{S}$.

Proof. This is essentially a rephrasing of the standard result with $\alpha = \epsilon m(\nu) M$ and $\eta = \| \mathbf{y}_0(\cdot)\| + m(\nu)\{\epsilon \| f(\mathbf{y}_{0,1}(\cdot), \cdot)\| + \| g(\cdot)\|\}$. We note that T^J is given by

$$T^J(\mathbf{y})(t) = \begin{bmatrix} -\epsilon \int_0^\pi G_{12}^J(t, s)\{f(y_1(s), s) - g(s)\}\, ds \\ \\ -\epsilon \int_0^\pi G_{22}^J(t, s)\{f(y_1(s), s) - g(s)\}\, ds \end{bmatrix} \tag{3.44}$$

and that $(T^J)'$ is given by

$$(T_{\mathbf{y}}^J)'\, v(t) = \begin{bmatrix} -\epsilon \int_0^\pi G_{12}^J(t, s) \dfrac{\partial f}{\partial x}(y_1(s), s)\, v_1(s)\, ds \\ \\ -\epsilon \int_0^\pi G_{22}^J(t, s) \dfrac{\partial f}{\partial x}(y_1(s), s)\, v_1(s)\, ds \end{bmatrix} \tag{3.45}$$

for $v(\cdot)$ in $\mathscr{C}([0, \pi], R_2)$.

An analogous result can be obtained when $f(x, s)$ is Lipschitz in x by using the results of the appendix to Chapter 3. We leave this to the reader. We note also that if $\mathbf{y}_0(\cdot)$ is a solution of the linear problem $\ddot{x} + \lambda x = g(t)$, $x(0) - x(\pi) = 0$, $\dot{x}(0) - \dot{x}(\pi) = 0$, then the estimate (3.43) will take the form

$$\epsilon m(\nu) \| f(\mathbf{y}_{0,1}(\cdot), \cdot)\| \leqslant (1 - \epsilon m(\nu) M) r. \tag{3.46}$$

Now let us examine an explicit example. Consider the TPBVP

$$\begin{gathered} \ddot{x} + \omega^2 x + \epsilon \left(\sum_{j=1}^{p} a_j(t) x^j \right) = a \cos 2t \\ x(0) - x(\pi) = 0, \qquad \dot{x}(0) - \dot{x}(\pi) = 0 \end{gathered} \tag{3.47}$$

with $\omega \neq 2k$. We observe that $x(t) \equiv 0$ is a solution of the linear problem associated with (3.47) [i.e., of $\ddot{x} + \omega^2 x = 0$, $x(0) = x(\pi)$, $\dot{x}(0) = \dot{x}(\pi)$]. So we let $\mathbf{y}_0(\cdot) = \mathbf{0}(\cdot)$. Then $\| \mathbf{y}_0(\cdot)\| = 0$ and $\| f(\mathbf{y}_{0,1}(\cdot), \cdot)\| = \| a_0(\cdot)\|$. Since $(\partial f/\partial x)(x, t) = \sum_{j=1}^{p} a_j(t) j x^{j-1}$, we have

$$\left\| \frac{\partial f}{\partial x}(x, t) \right\| \leqslant \sum_{j=1}^{p} | a_j(t)| j r^{j-1}. \tag{3.48}$$

If $r < 1$, then we may take

$$M = \sum_{j=1}^{p} j \int_0^{\pi} | a_j(s)| \, ds \tag{3.49}$$

if the $a_j(\cdot)$ are integrable. Thus, the estimate (3.42) will be satisfied if

$$\epsilon m(\omega) \left[\sum_{j=1}^{p} j \int_0^{\pi} | a_j(s)| \, ds \right] < 1 \tag{3.50}$$

and the estimate (3.43) will hold if

$$\frac{\epsilon m(\omega) \| a_0(\cdot)\| + m(\omega) a}{1 - \epsilon m(\omega) [\sum_{j=1}^{p} j \int_0^{\pi} | a_j(s)| \, ds]} \leqslant r < 1. \tag{3.51}$$

If (3.50) and (3.51) are satisfied, then (3.47) will have a unique solution in the sphere $\bar{S}(\mathbf{0}, r)$. In particular, if $a \geqslant 0$, then we will have a periodic solution if

$$m(\omega)\left\{\epsilon \| a_0(\cdot)\| + a + \epsilon\left(\sum_{j=1}^{p} j \int_0^{\pi} | a_j(s)| \, ds\right)\right\} < 1. \tag{3.52}$$

If $\omega \geqslant 1$, then $m(\omega) = 1/(1 - \cos \omega\pi)$ and (3.51) becomes

$$\epsilon\left\{\| a_0(\cdot)\| + \sum_{j=1}^{p} j \int_0^{\pi} | a_j(s)| \, ds\right\} < 1 - \cos \omega\pi - a \tag{3.53}$$

and so we will have a periodic solution if $1 - \cos \omega\pi - a > 0$ and ϵ is sufficiently small. Suppose now that instead of taking $\mathbf{y}_0(\cdot) = \mathbf{0}(\cdot)$ we take $\mathbf{y}_{0,1}(\cdot) = [a/(\omega^2 - 4)] \cos 2t$ and $\mathbf{y}_{0,2}(\cdot) = -[2a/(\omega^2 - 4)] \sin 2t$ so that $\mathbf{y}_0(\cdot)$ is the solution of the linear problem associated with (3.47). Then

$$\left\| \frac{\partial f}{\partial x}(t, x) \right\| \leqslant \sum_{j=1}^{p} j \,| a_j(t)| \left(\frac{2a}{\omega^2 - 4} + r\right)^{j-1} \tag{3.54}$$

and we have

$$M = M(r) = \sum_{j=1}^{p} j \left(\frac{2a}{\omega^2 - 4} + r\right)^{j-1} \int_0^{\pi} | a_j(s)| \, ds \tag{3.55}$$

if the $a_j(\cdot)$ are integrable. Thus, the estimate (3.42) will be satisfied if

$$\epsilon m(\omega)\left\{\sum_{j=1}^{p} j \left(\frac{2a}{w^2 - 4} + r\right)^{j-1} \int_0^{\pi} | a_j(s)| \, ds\right\} < 1 \tag{3.56}$$

and the estimate (3.46) will be satisfied if

$$\epsilon m(\omega)\left\{\sum_{j=1}^{p} \| a_j(\cdot)\| \left(\frac{a}{\omega^2 - 4}\right)^{j}\right\} \leqslant (1 - \epsilon m(\omega)\, M(r))r \tag{3.57}$$

with $M(r)$ given by (3.55). For suitable choices of ϵ and r, we can see that the periodic solution obtained will differ from that obtained for the initial guess $\mathbf{0}(\cdot)$.

We conclude with a consideration of problems of the form

$$\ddot{x} + \lambda x + \epsilon f(x, \dot{x}, t) = g(t) \tag{3.58}$$

$$x(0) - x(\pi) = 0, \qquad \dot{x}(0) - \dot{x}(\pi) = 0 \tag{3.59}$$

where $\lambda > 0$ and ϵ are parameters. The basic convergence theorem becomes the following.

THEOREM 3.60. Let $\mathbf{y}_0(\cdot)$ be an element of $\mathscr{C}([0, \pi], R_2)$ and let $\bar{S} = \bar{S}(\mathbf{y}_0, r)$. Suppose that $g(\cdot)$ is continuous and that $\|f(y_1, y_2, s)\| \leqslant \mu_1(s)$, $\|(\partial f/\partial \mathbf{y})(y_1, y_2, s)\| \leqslant (\mu/2)(s)$ on the range of $\bar{S}$ where $\int_0^\pi \mu(s)\,ds = M < \infty$. If

$$\epsilon m(\nu) M < 1 \tag{3.61}$$

and

$$\|\mathbf{y}_0(\cdot)\| + m(\nu)\{\epsilon \|f(\mathbf{y}_{0,1}(\cdot), \mathbf{y}_{0,2}(\cdot), \cdot)\| + \|g(\cdot)\|\} \leqslant (1 - \epsilon m(\nu) M) r \tag{3.62}$$

where $m(\nu)$ is given by (3.23), then (3.58), (3.59) has a unique solution $\mathbf{y}^*(\cdot)$ in $\bar{S}$.

An analogous result can be obtained when $f(y_1, y_2, s)$ is Lipschitz in y_1, y_2 using the results of the appendix to Chapter 3. We also note that if $\mathbf{y}_0(\cdot)$ is a solution of the linear problem $\ddot{x} + \lambda x = g(t)$, $x(0) - x(\pi) = 0$, $\dot{x}(0) - \dot{x}(\pi) = 0$, then the estimate (3.62) takes the form

$$\epsilon m(\omega) \|f(\mathbf{y}_{0,1}(\cdot), \mathbf{y}_{0,2}(\cdot), \cdot)\| \leqslant (1 - \epsilon m(\nu) M) r. \tag{3.63}$$

Consider the TPBVP [H1]

$$\begin{aligned} &\ddot{x} + \omega^2 x = B \cos 2t + \epsilon \left(\sum_{j=0}^{p} b_j x^{2j+1} - \epsilon^s c \dot{x} \right) \\ &x(0) - x(\pi) = 0, \qquad \dot{x}(0) - \dot{x}(\pi) = 0 \end{aligned} \tag{3.64}$$

with $\omega = (2n+1)^{-1}$, $n \geqslant 1$. We let $\mathbf{y}_0(\cdot)$ be the solution of the forced linear problem associated with (3.64) so that $\mathbf{y}_{0,1}(t) = A \cos 2t$ and $\mathbf{y}_{0,2}(t) = -2A \sin 2t$ with $A = B/[1/(2n+1)^2 - 4]$. Now

$$\frac{\partial f}{\partial y_1}(y_1, y_2, s) = \sum_{j=0}^{p} b_j (2j) y_1^{2j} \qquad \text{and} \qquad \frac{\partial f}{\partial y_2}(y_1, y_2, s) = -\epsilon^s c$$

and so we may take as an estimate (somewhat crude)

$$M = M(r) = \left(\sum_{j=0}^{p} b_j(2_j)(2A + r)^{2j}\pi \right) + \epsilon^s c. \tag{3.65}$$

The estimate (3.61) will then be satisfied if

$$\frac{\epsilon(2n+1)}{1 - \cos[\pi/(2n+1)]} \left\{ \left[\sum_{j=0}^{p} b_j(2_j)(2A + r)^{2j}\pi \right] + \epsilon^s c \right\} < 1 \tag{3.66}$$

and the estimate (3.63) will be satisfied if

$$\frac{\epsilon(2n+1)}{1 - \cos[\pi/(2n+1)]} \left\{ \left[\sum_{j=0}^{p} b_j A^{2j+1} \right] + \epsilon^s c 2A \right\} \leqslant \left(1 - \frac{\epsilon(2n+1)\, M(r)}{1 - \cos[\pi/(2n+1)]} \right) r. \tag{3.67}$$

Thus, if both (3.66) and (3.67) hold, then (3.64) will have a periodic solution in $\bar{S}$.

CHAPTER 6

SOME NUMERICAL EXAMPLES

6.1. Introduction

We examine the numerical solution of some simple problems in order to obtain a better appreciation for the practical aspects of the iterative methods discussed in Chapters 4 and 5. We consider two "standard" trajectory optimization problems and a simple oscillation problem. Both trajectory problems are concerned with a low-thrust orbital transfer from an Earth to a Mars orbit. The oscillation problem is concerned with a simple spring having a nonlinear restoring force.

The first trajectory problem is solved by Newton's method using three different procedures for converting the variable-interval TPBVP into a fixed-interval TPBVP. We compare these procedures and also discuss the effect of different initial guesses and of different grid sizes for the numerical integration routine on the "convergence" of the method. In addition, we consider the modified Newton method and evaluate the convergence factor K of Kantorovich's theorem.

The second trajectory problem is solved by Picard's method. We examine a procedure for converting this orbital transfer problem into an almost linear rendezvous problem and then apply Picard's method.

The oscillation problem is solved by the third-order multipoint method. We discuss the applicability of the main convergence theorem on multipoint methods in the light of this problem. A particular version of the convergence theorem is also given.

A final remark concerning the computer programs is in order. The programs were designed primarily for illustrative purposes and not necessarily for maximum accuracy and efficiency. Thus, the actual numerical results are not optimally precise but rather are indicative.

6.2. Constant Low-Thrust Earth-to-Mars Orbital Transfer

The problem considered in this section is probably one of the best known trajectory optimization examples in the literature. It has been treated by various authors using a variety of methods (e.g., Lindorfer and Moyer [L1], Kelley *et al.* [K6], McGill and Kenneth [M3], Kopp *et al.* [K10], and Handelsman [H5]). The problem involves the determination of the thrust angle history for the minimum time transfer from an Earth orbit to a Mars orbit of a low-thrust space vehicle. The problem is simplified in that the orbits of both Earth and Mars are assumed to be circular and coplanar. In addition, the gravitational attractions of the two planets on the space vehicle are neglected. The following equations are assumed to govern the transfer [M3]

$$\dot{r} = u$$

(2.1)
$$\dot{u} = \frac{v^2}{r} - \frac{\mu}{r^2} + \frac{T \sin \theta}{m_0 + \dot{m}t}$$

$$\dot{v} = -\frac{uv}{r} + \frac{T \cos \theta}{m_0 + \dot{m}t}.$$

Here r is the distance from the sun, u is the radial velocity, v is the tangential velocity, μ is the gravitational constant, T is the thrust, θ is the control angle (measured relative to the tangent of the local circular orbit), m_0 is the initial mass, and $\dot{m}$ is the propellant consumption rate. (Numerical values for T, m_0, and $\dot{m}$ are given by McGill and Kenneth [M3, p. 1764].) At the beginning of the maneuver the space vehicle is assumed to have a velocity and radial position corresponding to the orbit of the Earth, while at the end, its velocity and radial position correspond to the orbit of Mars. This leads to the boundary conditions (see McGill and Kenneth [M3, p. 1765])

(2.2)
$$\begin{aligned} r(t_0) &= 1.000, & r(t_f) &= 1.525 \\ u(t_0) &= 0.000, & u(t_f) &= 0.000 \\ v(t_0) &= 1.000, & v(t_f) &= (1.525)^{-1/2} \end{aligned}$$

in dimensionless variables. A gravitational constant $\mu = 1.0$ and a time unit equal to the time it takes the Earth to cover one radian (58.18 days) are used.

Application of the Pontryagin principle to this minimum-time problem leads to a TPBVP defined on an interval with a free end point. In order to apply any of the iterative methods discussed, it is necessary to convert the TPBVP into a problem defined on a fixed time interval. Several procedures can be used for this conversion. First, there is the procedure followed by McGill and Kenneth [M3], who replace the minimum time problem by a sequence of radius maximization problems and iteratively adjust the final time so that the maximum radius coincides with the required value of the radius at the end of the maneuver. Another procedure is to treat the problem as a regular minimum-time problem and to standardize the resulting TPBVP using Long's method [L2]. For that purpose, the time variable t is replaced by the product of a variable scale factor "a" and a new independent variable s which varies between 0 and 1, i.e.,

$$t = as. \tag{2.3}$$

(In the case at hand, we can conveniently set $t_0 = 0$.) The first effect of this change of variable is that all right-hand sides of the differential equations are multiplied by a since $dy/ds = a(dy/dt)$. A second and more important effect of this change of variable is that the scale factor "a" can be considered a new state variable defined by the trivial differential equation $da/ds = 0$. As pointed out by Long [L2], this leads to a more unified application of the iterative methods than the "mixed" procedure of McGill and Kenneth. A third procedure which differs only slightly from the second consists of the introduction of the change of the time variable before, instead of after, the application of the Pontryagin principle. The scale factor a is then treated as an ordinary state variable and the optimization problem consists of the minimization of this new state variable. This leads to still another TPBVP. We discuss the computational aspects of each of these three procedures, which we call, respectively, Procedures A, B, and C, in the sequel.

In their procedure for the solution of the problem, McGill and Kenneth start with a guess $t_{f,0}$ for the total flight time and determine (with the aid of the Pontryagin principle and Newton's method) the maximum radius $r_{f,0}$ that can be reached in that time. If this radius does not correspond to the radius of the orbit of Mars, then a new guess for the final time is determined from the general algorithm

$$t_{f,k+1} = t_{f,k} + \frac{t_{f,k} - t_{f,k-1}}{r_{f,k} - r_{f,k-1}} (r_{\text{Mars}} - r_{f,k}), \qquad k = 0, 1, 2, \ldots \tag{2.4}$$

where $t_{f,-1} = 0$ and $r_{f,-1} = 1$. The actual optimization problem which is (repeatedly) solved in this procedure is thus a maximum radius problem rather than a minimum time problem. Application of the Pontryagin principle to this maximum radius problem proceeds as follows: the Hamiltonian function for the problem is given by

$$H = \lambda_r u + \lambda_u \frac{v^2}{r} - \lambda_u \frac{\mu}{r^2} + \lambda_u \frac{T \sin \theta}{m_0 + \dot{m}t} - \lambda_v \frac{uv}{r} + \lambda_v \frac{T \cos \theta}{m_0 + \dot{m}t} \tag{2.5}$$

From

$$\frac{\partial H}{\partial \theta} = 0 = \lambda_u \frac{T \cos \theta}{m_0 + \dot{m}t} - \lambda_v \frac{T \sin \theta}{m_0 + \dot{m}t}$$

and

$$\frac{\partial^2 H}{\partial \theta^2} = -\lambda_u \frac{T \sin \theta}{m_0 + \dot{m}t} - \lambda_v \frac{T \cos \theta}{m_0 + \dot{m}t}$$

it follows that the Hamiltonian has a maximum for

$$\theta = \arctan \frac{\lambda_u}{\lambda_v} \tag{2.6}$$

or equivalently, for

$$\sin \theta = \frac{\lambda_u}{\sqrt{\lambda_u^2 + \lambda_v^2}}, \qquad \cos \theta = \frac{\lambda_v}{\sqrt{\lambda_u^2 + \lambda_v^2}}. \tag{2.7}$$

Substituting this value for θ back into the equations of motion (2.1), adding the equations for the adjoint variables and employing the change of variables (2.3), where "a" is now a known scale factor ($a = t_f$), we obtain the TPBVP*

$$\begin{aligned}
r' &= a[u] \\
u' &= a\left[\frac{v^2}{r} - \frac{\mu}{r^2} + \frac{T}{m_0 + \dot{m}t}\frac{\lambda_u}{(\lambda_u^2 + \lambda_v^2)^{1/2}}\right] \\
v' &= a\left[-\frac{uv}{r} + \frac{T}{m_0 + \dot{m}t}\frac{\lambda_u}{(\lambda_u^2 + \lambda_v^2)^{1/2}}\right] \\
\lambda_r' &= a\left[-\lambda_u\left(-\frac{v^2}{r^2} + 2\frac{\mu}{r^3}\right) - \lambda_v\left(+\frac{uv}{r^2}\right)\right] \\
\lambda_u' &= a\left[-\lambda_r + \lambda_v \frac{v}{r}\right] \\
\lambda_v' &= a\left[-\lambda_u \frac{2v}{r} + \lambda_v \frac{u}{r}\right]
\end{aligned} \tag{2.8}$$

* We use the prime to denote differentiation with respect to s.

with boundary conditions

$$
\begin{aligned}
&r(0) = 1.000, && r(1) \quad \text{free} \\
&u(0) = 0.000, && u(1) = 0.000 \\
&v(0) = 1.000, && v(1) = (1.525)^{-1/2} = 0.8098 \\
(2.9) \qquad &\left.\begin{aligned}\lambda_r(0) &= \alpha_1 \\ \lambda_u(0) &= a_2 \\ \lambda_v(0) &= \alpha_3\end{aligned}\right\} \text{free,} && \begin{aligned}\lambda_r(1) &= \lambda_0 \frac{\partial K}{\partial r} = \lambda_0(-1) \\ &\left.\begin{aligned}\lambda_u(1) &= \beta_1 \\ \lambda_u(2) &= \beta_2\end{aligned}\right\} \text{free}\end{aligned}
\end{aligned}
$$

The Pontryagin principle implies that if λ_0 is nonpositive,* then the solution of this TPBVP is a candidate for the solution of the optimal control problem.

McGill and Kenneth [M3] make use of a very interesting choice for the scale factor λ_0. Instead of choosing the "usual" value $\lambda_0 = -1$ which would have led to $\lambda_r(1) = 1.0$, they choose a value for λ_0 which makes $\lambda_r(0) = 1.0$. Practically, this means that they fix the initial value of λ_r instead of its final value. This choice for λ_0 leads to a considerable simplification of the numerical computations as there are now only two final conditions to be satisfied. The boundary conditions which have to be satisfied in McGill and Kenneth's procedure (or Procedure A) now become

$$
(2.10) \qquad
\begin{aligned}
r(0) &= 1.000 \\
u(0) &= 0.000, \qquad u(1) = 0.000 \\
v(0) &= 1.000, \qquad v(1) = 0.8098 \\
\lambda_r(0) &= 1.000
\end{aligned}
$$

In Procedure B, the problem is treated as a regular minimum-time problem. The Hamiltonian in this case is

(2.11)

$$
H = \lambda_0 + \lambda_r u + \lambda_u \frac{v^2}{r} - \lambda_u \frac{\mu}{r^2} + \lambda_u \frac{T \sin \theta}{m_0 + \dot{m}t} - \lambda_v \frac{uv}{r} + \lambda_v \frac{T \cos \theta}{m_0 + \dot{m}t} .
$$

As before, the Hamiltonian has a maximum for θ given by (2.6) or

* In order to be consistent with the literature we follow the convention of Pontryagin {*P*3} and take λ_0 to be nonpositive.

(2.7). The TPBVP that results from the substitution of (2.7) into the equations of motion, the addition of the adjoint equations and the introduction of the change of variable (2.3) is given by the same differential equation (2.8) and almost the same boundary conditions. The difference in the boundary conditions lies in the conditions for $r(1)$ and $\lambda_r(1)$, which now become

$$r(1) = 1.525 \quad \text{and} \quad \lambda_r(1) \ \text{free}. \tag{2.12}$$

The other boundary conditions remain the same. The scale factor "a," which equals the final time, is now considered a variable rather than a given constant. Therefore, the trivial equation

$$a' = 0$$

is added to the set of differential equations (2.9). The boundary condition corresponding to this extra state variable follows from the condition that the Hamiltonian at the endpoint equals zero. This yields

$$\begin{aligned} H(1) = 0 = \lambda_0 + \lambda_r(1)\,u(1) + \lambda_u(1)\left[\frac{v^2(1)}{r(1)}\right] \\ + \frac{T}{m_0 + \dot{m}a} \cdot \frac{\lambda_u^2(1)}{[\lambda_u^2(1) + \lambda_v^2(1)]^{1/2}} - \lambda_v(1)\,\frac{u(1)\,v(1)}{r(1)} \\ + \frac{T}{m_0 + \dot{m}a} \cdot \frac{\lambda_v^2(1)}{[\lambda_u^2(1) + \lambda_v^2(1)]^{1/2}} - \lambda_u(1)\,\frac{\mu}{r^2(1)} \end{aligned}$$

or, after substitution of the known values for $r(1)$, $u(1)$, $v(1)$, and μ,

$$\lambda_0 + \frac{T}{m_0 + \dot{m}a}\,[\lambda_u^2(1) + \lambda_v^2(1)]^{1/2} = 0. \tag{2.13}$$

The TPBVP that has to be solved in Procedure B is thus given by the differential equations (2.9) combined with $a' = 0$ and the boundary conditions

$$\begin{aligned} r(0) &= 1.000, & r(1) &= 1.525 \\ u(0) &= 0.000, & u(1) &= 0.000 \\ v(0) &= 1.000, & v(1) &= 0.8098 \end{aligned} \tag{2.14}$$

$$\frac{T}{m_0 + \dot{m}a}\,[\lambda_u^2(1) + \lambda_v^2(1)]^{1/2} = -\lambda_0 .$$

In contrast to the boundary conditions for Procedure A, these boundary conditions involve a nonlinear condition. In addition, there are four conditions to be satisfied at the end point instead of two. On the other hand, the solution of this TPBVP is the actual candidate for the solution of the optimization problem and not an intermediate result as in Procedure A.

In Procedure C, the new state variable a defined by (2.3) is introduced before the application of the Pontryagin principle. This means that instead of the equations of motion (2.11) the system equations are taken to be

$$\begin{aligned} r' &= a[u] \\ u' &= a\left[\frac{v^2}{r} - \frac{\mu}{r^2} + \frac{T \sin\theta}{m_0 + \dot{m}as}\right] \\ v' &= a\left[-\frac{uv}{r} + \frac{T\cos\theta}{m_0 + \dot{m}as}\right] \\ a' &= 0. \end{aligned} \tag{2.15}$$

The objective now is to minimize the value of a at the terminal point, i.e., $K = a(1) = a$. The Hamiltonian for this minimization problem is

$$\begin{aligned} H = \lambda_r a[u] &+ \lambda_u a\left[\frac{v^2}{r} - \frac{\mu}{r^2} + \frac{T\sin\theta}{m_0 + \dot{m}as}\right] \\ &+ \lambda_v a\left[-\frac{uv}{r} + \frac{T\cos\theta}{m_0 + \dot{m}as}\right] + \lambda_a[0]. \end{aligned} \tag{2.16}$$

As before, this Hamiltonian has a maximum for θ given by (2.6) or (2.7). Substitution of this value of θ into the equations of motion (2.15) and addition of the adjoint equations leads to a TPBVP given by the set of differential equations (2.8) together with the trivial equation $a' = 0$ and the equation for the adjoint variable λ_a corresponding to "a"

$$\begin{aligned} \lambda_a' = &-\lambda_r u - \lambda_u\left[\frac{v^2}{r} - \frac{\mu}{r^2} + \frac{T}{m_0 + \dot{m}as}\frac{\lambda_u}{(\lambda_u^2 + \lambda_v^2)^{1/2}}\right] \\ &- \lambda_v\left[-\frac{uv}{r} + \frac{T}{m_0 + \dot{m}as}\frac{\lambda_v}{(\lambda_u^2 + \lambda_v^2)^{1/2}}\right] \\ &+ \lambda_u a\left[\frac{T\dot{m}s}{(m_0 + \dot{m}as)^2}\frac{\lambda_u}{(\lambda_u^2 + \lambda_v^2)^{1/2}}\right] \\ &+ \lambda_v a\left[\frac{T\dot{m}s}{(m_0 + \dot{m}as)^2}\cdot\frac{\lambda_v}{(\lambda_u^2 + \lambda_v^2)^{1/2}}\right] \end{aligned}$$

or

$$\text{(2.17)} \quad \lambda_a' = -\lambda_r u - \lambda_u \left[\frac{v^2}{r} - \frac{\mu}{r^2} \right] - \lambda_v \left[-\frac{uv}{r} \right] - \frac{Tm_0}{(m_0 + \dot{m}as)^2} (\lambda_u^2 + \lambda_v^2)^{1/2}.$$

The boundary conditions for the TPBVP are given by

$$\text{(2.18)} \quad \begin{aligned} r(0) &= 1.000, & r(1) &= 1.525 \\ u(0) &= 0.000, & u(1) &= 0.000 \\ v(0) &= 1.000, & v(1) &= 0.8098 \\ \lambda_a(0) &= 0.000, & \lambda_a(1) &= \lambda_0(\leqslant 0). \end{aligned}$$

In comparison with both Procedures A and B, the TPBVP to be solved in Procedure C is of eighth order with four boundary conditions at the initial point and four at the final point. In contrast with the TPBVP in Procedure B, the boundary conditions are linear and in contrast with Procedure A, the solution of the TPBVP is a candidate for the solution of the minimum-time problem instead of just an intermediate result.

The nonlinear TPBVP's corresponding to each of the Procedures A, B, and C were numerically solved by means of Newton's method. As initial guess for the trajectory, we chose that used by McGill and Kenneth [M3, p. 1765]), i.e.,

$$\begin{aligned} r_0(s) &= 1.000 + 0.525s \\ u_0(s) &= 0.000 \\ v_0(s) &= [r_0(s)]^{-1/2} \\ \lambda_{r,0}(s) &= 1.000 \\ \lambda_{u,0}(s) &= 0.5200 && \text{for} \quad 0 \leqslant s < 0.5 \\ &= -0.5000 && \text{for} \quad 0.5 \leqslant s \leqslant 1.0 \\ \lambda_{v,0}(s) &= 0.3000 && \text{for} \quad 0 \leqslant s < 0.5 \\ &= 0.000 && \text{for} \quad 0.5 \leqslant s \leqslant 1.0.^* \end{aligned}$$

* These functions are discontinuous at $s = 0.5$ and so, theoretically, cannot be used as initial guesses. However, they may be used in the computer calculations since the calculations are discrete.

For the Procedure C, this guess was supplemented by an initial guess for the adjoint variable given by

$$\lambda_{a,0}(s) = -0.2000s.$$

Different guesses for the total flight time $a = (t_f)$ were tried for the TPBVP's of all three procedures. In addition, an initial guess having the same form as that of McGill and Kenneth but slightly different numerical values was tried for the Procedure C. This guess had the form

$$\begin{aligned}
r_0(s) &= 1.000 + 0.525s \\
u_0(s) &= 0.000 \\
v_0(s) &= [r_0(s)]^{-1/2} \\
\lambda_{r,0}(s) &= 0.5000 \\
\lambda_{u,0}(s) &= 0.5000 \qquad \text{for} \quad 0 \leqslant s < 0.5 \\
&= -0.5000 \qquad \text{for} \quad 0.5 \leqslant s \leqslant 1.0 \\
\lambda_{v,0}(s) &= 0.5000 \qquad \text{for} \quad 0 \leqslant s < 0.5 \\
&= 0.5000 \qquad \text{for} \quad 0.5 \leqslant s \leqslant 1.0 \\
\lambda_a(s) &= -0.2000s.
\end{aligned}$$

After storage of the current trajectory (or guess) $y_n(s)$, the linearized TPBVP's

$$y'_{n+1} = F(y_n(s), s) + \frac{\partial F}{\partial y}(y_n(s), s)(y_{n+1}(s) - y_n(s))$$

$$g(y_n(0)) + h(y_n(1)) + \frac{\partial g}{\partial y}(y_n(0))(y_{n+1}(0) - y_n(0))$$
$$+ \frac{\partial h}{\partial y}(y_n(1))(y_{n+1}(1) - y_n(1)) = c$$

are integrated by the same method as used for the derivation of the analytical solution of linear TPBVP's in Chapter 3. Assuming that the boundary conditions can be split into a set of initial conditions, $g_j(y(0)) = c_j$, $j = 1, 2, \ldots, m \leqslant p$ and a set of final conditions, $h_k(y(1)) = c_k$, $k = 1, 2, \ldots, p - m$, the method proceeds as follows (see McGill and Kenneth [M3]): first, the nonhomogeneous equation

$$y'_{n+1}(s) = F(y_n(s), s) + \frac{\partial F}{\partial y}(y_n(s), s)(y_{n+1}(s) - y_n(s))$$

is integrated starting from some initial vector $\hat{y}_{n+1}(0)$ which satisfies the linearized initial conditions

$$g_j(y_n(0)) + \left\langle \frac{\partial g_j}{\partial y}(y_n(0)), (\hat{y}_{n+1}(0) - y_n(0)) \right\rangle = c_j, \qquad j = 1, \ldots, m.$$

The generated errors in the linearized final conditions

$$\Delta e_k = h_k(y_n(1)) + \left\langle \frac{\partial h_k}{\partial y}(y_n(1)), (y_{n+1}(1) - y_n(1)) \right\rangle - c_k, \qquad k = 1, \ldots, p - m$$

are evaluated and stored. Next, the homogeneous linear equation

$$y'_{n+1}(s) = \frac{\partial F}{\partial y}(y_n(s))\, y_{n+1}(s)$$

is integrated $p - m$ times starting from $p - m$ independent initial vectors $y_{n+1}^{(l)}(0)$ which satisfy the homogeneous part of the linearized boundary conditions, i.e.,

$$\frac{\partial g}{\partial y}(y_n(0))\, y_{n+1}^{(l)}(0) = 0.$$

If the jth component of $y(0)$ does not appear in the initial conditions, then the vector

$$y_{n+1}^{(l)}(0) = [0, \ldots, 0, y_{n+1,j}^{(l)}(0), 0, \ldots, 0]$$

with $y_{n+1,j}^{(l)} = 1.0$ is a convenient choice for one of these $p - m$ independent vectors $y_{n+1}^{(l)}(0)$. After each integration, the numerical values of the homogeneous parts of the linearized final conditions

$$\Delta d_{k,l} = \left\langle \frac{\partial h_k}{\partial y}(y_n(1)), y_{n+1}(1) \right\rangle$$

are evaluated and stored. Forming the $(p - m) \times (p - m)$ matrix D of the elements $\Delta d_{k,l}$, i.e., $D = [\Delta d_{k,l}]$, the change $\Delta y(0)$ to be added to the initial vector $\hat{y}_{n+1}(0)$ in order to satisfy the terminal boundary conditions is given by a linear combination of the $p - m$ vectors

$y^{(l)}_{n+1}(0)$, $\Delta y(0) = \sum_{l=1}^{p-m} b_l y^{(l)}_{n+1}(0)$, where the coefficient vector b can be found as the solution of the linear equation $Db = -\Delta e$.

In order to have a basis for comparison, the same norm was used for measuring convergence as used by McGill and Kenneth [M3], namely

$$\| y_{k+1} - y_k \| = \sum_{i=1}^{p} \{ \max_{s \in [0,1]} | y_{k+1,i}(s) - y_{k,i}(s) | \}. \tag{2.19}$$

The iterative solution of the linearized differential equations was continued until this norm had a value smallert han some prescribed number (usually 1.0×10^{-5}). As a check on the accuracy of this limit solution, the nonlinear equations were integrated starting from the initial values of the limit solution. Then, the values of this trajectory at the terminal time were determined. The maximum absolute value of the difference between these terminal values and the given boundary conditions was taken as the accuracy or quality criterion of the limit solution.

For the numerical integration of the differential equations, a modified fourth-order Runge-Kutta method was used. The Runge-Kutta routine requires the value of the right-hand sides of the differential equations at points in between the points for which the routine yields the value of the solution and also at those points where the solution is obtained. In the present case, the right-hand sides of the differential equations depend on the value of the last-obtained trajectory at those intermediate points. Since these values were not available, they were obtained by linear interpolation. In the sequel, all points where the right-hand sides of the differential equations are evaluated are called grid points.

In order to limit the computer time, use was made in many of the cases treated of a rather coarse grid of only 20 points on the interval [0, 1]. To check the validity of the results thus obtained, the effect of the grid size on the convergence of Newton's method TPBVP's was investigated. Also considered were possible advantages of a procedure in which a coarse grid is used in the beginning and a fine grid at the end. The change of grid size occurs as soon as a convergence criterion is satisfied for the coarse grid iteration.

Some typical results of the investigation of the effect of initial guesses, grid sizes and procedures on the convergence of the application of Newton's method to the solution of the problem are given in

TABLE IV

NEWTON'S METHOD: COMPARISON OF DIFFERENT PROCEDURES

Procedure	Initial guess for "a"	Number of grid points	Total number of iterations	Computer time (sec)	Accuracy criterion	Final value for "a"
A	3.0	20	29	41.4	1.14×10^{-3}	3.31911373
		100	20	121 2	2.91×10^{-6}	3.31931227
		100	20	121.2	2.91×10^{-6}	3.31931227
		20/100[a]	$29 + 3 = 32$	60.6	5.10×10^{-5}	3.31911382
	4.0	20		Divergent after first shift of "a"		
B	4.0	20	8	16.2	1.14×10^{-3}	3.31911364
		100	6	50.4	2.93×10^{-6}	3.31931239
		20/100[a]	$8 + 3 = 11$	41.4	2.95×10^{-6}	3.31936227
	3.0	20	11	21.6	1.14×10^{-3}	3.31911382
C	4.0	20	8	18.0	1.14×10^{-3}	3.31911379
		60	7	40.8	1.97×10^{-5}	3.31931996
		100	7	66.6	2.84×10^{-6}	3.31931227
		20/100[a]	$8 + 3 = 11$	47.3	2.64×10^{-6}	3.31931174
	3.0	20	Divergent			

[a] Coarse grid of 20 grid points was (after convergence) changed into fine grid of 100 grid points. Total number of iterations is the sum of the iterations for the coarse and the fine grid, respectively.

TABLE V

NEWTON'S METHOD, PROCEDURE A: BREAKDOWN OF NUMBER OF ITERATIONS BETWEEN SHIFTS OF THE FINAL TIME

Initial guess for "a"	Number of grid points	Number of iterations between shifts of the final time "a"
3.0	20	$10 + 7 + 5 + 4 + 3 = 20$
3.0	100	$7 + 4 + 4 + 3 + 2 = 20$
4.0	20	$24 + \infty$ (divergence after 1st shift)
4.0	100	$6 + 5 + 4 + 3 + 2 = 20$
3.06	20	$10 + 6 + 5 + 4 + 2 = 27$

Comparable data reported by Moyer and Pinkham [K10]

3.06	100(?)	$5 + 3 + 3 + 2 = 13$

Tables IV and V and Figs. 6.1–6.4. In Table IV, criteria for the comparison of the convergence of the applications of Newton's method are listed for different procedures and grid sizes. The criteria are: the number of iterations, the total computer time required, the absolute value of the maximum violation of the boundary conditions by the solution of the nonlinear equations, and the value of the minimum time found. Table V gives a breakdown of the number of iterations required in Procedure A. The figures show the norms (2.19) plotted on a logarithmic scale versus the number of the corresponding iteration. These figures thus provide an illustration of the convergence rate (see Kopp *et al.* [K10, Fig. 4, p. 104]). We discuss these results in some detail.

With regard to the effect of the initial guess on the convergence of Newton's method, no definite trends were discovered. Of course, in those cases where the initial guess was very close to the exact solution, then convergence occurred. A good example of the unpredictability of the effect of initial guesses is provided by the convergence behavior in the case where Procedure C is used: For both sets of initial guesses considered in Figs. 6.1 and 6.2, a guessed value of $a = 4.0$ lead to a convergent iteration procedure, while the guessed value $a = 3.0$, which is actually closer to the correct value $a \simeq 3.32$ (see Table IV), lead to divergence.

It was found that in many of those cases where convergence did not occur, the well-known trick of applying a partial correction provided an answer. To be more specific, the new approximation $\hat{y}_{k+1}$, instead of being the solution y_{k+1} of the linearized TPBVP, is determined from the relation $\hat{y}_{k+1} = \hat{y}_k + q(y_{k+1} - \hat{y}_k)$ where q is the correction (or relaxation) factor. Comparison of the convergence behavior of those cases in Figures 6.1 and 6.2 where a correction factor $q = 0.5$ is used and those cases where $q = 1.0$ shows clearly the usefulness of this "practical" trick.

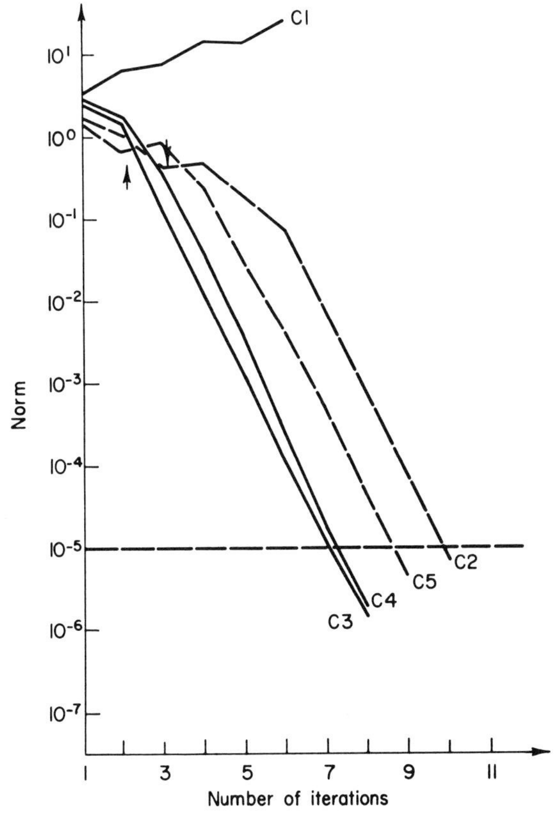

Fig. 6.1. Newton's method, Procedure C, 20 grid points. Comparison of different initial guesses for a and of different values for the correction factor q: C1, $a = 3.0$, $q = 1.0$; C2, $a = 3.0$, $q = 0.5$; C3, $a = 3.5$, $q = 1.0$; C4, $a = 4.0$, $q = 1.0$; C5, $a = 4$, $q = 0.5$. Note: arrow indicates iteration after which correction factor q is changed.

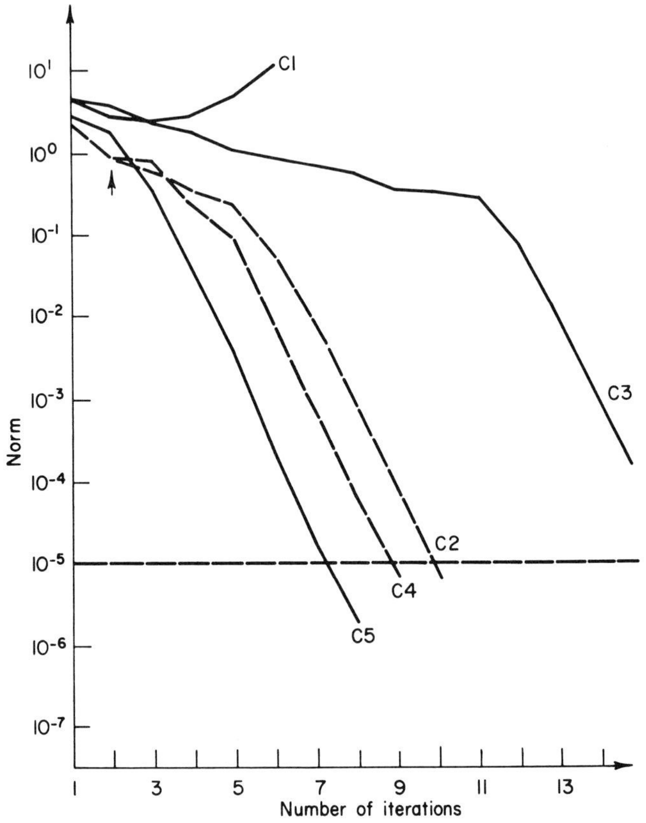

Fig. 6.2. Newton's method, Procedure C, 20 grid points. Comparison of different initial guesses for a and of different values for the correction factor q: C1, $a = 3.0$, $q = 1.0$; C2, $a = 30$, $q = 0.5$; C3, $a = 3.0$, $q = 1.0$; C4, $a = 4.0$, $q = 0.5$; C5, $a = 4$, $q = 1.0$. Note: arrow indicates iteration after which correction factor q is changed.

As shown in Fig. 6.3, we found that of the two grid sizes tried, the fine grid resulted in a faster convergence rate than the coarse grid. The difference was particularly noticeable when the actual solution was approached. The reason for the faster convergence probably lies in the smaller truncation error for a fine grid. In fact, it was noted that only in the case of a fine grid did the convergence rate resemble the quadratic convergence rate guaranteed by the theorems on Newton's method. In the coarse grid case, the rather large truncation error apparently obscured the quadratic character of the convergence of Newton's method. As follows from Tables IV–VI, the faster convergence rates for a fine grid resulted in a reduction of the total number of iterations of 2 and 1, respectively, for Procedures B and C. For Procedure A, the difference in the total number of iterations was much larger for two reasons. First, Procedure A consists of

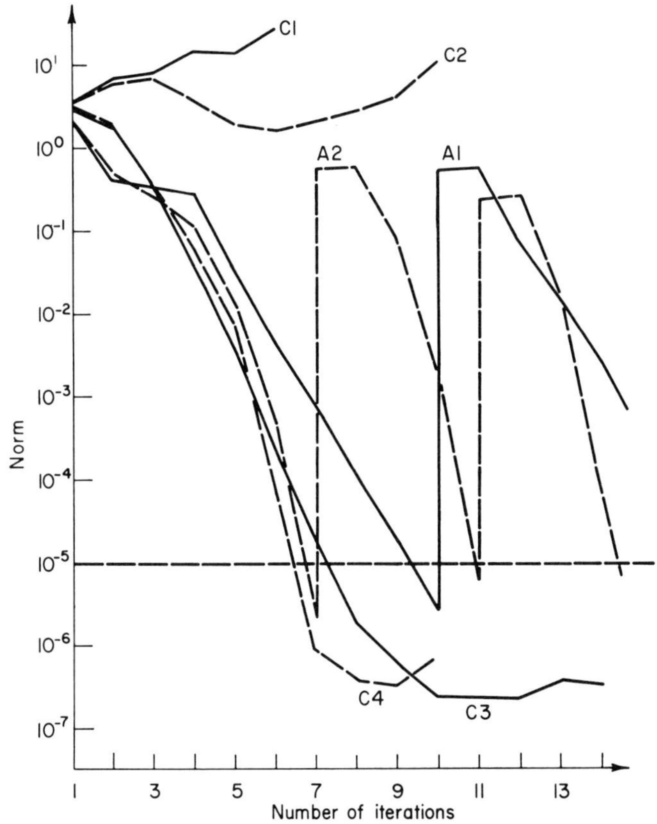

Fig. 6.3. Newton's method, Procedures A and C. Comparison of different numbers of grid points. Procedure A: A1, $a = 3.0$, 20 grid points; A2, $a = 3.0$, 100 grid points. Procedure C: C1, $a = 3.0$, 20 grid points; C2, $a = 3.0$, 20 grid points; C3, $a = 4.0$, 20 grid points; C4, $a = 4.0$, 100 grid points.

a sequence of several iterative solutions of radius maximization problems. Each of these solutions required a smaller number of iterations for the fine grid than for the coarse grid; the total number of iterations is thus the sum of these smaller numbers. Second, we found that the convergence rate in Procedure A was more sensitive to the grid size than the convergence rate in Procedures B and C. For the particular initial guess $a = 4.0$, this sensitivity was very marked (see Table V). In fact, we found that for $a = 4.0$ Procedure A was divergent (after the first shift of the time scale factor "a") for the coarse grid and convergent for the fine grid. A breakdown of the total number of iterations for Procedure A into the sum of the numbers of iterations required in between the successive shifts of the time scale factor a is given in Table IV. It may be remarked that the total number of iterations for Procedure A can be reduced if for the first few radius maximization problems the adjustment of the time scale factor a is effected as soon as the solutions of the linearized problems start to converge instead of after they have converged.

As would be expected, the grid size strongly affects the computer time per iteration and hence is one of the major factors determining the total computer time. Table IV shows that the grid size also strongly influences the accuracy of the final result, as indicated by the quality criterion. These effects suggest using a coarse grid for the initial steps and a fine grid for the final steps. The listings in Table IV of the cases where this procedure was applied show significant gains in computer time.

A comparison of the convergence of Newton's method following the three different Procedures A, B, and C is given in Fig. 6.4 and Table IV. The comparison is slightly complicated by the fact that Procedure A diverged for the initial guess $a = 4.0$ and a coarse grid, whereas Procedure C diverged for the initial guess $a = 3.0$ for both a coarse and a fine grid. Only Procedure B converged for both initial guesses for a. Neither of the initial guesses $a = 4.0$ and $a = 3.0$, which were used for most of the numerical experiments, could therefore be used as initial guess for all three procedures. As expected, Procedure A required the largest number of iterations. Since there are only two, instead of four, boundary conditions to be satisfied at the end point, each of those iterations take less computer time than the iterations in the other two procedures. Despite this fact, Procedure A took roughly twice as much computer time as the other

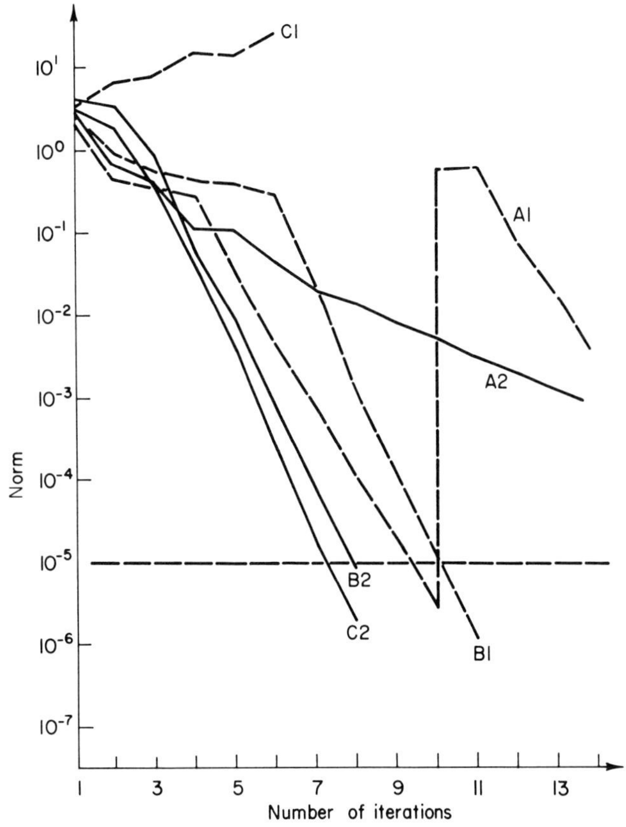

Fig. 6.4. Newton's method, 20 grid points. Comparison of the different procedures: A1, $a = 3.0$, Procedure A; A2, $a = 4.0$, Procedure A; B1, $a = 3.0$, Procedure B; B2, $a = 4.0$, Procedure B; C1, $a = 3.0$, Procedure C; C2, $a = 4.0$, Procedure C.

two procedures (see Table IV). With regard to Procedures B and C, it follows from both Fig. 6.4 and Table IV that Procedure B is preferable to Procedure C. First, for the initial guess $a = 3.0$, Procedure B leads to a convergent iteration sequence while Procedure C results in a divergent sequence. Second, comparing computer times, we note that, for the same number of iterations, Procedure B leads to the desired result faster than Procedure C. The reason for this difference between the two procedures lies in the fact that there are more differential equations to be solved in Procedure C than in Procedure B. Since the computer program was made most efficient for Procedure C, the comparison between Procedures B and C would be more striking if the program were written to be most efficient for Procedure B.

For the nonlinear TPBVP corresponding to Procedure C, the computational aspects of the modified Newton's method were investigated. The algorithm used requires the solution of the linearized TPBVP's

$$\dot{y}_{n+1} = F[y_n(t), t] + \left[\frac{\partial F}{\partial y}\right]_{(y_0(s))} (y_{n+1}(s) - y_n(s))$$

$$g[y_n(0)] + h[y_n(0)] + \left[\frac{\partial g}{\partial y}\right]_{(y_0(0))} (y_{n+1}(0) - y_n(0))$$

$$+ \left[\frac{\partial h}{\partial y}\right]_{(y_0(1))} (y_{n+1}(1) - y_n(1)) = c$$

where, in contrast with the algorithm of Newton's method, the matrices $\partial F/\partial y$, $\partial g/\partial y$, and $\partial h/\partial y$ are held fixed. For the numerical solution of this linearized TPBVP, the same procedures (of McGill and Kenneth) can be used. An important simplification arises as the homogeneous differential equation has to be integrated (as many times as there are unsatisfied boundary conditions) only for $y_0(s)$ instead of for each $y_n(s)$. It is clear that this simplification results in a considerable reduction of computer time per iteration.

A family of initial guesses for the modified Newton's method was generated by the application of Newton's method for the first few iterations. In this manner the influence of the initial guess on the convergence of the modified Newton's method could be readily determined. The results of this investigation are given in Fig. 6.5 and Table VI.

Figure 6.5 provides a good illustration of the importance of the initial guess for the convergence of the modified Newton's method. The data seem to indicate that the initial guess is more critical for the modified Newton method than for Newton's method. The improvement of convergence rate with a better initial guess is very clear in Fig. 6.5. Figure 6.5 also shows the surprising result that, when the change from Newton's method to the modified Newton method is made at a late stage, the convergence rate increases. One

TABLE VI

PROCEDURE C: COMPARISON OF NEWTON'S METHOD AND THE MODIFIED NEWTON'S METHOD

	Initial guess for "*a*"	Number of grid points	Number of iterations	Computer time (sec)	Accuracy criterion	Final value for "*a*"
Newton	4.0	20	8	18.0	1.14×10^{-3}	3.31911379
		100	7	66.6	2.84×10^{-6}	3.31931227
		20/100	$8 + 3 = 11$	47.3	2.64×10^{-6}	3.31931174
Modified after 3[a]	4.0	20	15	18.6	2.26×10^{-3}	3.32129359
Modified after 4[a]		20	9	15.6	9.97×10^{-4}	3.31911382
Modified after 5[a]		20	7	13.2	1.16×10^{-3}	3.31908238
Modified after 6[a]		20	7	15.0	1.14×10^{-3}	3.31911370
Modified after 4[a]	4.0	100	9	57.6	1.27×10^{-4}	3.31928119
Modified after 5[a]		100	7	55.8	1.21×10^{-4}	3.31930909

[a] Modified Newton's method started with the $(n - 1)$th iterate of Newton's method as initial guess.

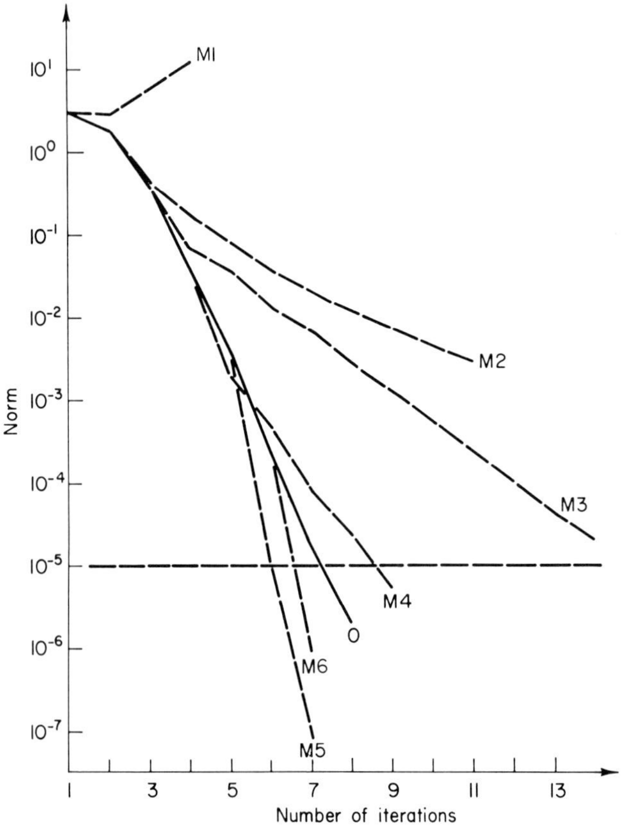

Fig. 6.5. Procedure C, 20 grid points. Comparison of Newton's method and the modified Newton's method: 0, Newton's method; M1, modified after 1; M2, modified after 2; M3, modified after 3; M4, modified after 4; M5, modified after 5; M6, modified after 6.

of the reasons for this strange result may well be a better adjustment to the truncation errors in the case of the modified Newton method. No significant improvement in convergence was found when the same cases were recomputed with a grid size of 100 points in the interval [0, 1].

Table VI clearly shows the reduction in computer time per iteration. In fact, the data show that if more than four Newton iterations are used, it is possible to achieve a reduction in overall computer time.

It should be noted, however, that the quality of the limit solution deteriorates if the modified Newton's method is used.

In order to evaluate the practicality of the theorems of Chapter 4, an estimate of the convergence factor K was determined for Procedure C. Since the boundary conditions of this TPBVP are linear, K is given by

$$\sup_{y\in\bar{S}} \sup_{t\in[0,1]} \left\{ \sum_{k=1}^{p} \sum_{l=1}^{p} \int_0^1 \left| g_{ij}^{J_0}(t, s) \frac{\partial^2 F_j}{\partial y_k \, \partial y_l} (y(s), s) \right| ds \right\} \leqslant K.$$

As noted in the remarks following the theorems in Chapter 4, this type of expression is difficult to evaluate. Simpler expressions which provide a majorization of K are

$$\sup_i \sup_{t\in[0,1]} \left\{ \sum_{j=1}^{p} \left[\int_0^1 | g_{ij}^{J_0}(t, s) | \, ds \right] \right.$$

$$\left. \times \left[\sup_{y\in\bar{S}} \sup_{t\in[0,1]} \left\{ \sum_{k=1}^{p} \sum_{l=1}^{p} \left| \frac{\partial^2 F_j}{\partial y_k \, \partial y_l} (y(t), t) \right| \right\} \right] \right\} \leqslant K'$$

or

$$\sup_i \left\{ \sum_{j=1}^{p} \left[\sup_{t\in[0,1]} \int_0^1 | g_{ij}^{J_0}(t, s) | \, ds \right] \right.$$

$$\left. \times \left[\sup_{y\in\bar{S}} \sup_{t\in[0,1]} \left\{ \sum_{k=1}^{p} \sum_{l=1}^{p} \left| \frac{\partial^2 F_j}{\partial y_k \, \partial y_l} (y(t), t) \right| \right\} \right] \right\} \leqslant K''.$$

These expressions can be computed by first evaluating a matrix $\mathbf{P}$ with elements

$$p_{ij} = \sup_{t\in[0,1]} \int_0^1 | g_{ij}^{J_0}(t, s) | \, ds$$

and a vector $\mathbf{x}$ with the components

$$x_j = \sup_{y\in\bar{S}} \sup_{t\in[0,1]} \left\{ \sum_{k=1}^{p} \sum_{l=1}^{p} \left| \frac{\partial^2 F_j}{\partial y_k \, \partial y_l} (y(t), t) \right| \right\}. \tag{2.20}$$

K'' is then given by

$$\| \mathbf{Px} \| = \sup_i \left\{ \sum_{j=1}^{p} p_{ij} x_j \right\} \leqslant K''.$$

Since it was clear that K'' would be rather large, the convergence condition $K\eta \leqslant \frac{1}{2}$ will only be satisfied for very small η. No effort was made to evaluate the supremum over the small sphere $S(y_0, r)$. Instead the second derivatives in (2.20) were evaluated for the limit solution obtained by the application of Newton's method. The elements x_j were taken equal to the suprema over t of the sums of the absolute values of these second derivatives.

The numerical computation of the elements p_{ij} of the matrix $\mathbf{P}$ can be carried out by determining, for particular i and j, the function $g_{ij}^{J_0}(t, s)$ for all points of a grid in the square $[0, 1] \times [0, 1]$ of the t–s plane and integrating this function over all lines of constant s and determining the largest of these integrals. This involves integrations which are complicated by the fact that there is a jump in many of the functions $g_{ij}^{J_0}(t, s)$ at the line $t = s$. To keep the computation simple no attempt was made to use an elaborate integration scheme for these integrals; instead the average values of the functions $| g_{ij}^{J_0}(t, s)|$ at the grid points along lines of constant t are taken as the values of the integrals (the interval of integration has length 1.0).

Even with these simplifications, the computer program to determine K'' was complicated. All second derivatives (for all t) and all elements of the Green's function matrix (for all t and s) had to be evaluated. The Green's function matrix was determined as a matrix product. This product involves both the fundamental matrix and its inverse. These matrices were found, in turn, as the solutions of linear matrix differential equations. As a measure of the complexity of the computer program, it may be mentioned that the total number of computer instructions was comparable to the number of instructions in the original basic program for the application of Newton's method.

The actual computation of the number K'' was carried out for the TPBVP of Procedure C using a coarse grid (20 divisions). This resulted in an estimate for K given by $K'' \cong 5.3 \times 10^3$. From this estimate, it follows that the practical application of the theorem can be considered as soon as the uniform norm of the difference between two successive iterations is smaller than $\eta \leqslant 1/2K'' \cong 9.4 \times 10^{-5}$.

6.3. Variable Low-Thrust Earth-to-Mars Orbital Transfer

The second example concerns the optimization of the transfer of a low-thrust space vehicle from an orbit of Earth to an orbit of Mars. The difference between this and the previous example lies in the assumption of a thrust which is variable in both magnitude and direction and in the use of a different optimization criterion. Instead of time, the criterion to be optimized is

$$J[a] = \int_0^T (a_x^2 + a_y^2)\, dt \tag{3.1}$$

where a_x and a_y are the planar accelerations and T is a fixed total flight time. It has been shown by Irving [I1] that in the case of a power-limited rocket $J[a]$ is monotonically related to the total fuel consumption. Minimization of (3.1) is therefore the same as the minimization of total fuel consumption. The variable low-thrust Earth-to-Mars orbital transfer problem has been treated before by several authors (e.g., Melbourne and Sauer [M4, M5], and Van Dine *et al.* [V1]) and numerical data have been published. The treatment of this problem as an almost linear optimization problem is undertaken here.

To convert the problem into an almost linear optimization problem, the motion of the space vehicle is considered relative to a coordinate system which is fixed to a hypothetical body moving in a circular orbit (around the Sun) between the orbits of the Earth and Mars. Coordinate systems of this type are rather common in studies of rendezvous maneuvers and transfers of space vehicles between neighboring orbits. Under the condition that the distance (and/or the velocity) of the space vehicle relative to the origin of the coordinate system is small in comparison with the radius of the orbit (or the orbital velocity, respectively), the equations of motion may be linearized. The resulting linearized transfer problem then becomes a linear optimization problem with a quadratic cost criterion and unconstrained control. This problem can be solved analytically. Solutions for the linear problem have been derived, among others, by Billik [B5] and Gobetz [G2]. Our treatment of the optimal low-thrust Earth-to-Mars orbital transfer can be considered as a nonlinear extension of Gobetz's work. Instead of neglecting the higher-order nonlinear terms, we carry these terms along as small perturbations.

Neglecting, as before, the gravitational attraction of the two planets and considering only planar motion, the equations of motion of the space vehicle are

$$\begin{aligned} \ddot{r} - r\dot{\theta}^2 &= -\frac{\mu}{r^2} + a_y \\ 2\dot{r}\dot{\theta} + r\ddot{\theta} &= -a_x . \end{aligned} \tag{3.2}$$

Here r is the distance to the Sun, θ is the angular position of the space vehicle measured in the direction of the orbital motion, μ is the gravitational constant, a_x is the tangential thrust acceleration which is taken to be positive in the direction of decreasing θ (i.e., opposite to the orbital motion), and a_y is the radial thrust acceleration which is taken to be positive in the direction of increasing r. Employing the usual perturbation procedure consisting of replacing r and θ by, respectively,

$$r = r_0 + \Delta r, \qquad \theta = \theta_0 + \Delta\theta \tag{3.3}$$

where r_0 and θ_0 are the coordinates of the origin of the coordinate system, and substituting the known relations for the circular reference orbit

$$\ddot{r}_0 = 0, \qquad \dot{r}_0 = 0, \qquad \ddot{\theta}_0 = 0, \qquad \dot{\theta}_0 = \omega_0, \qquad \frac{\mu}{r^2} = \omega_0^2 r_0, \tag{3.4}$$

we can write the (3.2) in the form

$$\begin{aligned}
(\Delta\ddot{r}) &= 3\omega_0^2\,\Delta r + 2\omega_0 r_0(\Delta\dot{\theta}) + r_0(\Delta\dot{\theta})^2 + 2\omega_0\,\Delta r(\Delta\dot{\theta}) + \Delta r(\Delta\dot{\theta})^2 \\
&\quad - 3\omega_0^2 r_0 \frac{(\Delta r)^2}{(r_0 + \Delta r)^2} - 2\omega_0^2 \frac{(\Delta r)^3}{(r_0 + \Delta r)^2} + a_y \\
(\Delta\ddot{\theta}) &= -\frac{1}{r_0}[2\omega_0(\Delta\dot{r}) + 2(\Delta\dot{r})(\Delta\dot{\theta}) + a_x] \\
&\quad + \frac{\Delta r}{r_0(r_0 + \Delta r)}[2\omega_0(\Delta\dot{r}) + 2(\Delta\dot{r})(\Delta\dot{\theta}) + a_x].
\end{aligned} \tag{3.5}$$

In terms of the new variables (see Gobetz [G2]) $x = -\Delta\theta$, $y = \Delta r/r_0$, $\tau = \omega_0 t$, and the dimensionless thrust accelerations $\tilde{a}_x = a_x/\omega_0^2 r_0$, $\tilde{a}_y = a_y/\omega_0^2 r_0$, the equations of motion (3.5) can be written as a set of first-order equations of the form

$$\begin{aligned}
x' &= u \\
u' &= 2v + \tilde{a}_x - \frac{1}{1+y}(2vy + 2uv + \tilde{a}_x y) \\
y' &= v \\
v' &= -2u + 3y + \tilde{a}_y + (1+y)u^2 - 2yu - \frac{1}{(1+y)^2}(3y^2 + 2y^3)
\end{aligned} \tag{3.6}$$

where the prime denotes differentiation with respect to τ.

If y, u, and v are small (i.e., if the radial distance from the reference orbit and the velocities of the space vehicle relative to the origin of the reference orbit are small in comparison with the radius and the orbital velocity of the reference orbit), then the second- and higher-order terms in (3.6) are small in comparison with the first-order terms. Under these conditions, the system of equations is almost linear. (Given the upper and lower limits of y, u, and v, it would be possible in theory to determine a number ϵ and write the equations in the proper form. For practical purposes this is neither necessary, nor desirable.) The underlying linear system is

$$\begin{aligned} x' &= u \\ u' &= 2v + \tilde{a}_x \\ y' &= v \\ v' &= -2u + 3y + \tilde{a}_y \,. \end{aligned} \tag{3.7}$$

The boundary conditions for an orbital transfer follow from the condition that the space vehicle at the beginning and at the end of the maneuver should have the velocity and radial position of the corresponding orbit. Assuming both orbits to be circular and coplanar with the reference orbit, the boundary conditions for the optimization problem are

$$\begin{aligned} x(0) &= 0, & x(\tau_f) &\quad \text{free} \\ u(0) &= (1 + y_{\mathrm{E}})^{-3/2} - 1, & u(\tau_f) &= (1 + y_{\mathrm{M}})^{-3/2} - 1 \\ y(0) &= y_{\mathrm{E}}\,, & y(\tau_f) &= y_{\mathrm{M}} \\ v(0) &= 0, & v(\tau_f) &= 0. \end{aligned} \tag{3.8}$$

Here y_{E} and y_{M} are the radial distances from the reference orbit of the Earth and Mars, respectively.

If a new cost criterion

$$\tilde{J}[\tilde{a}] = \frac{1}{2}\int_0^{\tau_f} [\tilde{a}_x^2 + \tilde{a}_y^2]\, d\tau \tag{3.9}$$

which is clearly proportional to the original cost criterion, is introduced, then it follows that the variable low-thrust Earth-to-Mars orbital transfer problem can be formulated as the following almost linear control problem: determine $\tilde{a}_x(\tau)$ and $\tilde{a}_y(\tau)$ which transfer the state of the almost linear system (3.6) from the initial state, given in

(3.8), to the set of final states, given in (3.8), and which in so doing minimizes the cost (3.9).

The Hamiltonian of the almost linear optimization problem takes the form

$$H = \tfrac{1}{2} p_0(\tilde{a}_x^2 + \tilde{a}_y^2) + p_x u + p_u \left[2v + \tilde{a}_x - \frac{1}{1+y}(2vy + 2uv + \tilde{a}_x y)\right]$$
$$+ p_y v + p_v \left[-2u + 3y + \tilde{a}_y + (1+y)u^2 - 2yu - \frac{1}{(1+y)^2}(3y^2 + 2y^3)\right].$$

From

$$\frac{\partial H}{\partial \tilde{a}_x} = p_0 \tilde{a}_x + p_u \left(\frac{1}{1+y}\right), \qquad \frac{\partial H}{\partial \tilde{a}_y} = p_0 \tilde{a}_y + p_v$$

and

$$\frac{\partial^2 H}{\partial \tilde{a}_x^2} = p_0, \qquad \frac{\partial^2 H}{\partial \tilde{a}_x \, \partial \tilde{a}_y} = 0, \qquad \frac{\partial^2 H}{\partial \tilde{a}_y^2} = p_0,$$

it follows that if $p_0 > 0$, then the Hamiltonian has an absolute minimum for

$$\tilde{a}_x = -\frac{p_u}{p_0}\left(\frac{1}{1+y}\right), \qquad \tilde{a}_y = -\frac{p_v}{p_0}.$$

Substitution of these expressions into the equations of motion and addition of the adjoint equations with their boundary conditions results in the TPBVP given by

$$
\begin{aligned}
x' &= u \\
u' &= 2v - \frac{p_u}{p_0} - \frac{1}{(1+y)}[2vy + 2uv] + \frac{1}{(1+y)^2}\frac{p_u}{p_0}[2y + y^2] \\
y' &= v \\
v' &= -2u + 3y - \frac{p_v}{p_0} + (1+y)u^2 - 2yu - \frac{1}{(1+y)^2}[3y^2 + 2y^3] \\
p_x' &= 0 \\
p_u' &= -p_x + 2p_v + p_u \frac{1}{(1+y)}[2v] - 2p_v[(1+y)u - y] \\
p_y' &= -3p_v - p_u \frac{1}{(1+y)^2}[2uv - 2v] - p_u \frac{p_u}{p_0(1+y)^3} - p_v[u^2 - 2u] \\
&\quad + 2p_v \frac{1}{(1+y)^3}[3y + 3y^2 + y^3] \\
p_v' &= -p_y - 2p_u + p_u \frac{1}{(1+y)}[2y + 2u]
\end{aligned}
\tag{3.10}
$$

$$
(3.11)\quad
\begin{aligned}
x(0) &= 0, & x(\tau_f) &\quad \text{free} \\
u(0) &= (1 + y_{\mathrm{E}})^{-3/2} - 1, & u(\tau_f) &= (1 + y_{\mathrm{M}})^{-3/2} - 1 \\
y(0) &= y_{\mathrm{E}}, & y(\tau_f) &= y_{\mathrm{M}} \\
v(0) &= 0, & v(\tau_f) &= 0 \\
p_x(0) &= \alpha_1 & p_x(\tau_f) &= 0 \\
p_u(0) &= \alpha_2 & p_u(\tau_f) &= \beta_1 \\
p_y(0) &= \alpha_3 \quad \text{free,} & p_y(\tau_f) &= \beta_2 \quad \text{free.} \\
p_v(0) &= \alpha_4 & p_v(\tau_f) &= \beta_3
\end{aligned}
$$

The Pontryagin principle implies that the solution of the optimization problem satisfies the TPBVP.

It may be noted that the differential equation for p_x, together with the corresponding boundary condition, result in the trivial solution

$$p_x(\tau) \equiv 0.$$

This reduces the order of the TPBVP by one.

If it can be assumed that, in addition to the earlier assumptions on y, u, and v, that pu/p_0 (or $\tilde{a}_x$) is small, then the TPBVP given by (3.10) and (3.11) can be considered an almost linear problem. In that case an iterative solution by means of Picard's method, can be considered.

The numerical solution of the TPBVP given by (3.10) and (3.11) by means of Picard's method was carried out for numerical data corresponding to an Earth to Mars orbital transfer in 160 days. The reference orbit was chosen so that the unit of time (i.e., the time in which a body in orbit covers one radian) was equal to 80 days. For this orbit the relation $r/r_{\mathrm{E}} = 1.23724$ holds. The resulting initial and final conditions for the Earth-to-Mars orbital transfer are

$$
\begin{aligned}
x(0) &= 0, & x(2) &\quad \text{free} \\
u(0) &= -0.37620, & u(2) &= 0.26924 \\
y(0) &= -0.19175, & y(2) &= 0.23258 \\
v(0) &= 0, & v(2) &= 0.
\end{aligned}
$$

These numerical data give an idea of the magnitudes of the numbers involved.

Since the procedure of Picard's method is quite similar to the procedure of the modified Newton's method, the computer program used was basically the same as the computer program for Newton's method. The numerical results are given in Figs. 6.6 and 6.7. These figures show the total thrust and thrust angle programs, respectively, as found by solving the linearized version of the TPBVP and the exact nonlinear version using Picard's method. In addition, the results published by Melbourne and Sauer [M5] are plotted for comparison. The agreement of the results of Picard's method with the results of Melbourne and Sauer, which were obtained by a method based on the calculation of the orbital elements and computed for an elliptic Martian orbit, is seen to be poor. The reason for the discrepancy may well be the important effect (see Melbourne [M4, p. 1727]) of the eccentricity of the Martian orbit on the minimum fuel control history. From a comparison of the solution of the linearized equations with Picard's solution, the improvement of Picard's solution over the linear solution is evident.

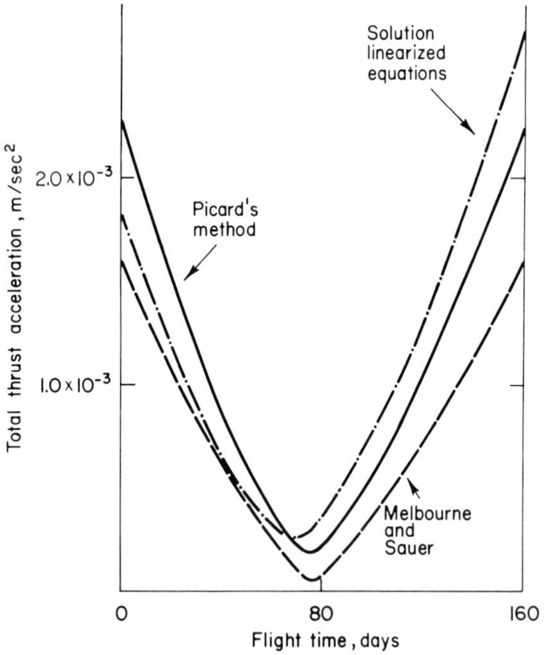

Fig. 6.6. Earth–Mars orbital transfer in 160 days: total thrust acceleration $a = (a_x^2 + a_y^2)^{1/2}$ program from different solution procedures (Melbourne and Sauer [M5]).

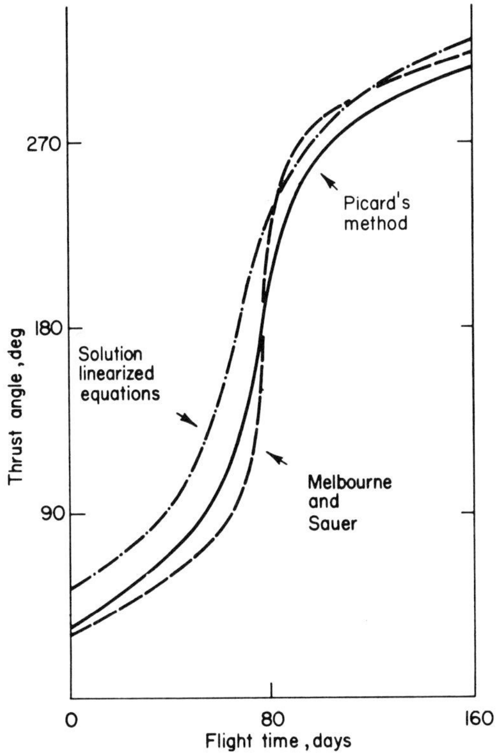

Fig. 6.7. Earth–Mars orbit transfer in 160 days: thrust angle program from different solution procedures (Melbourne and Sauer [M5]).

In order to check the dependence of the convergence of Picard's method on the initial conditions, several different conditions were tried for the same program. The results of these numerical experiments are given in Table VII. This table shows the grid size, the number of iterations, the total computer time, and the quality criterion for the solution. It follows immediately from the table that, as the absolute values of the initial conditions increase (which implies that the solution of the linear system becomes a worse approximation to the solution), the number of total iterations increases and the quality of the solutions degrades. This result is in line with the results for the modified Newton method. It may also be noted from the table that the total computer times in all cases was relatively short.

The numerical results discussed in this section clearly show the

TABLE VII

PICARD'S METHOD: COMPARISON OF DIFFERENT INITIAL AND FINAL RADII[a]

Algorithm	Initial value for y	Final value for y	Number of grid points	Number of iterations	Computer time(sec)	Accuracy criterion
Picard	-0.19175	$+0.23258$	20	13	9.0	1.56×10^{-2}
	-0.19175	$+0.23258$	100	13	26.4	6.35×10^{-4}
	-0.1975	$+0.23258$	20/100	$13 + 9$	27.2	6.35×10^{-4}
	0	$+0.1$	20	7	6.0	3.31×10^{-3}
	-0.1	$+0.1$	20	7	6.0	3.07×10^{-3}
	0	$+0.3$	20	12	8.4	2.08×10^{-3}
	-0.3	$+0.3$	20	32	16.8	4.42×10^{-2}
	0	$+0.525$	20	17	10.8	4.25×10^{-3}
	-0.5	$+0.5$	20	Divergent		

[a] Picard's algorithm throughout.

feasibility of Picard's method for TPBVP's for which approximate solutions can be determined from the linearized equations. For that type of problem Picard's method provides a fast computational scheme for the related nonlinear problem.

6.4. An Oscillation Problem*

Consider the nonlinear differential equation

$$\ddot{y}(t) + 6y(t) + \beta y^2(t) + \cos t = 0 \tag{4.1}$$

which describes an oscillator with a nonlinear restoring force. We wish to determine periodic solutions of (4.1) with period 2π and so we impose the boundary conditions

$$y(0) - y(2\pi) = 0, \qquad \dot{y}(0) - \dot{y}(2\pi) = 0. \tag{4.2}$$

* See Bosarge and Falb [B7].

The boundary value problem (4.1), (4.2) can be written in vector form as

$$\begin{bmatrix} \dot{x}_1 \\ \dot{x}_2 \end{bmatrix} = \begin{bmatrix} x_2 \\ -6x_1 - \beta x_1^2 - \cos t \end{bmatrix}, \tag{4.3}$$

$$\begin{bmatrix} 1 & 0 \\ 0 & 1 \end{bmatrix} \begin{bmatrix} x_1(0) \\ x_2(0) \end{bmatrix} + \begin{bmatrix} -1 & 0 \\ 0 & -1 \end{bmatrix} \begin{bmatrix} x_1(2\pi) \\ x_2(2\pi) \end{bmatrix} = \begin{bmatrix} 0 \\ 0 \end{bmatrix}$$

where $x_1(t) = y(t)$ and $x_2(t) = \dot{y}(t)$. We now have the following.

THEOREM 4.4. Suppose that $0 < \beta \leqslant 0.5$ and that $r = \frac{16}{11}\eta_0$ where $\eta_0 = d_0(1 + 4.16\beta d_0/2)$ and $d_0 = 0.2$. Then the multipoint sequence $\mathbf{x}_{n+1} = \psi_2(\mathbf{x}_n)$ with $\mathbf{x}_0(\cdot) = \mathbf{0}(\cdot)$ converges to a solution $\mathbf{x}^*$ of (5.3) in $\bar{S} = \bar{S}(\mathbf{x}_0, r)$ and the rate of convergence is given by

$$\| \mathbf{x}^* - \mathbf{x}_n \| \leqslant \frac{16}{11} \left(\frac{5}{16}\right)^n (2h_0)^{3^n - 1} \eta_0 \tag{4.5}$$

where $h_0 = 4.16\beta\eta_0 \leqslant 0.5$.

Proof. We simply verify the hypotheses of Theorem 8.1 of Chapter 4. We first observe that

$$\frac{\partial f}{\partial \mathbf{x}} = \begin{bmatrix} 0 & 1 \\ -6 - 2\beta x_1 & 0 \end{bmatrix}, \qquad \frac{\partial g}{\partial \mathbf{x}} = \mathbf{I}, \qquad \frac{\partial h}{\partial \mathbf{x}} = -\mathbf{I} \tag{4.6}$$

and that

$$\frac{\partial^2 f}{\partial \mathbf{x}^2} = \left[\frac{\partial}{\partial x_j} \left[\frac{\partial f_i}{\partial x_k} \right] \right]_{j=1,2} = \begin{bmatrix} 0 & 0 \\ -2\beta & 0 \end{bmatrix}, \qquad j = 1 \tag{4.7}$$

$$= \begin{bmatrix} 0 & 0 \\ 0 & 0 \end{bmatrix}, \qquad j = 2$$

$$\frac{\partial^2 g}{\partial \mathbf{x}^2} = \mathbf{0}, \qquad \frac{\partial^2 h}{\partial \mathbf{x}^2} = \mathbf{0}. \tag{4.8}$$

Thus, the hypotheses (i), (ii), and (iii) of Theorem 8.1 are satisfied.

Moreover, if we let $\mathbf{A}(t) = (\partial f/\partial \mathbf{x})(\mathbf{x}_0(t))$, $\mathbf{B} = \partial g/\partial \mathbf{x}$, and $\mathbf{C} = \partial h/\partial \mathbf{x}$, then the set $J = \{\mathbf{A}(t), \mathbf{B}, \mathbf{C}\}$ is a boundary-compatible set (as is easily checked).

Now let $\delta = 0$. Then the inequality (8.2) holds in our case in view of the definition of J and (4.8). Moreover, the operator T^J is given by

$$T^J(\mathbf{x}) = \int_0^{2\pi} G^J(t, s) \begin{bmatrix} 0 \\ -\beta x_1^2(s) - \cos s \end{bmatrix} ds \tag{4.9}$$

where $G^J(t, s)$ is the Green's matrix which corresponds to J. Writing (4.9) in component form, we have

$$\begin{aligned} T^J(\mathbf{x})_1(t) &= \int_0^{2\pi} \gamma_{12}^J(t, s)[-\beta x_1^2(s) - \cos s]\, ds \\ T^J(\mathbf{x})_2(t) &= \int_0^{2\pi} \gamma_{22}^J(t, s)[-\beta x_1^2(s) - \cos s]\, ds \end{aligned} \tag{4.10}$$

where

$$\begin{aligned} \gamma_{12}^J(t, s) &= -\frac{1}{c} \cos a(\pi - s + t), & t \leqslant s \\ &= -\frac{1}{c} \cos 2(\pi - t + s), & s < t \end{aligned} \tag{4.11}$$

$$\begin{aligned} \gamma_{22}^J(t, s) &= \frac{a}{c} \sin a(\pi - s + t), & t \leqslant s \\ &= \frac{a}{c} \cos a(\pi - t + s), & s < t \end{aligned} \tag{4.12}$$

for $0 \leqslant s \leqslant 2\pi$, $0 \leqslant t \leqslant 2\pi$ and where $a = \sqrt{6}$ and $c = 2\sqrt{6}\sin(\pi\sqrt{6})$. Using (4.7) and the estimates

$$\int_0^{2\pi} |\gamma_{12}^J(t, s)|\, ds \leqslant \frac{2}{c}\left\{4 + \frac{\sin(\pi a)}{a}\right\}$$

$$\int_0^{2\pi} |\gamma_{22}^J(t, s)|\, ds \leqslant \frac{2a}{c}[5 - \cos(\pi a)]$$

we deduce that (8.4) holds in our case for $K = 4.16\beta$. Moreover, in view of the definition of T^J, we can readily check that (8.3) will be satisfied with $d_0 = 0.2$ since $T^J(\mathbf{0})_1(t) = (\cos t)/5$ and $T^J(\mathbf{0})_2(t) =$

(sin t)/5. As 8.5) holds by the definition of η_0, all that remains is to verify (8.7) and (8.9).

$$h_0 = K1\eta_0 = (4.16)\,\beta(.2)\left[1 + \frac{4.16\beta(.2)}{2}\right] \leqslant \tfrac{1}{2} \tag{4.13}$$

since $\beta \leqslant 0.5$. Morevoer, since $\gamma_{0,2}^{(2)} = 1 + Kd_0/2$, (8.9) is clearly satisfied here. Thus, the theorem is established.

Again an analogous theorem could be proved for any of the multipoint algorithms.

The pair of linear TPBVP's (8.14a) and (8.14b) here take the form

$$\begin{aligned} \dot{z}_{n,1} &= z_{n,2} \\ \dot{z}_{n,2} &= -(6 + 2\beta x_{n,1}(t))z_{n,1} + \beta x_{n,2}^2(t) - \cos t \\ z_{n,1}(0) &= z_{n,1}(2\pi), \qquad z_{n,2}(0) = z_{n,2}(2\pi) \end{aligned} \tag{4.13a}$$

$$\begin{aligned} \dot{x}_{n+1,1} &= x_{n+1,2} \\ \dot{x}_{n+2,2} &= -(6 + 2\beta x_{n,1}(t))x_{n+1,1} + \beta z_{n,1}(2x_{n,1}(t) - z_{n,1}) - \cos t \\ x_{n+1,1}(0) &= x_{n+1,1}(2\pi), \qquad x_{n+1,2}(0) = x_{n+1,2}(2\pi) \end{aligned} \tag{4.13b}$$

and Theorem 4.4 insures the convergence of the sequence $\mathbf{x}_{n+1}(\cdot)$ to the solution of (4.3). The equations (4.13a) and (4.13b) were integrated numerically using a modified Runge-Kutta method and the results of the computations are indicated in Tables VIII and IX. Table VIII contains the number of iterations required for "convergence"* for

TABLE VIII

β	0.1	0.2	0.3	0.4	0.5	0.6	0.7	0.8	0.9	1.0
Iterations required	2	2	3	3	3	3	3	3	3	4

* Convergence is here construed to mean that

$$\| \mathbf{x}_{n+1} - \mathbf{x}_n \| = \sum_{i=1}^{2} \{\max_k | x_{n+1,i}(t_k) - x_{n,i}(t_k)|\} \leqslant 10^{-6}$$

where the t_k are the points in the integration routine.

various values of β, while Table IX contains the actual solutions. We note that the actual computations converge for larger values of β than 0.5. In other words, the convergence theorem is conservative as was to be expected.

TABLE IX

MULTIPOINT METHOD SOLUTION OF OSCILLATION PROBLEM: ACTUAL SOLUTIONS VERSUS β

t \ β	0.1	0.2	0.3	0.4	0.5
0.0	−0.201338	−0.202672	−0.204007	−0.205343	−0.206682
0.2π	−0.162459	−0.163124	−0.163804	−0.164500	−0.165212
0.4π	−0.061336	−0.060884	−0.060445	−0.060022	−0.059614
0.6π	+0.062288	+0.062786	0.063299	+0.063827	+0.064369
0.8π	+0.161170	+0.160549	0.159944	+0.159352	+0.158775
π	+0.198668	+0.197334	0.195999	.194663	+0.193325
1.2π	+0.161173	+0.160553	0.159947	0.159355	+0.158778
1.4π	+0.062295	+0.062793	0.063306	0.063834	+0.064376
1.6π	−0.161173	−0.060876	−0.060472	−0.060014	−0.059606
1.8π	−0.162454	−0.163118	−0.163798	−0.164495	−0.165206
2π	−0.201338	−0.202672	−0.204007	−0.205343	−0.206682

t \ β	0.6	0.7	0.8	0.9	1.0
0.0	−0.208022	−0.209365	−0.210712	−0.212062	−0.213416
0.2π	−0.165940	−0.166685	−0.167446	−0.168224	−0.169020
0.4π	−0.059221	−0.058844	−0.058481	−0.058135	−0.057805
0.6π	+0.064927	+0.065499	+0.066087	+0.066688	+0.067305
0.8π	+0.158212	+0.157662	+0.157126	+0.156604	+0.156095
π	+0.191984	+0.190641	+0.189296	+0.187946	+0.186593
1.2π	+0.158215	+0.157665	+0.157129	+0.156607	+0.156097
1.4π	+0.064934	+0.065506	+0.066093	+0.066695	+0.067312
1.6π	−0.059213	−0.058835	−0.058473	−0.058126	−0.057796
1.8π	−0.165934	−0.166678	−0.167440	−0.168218	−0.169013
2π	−0.208022	−0.209365	−0.210712	−0.212062	−0.213416

REFERENCES

A1. H. A. Antosiewicz, Newton's method and boundary value problems (to be published).

A2. H. A. Antosiewicz and W. C. Rheinboldt, Numerical analysis and functional analysis, Ch. 14 of "Survey of Numerical Analysis" (J. Todd, ed.), Chapter 14. McGraw-Hill, New York, 1962.

A3. M. Athans and P. L. Falb, "Optimal Control: An Introduction to the Theory and Its Applications." McGraw-Hill, New York, 1966.

A3. M. Athans, The status of optimal control theory and applications for deterministic systems, *IEEE Trans. Autom. Control* **AC-11**, 580–596 (1966).

B0. S. Banach, "Theorie des Opèrations Linéaires." Chelsea, New York, 1955.

B1. R. O. Barr and E. G. Gilbert, Some iterative procedures for computing optimal controls, *Proc. IFAC Congress, 3rd, London, 1967.*

B2. R. E. Bellman, "Dynamic Programming." Princeton Univ. Press, Princeton, N. J., 1957.

B3. R. E. Bellman and R. E. Kalaba, "Quasilinearization and Nonlinear Boundary-Value Problems." Elsevier, New York, 1965.

B4. L. D. Berkovitz, Variational methods in problems of control and programming, *J. Math. Anal. Appl.* **3**, 145–169 (1961).

B5. B. H. Billik, Some optimal low-acceleration rendezvous maneuvers, *AIAA J.* **2**, 510–516 (1964).

B6. G. A. Bliss, "Lectures on the Calculus of Variations." Univ. of Chicago Press, Chicago, 1946.

B7. W. E. Bosarge, Jr., and P. L. Falb, Infinite dimensional multipoint methods and the solution of boundary value problems (to be published).

B8. J. V. Breakwell, The optimization of trajectories, *J. SIAM* **7**, 215–247 (1959).

B9. J. V. Breakwell, J. L. Speyer, and A. E. Bryson, Optimization and control of nonlinear systems using the second variation, *J. SIAM Control Ser. A* **1**, 193–223 (1963).

B10. A. E. Bryson and W. F. Denham, A steepest-ascent method for solving optimum programming problems, *Trans. ASME Ser. E*; *J. Appl. Mech.* **29**, 247–257 (1962).

C0. M. Canon, C. Cullum, and E. Polak, Constrained minimization problems in finite dimensional spaces, *SIAM J. Control* **4**, 528–547 (1967).

C1. E. A. Coddington and N. Levinson, "Theory of Ordinary Differential Equations." McGraw-Hill, New York, 1955.

C2. L. Collatz, Einige Anwendungen funktionalanalytischer Methoden in der praktischen Analysis, *Z. Angew. Math. Phys.* **4**, 327–357 (1953).
C3. L. Collatz, Das vereinfachte Newtonsche Verfahren bei nicht lineare Randwertaufgaben, *Arch. Math.* **5**, 233–240 (1954).
C4. L. Collatz, "Funktionalanalysis und numerische Mathematik." Springer, Berlin, 1964; "Functional Analysis and Numerical Mathematics" (English translation by H. Oser). Academic Press, New York, 1966.
C5. R. Conti, Recent trends in the theory of boundary value problems for ordinary differential equations, *Boll. Un. Mat. Ital.* **22**, 135–178 (1967).
D1. J. Dieudonné, "Foundations of Modern Analysis." Academic Press, New York, 1960.
G1. F. R. Gantmacher, "The Theory of Matrices," Vol. I. Chelsea, New York, 1959.
G2. F. W. Gobetz, Optimal variable-thrust transfer of a power-limited rocket between neighboring circular orbits, *AIAA J.* **2**, 339–343 (1964); Errata, *AIAA J.* **2**, 2237 (1964).
G3. A. A. Goldstein, "Constructive Real Analysis." Harper and Row, New York, 1967.
H1. J. Hale, On differential equations containing a small parameter, *Control. Diff. Eq.* **1**, 215–250 (1962).
H2. J. Hale, "Oscillations in Nonlinear Systems." McGraw-Hill, New York, 1963.
H3. H. Halkin, A maximum principle of the Pontryagin type for systems described by nonlinear difference equations, *SIAM J. Control* **4**, 90–111 (1966).
H4. H. Halkin, An abstract framework for the theory of process optimization, *Bull. Amer. Math. Soc.* (to be published).
H5. M. Handelsman, Optimal free space fixed thrust trajectories using impulsive trajectories as starting iteratives, *AIAA J.* **4**, 1077–1082 (1966).
I1. J. H. Irving, Low-thrust flight: variable exhaust velocity in gravitational fields, *in* "Space Technology" (H. S. Seifert, ed.), Chapter 10. Wiley, New York, 1959.
K1. R. E. Kalaba, On nonlinear differential equations, the maximum operation, and monotonic convergence, *J. Math. Mech.* **8**, 519–575 (1959).
K2. L. V. Kantorovich, The method of successive approximations for functional equations, *Acta Math.* **71**, 63–97 (1939).
K3. L. V. Kantorovich and G. P. Akilov, "Functional Analysis in Normed Spaces." Macmillan, New York, 1964.
K4. W. Kaplan, "Ordinary Differential Equations." Addison-Wesley, Reading, Mass., 1958.
K5. H. J. Kelley, Method of gradients, *in* "Optimization Techniques" (G. Leitman, ed.) Chapter 6. Academic Press, New York, 1962.
K6. H. J. Kelley, R. E. Kopp, and H. G. Moyer, A trajectory optimization technique using the second variation, *Progr. Astron. Aeronaut.* **14** ("Celestial Mechanics and Astrodynamics," V. G. Szebehely, ed.), Academic Press, New York (1964).
K7. P. Kenneth and R. McGill, Two-point boundary-value-problem techniques, *Advan. Control Systems* **3** (1966).
K8. P. Kenneth and G. E. Taylor, Solution of variational problems with bounded control variables by means of the generalized Newton-Raphson method, *in* "Recent Advances in Optimization Techniques" (A. Lavi and T. P. Vogl, eds.). Wiley, New York, 1966.

K9. A. N. Kolmogorov and S. V. Fomin, "Elements of the Theory of Functions and Functional Analysis," Vol. I. Graylock Press, Rochester, New York, 1957.
K10. R. E. Kopp, R. McGill, H. G. Moyer, and G. Pinkham, Several trajectory optimization techniques, *in* "Computing Methods in Optimization Problems" (A. V. Balakrishnan and L. W. Neustadt, eds.). Academic Press, New York, 1964.
L1. W. Lindorfer and H. G. Moyer, Application of a low thrust trajectory optimization scheme to planar Earth–Mars transfer, *ARS J.* **32**, 260–262 (1962).
L2. R. S. Long, "Newton-Raphson Operator; Problems with Undetermined Endpoints," *AIAA J.*, **3**, 1351–1352 (1965).
M1. R. McGill, Optimal control, inequality state constaints, and the generalized Newton-Raphson algorithm, *J. SIAM Control* **3**, 291–298 (1966).
M2. R. McGill and P. Kenneth, A convergence theorem on the iterative solution of non-linear two-point boundary-value systems, *Proc. Int. Astron. Cong., 14th, Paris, 1963.*
M3. R. McGill and P. Kenneth, Solution of variational problems by means of a generalized Newton-Raphson operator, *AIAA J.* **2**, 1761–1766 (1964).
M4. W. G. Melbourne, Three-dimensional optimum thrust trajectories for power limited propulsion systems, *ARS J.* **31**, 1723–1728 (1961).
M5. W. G. Melbourne and C. G. Sauer, Optimum thrust programs for power-limited propulsion systems, *Astron. Acta* **8**, 205–226 (1962).
N1. E. G. Nering, "Linear Algebra and Matrix Theory." Wiley, New York, 1963.
N2. L. W. Neustadt, Synthesizing time optimal control systems, *J. Math. Anal. Appl.* **1**, 484–493 (1960).
N3. L. W. Neustadt, An abstract variational theory with applications to a broad class of optimization problems. I. General theory, *J. SIAM Control* **4**, 505–528 (1966).
P1. B. Paiewonski, Optimal control: A review of theory and practice, *AIAA J.* **3**, 1985–2006 (1965).
P2. E. Picard, "Traite d'Analyse," 3rd ed., Vol. III. Gauthiers-Villars, Paris, 1928.
P3. L. S. Pontryagin, V. G. Boltyanskii, R. V. Gamkrelidze, and E. F. Mishchenko, "The Mathematical Theory of Optimal Processes." Wiley, New York, 1962.
P4. W. A. Porter, "Modern Foundations of Systems Engineering." Macmillan, New York, 1966.
R1. W. Rudin, "Principles of Mathematical Analysis, 2nd ed. McGraw-Hill, New York, 1964.
S1. J. Schroder, Neue Fehlerabschatzungen für verschiedene Iterations verfahren, *Z. Angew. Math. Mech.* **36**, 168–181 (1956).
V1. C. P. Van Dine, W. R. Fimple, and T. N. Edelbaum, Application of a finite-difference Newton-Raphson algorithm to problems of low-thrust trajectory optimization, *Advan. Astron. Aeronaut.* **17** (1966).
V2. B. S. Vulikh, "Introduction to Functional Analysis for Scientists and Technologists." Pergamon Press, New York, 1963.
W1. J. Warga, On a class of iterative procedures for solving normal systems of ordinary differential equations, *J. Math. Phys.* **31**, 223–243 (1953).
W2. H. Witsenhausen, Note on some iterative methods using partial order for solution of boundary-value problems, Lecture notes, Harvard-MIT-Brown-Lincoln, 1966.

AUTHOR INDEX

Numbers in parentheses are reference numbers and indicate that an author's work is referred to, although his name is not cited in the text. Numbers in italics show the page on which the complete reference is listed.

SUBJECT INDEX

Q

R

S

T

Mathematics in Science and Engineering

A Series of Monographs and Textbooks

Edited by RICHARD BELLMAN, ***University of Southern California***

1. T. Y. Thomas. Concepts from Tensor Analysis and Differential Geometry. Second Edition. 1965

2. T. Y. Thomas. Plastic Flow and Fracture in Solids. 1961

3. R. Aris. The Optimal Design of Chemical Reactors: A Study in Dynamic Programming. 1961

4. J. LaSalle and S. Lefschetz. Stability by by Liapunov's Direct Method with Applications. 1961

5. G. Leitmann (ed.). Optimization Techniques: With Applications to Aerospace Systems. 1962

6. R. Bellman and K. L. Cooke. Differential-Difference Equations. 1963

7. F. A. Haight. Mathematical Theories of Traffic Flow. 1963

8. F. V. Atkinson. Discrete and Continuous Boundary Problems. 1964

9. A. Jeffrey and T. Taniuti. Non-Linear Wave Propagation: With Applications to Physics and Magnetohydrodynamics. 1964

10. J. T. Tou. Optimum Design of Digital Control Systems. 1963.

11. H. Flanders. Differential Forms: With Applications to the Physical Sciences. 1963

12. S. M. Roberts. Dynamic Programming in Chemical Engineering and Process Control. 1964

13. S. Lefschetz. Stability of Nonlinear Control Systems. 1965

14. D. N. Chorafas. Systems and Simulation. 1965

15. A. A. Pervozvanskii. Random Processes in Nonlinear Control Systems. 1965

16. M. C. Pease, III. Methods of Matrix Algebra. 1965

17. V. E. Benes. Mathematical Theory of Connecting Networks and Telephone Traffic. 1965

18. W. F. Ames. Nonlinear Partial Differential Equations in Engineering. 1965

19. J. Aczel. Lectures on Functional Equations and Their Applications. 1966

20. R. E. Murphy. Adaptive Processes in Economic Systems. 1965

21. S. E. Dreyfus. Dynamic Programming and the Calculus of Variations. 1965

22. A. A. Fel'dbaum. Optimal Control Systems. 1965

23. A. Halanay. Differential Equations: Stability, Oscillations, Time Lags. 1966

24. M. N. Oguztoreli. Time-Lag Control Systems. 1966

25. D. Sworder. Optimal Adaptive Control Systems. 1966

26. M. Ash. Optimal Shutdown Control of Nuclear Reactors. 1966

27. D. N. Chorafas. Control System Functions and Programming Approaches (In Two Volumes). 1966

28. N. P. Erugin. Linear Systems of Ordinary Differential Equations. 1966

29. S. Marcus. Algebraic Linguistics; Analytical Models. 1967

30. A. M. Liapunov. Stability of Motion. 1966

31. G. Leitmann (ed.). Topics in Optimization. 1967

32. M. Aoki. Optimization of Stochastic Systems. 1967

33. H. J. Kushner. Stochastic Stability and control. 1967

34. M. Urabe. Nonlinear Autonomous Oscillations. 1967

35. F. Calogero. Variable Phase Approach to Potential Scattering. 1967

36. A. Kaufmann. Graphs, Dynamic Programming, and Finite Games. 1967

37. A. Kaufmann and R. Cruon. Dynamic Programming: Sequential Scientific Management. 1967

38. J. H. Ahlberg, E. N. Nilson, and J. L. Walsh. The Theory of Splines and Their Applications. 1967

39. Y. Sawaragi, Y. Sunahara, and T. Nakamizo. Statistical Decision Theory in Adaptive Control Systems. 1967

40. R. Bellman. Introduction to the Mathematical Theory of Control Processes Volume I. 1967 (Volumes II and III in preparation)

41. E. S. Lee. Quasilinearization and Invariant Imbedding. 1968

42. W. Ames. Nonlinear Ordinary Differential Equations in Transport Processes. 1968

43. W. Miller, Jr. Lie Theory and Special Functions. 1968

44. P. B. Bailey, L. F. Shampine, and P. E. Waltman. Nonlinear Two Point Boundary Value Problems. 1968.

45. Iu. P. Petrov. Variational Methods in Optimum Control Theory. 1968

46. O. A. Ladyzhenskaya and N. N. Ural'tseva. Linear and Quasilinear Elliptic Equations. 1968

47. A. Kaufmann and R. Faure. Introduction to Operations Research. 1968

48. C. A. Swanson. Comparison and Oscillation Theory of Linear Differential Equations. 1968

49. R. Hermann. Differential Geometry and the Calculus of Variations. 1968

50. N. K. Jaiswal. Priority Queues. 1968

51. H. Nikaido. Convex Structures and Economic Theory. 1968

52. K. S. Fu. Sequential Methods in Pattern Recognition and Machine Learning. 1968

53. Y. L. Luke. The Special Functions and Their Approximations (In Two Volumes). 1969

54. R. P. Gilbert. Function Theoretic Methods in Partial Differential Equations. 1969

55. V. Lakshmikantham and S. Leela. Differential and Integral Inequalities (In Two Volumes). 1969

56. S. H. Hermes and J. P. LaSalle. Functional Analysis and Time Optimal Control. 1969.

57. M. Iri. Network Flow, Transportation, and Scheduling: Theory and Algorithms. 1969

58. A. Blaquiere, F. Gerard, and G. Leitmann. Quantitative and Qualitative Games. 1969

59. P. L. Falb and J. L. de Jong. Successive Approximation Methods in Control and Oscillation Theory. 1969

In preparation

R. Bellman. Methods of Nonlinear Analysis, Volume I

R. Bellman, K. L. Cooke, and J. A. Lockett. Algorithms, Graphs, and Computers

A. H. Jazwinski. Stochastic Processes and Filtering Theory

S. R. McReynolds and P. Dyer. The Computation and Theory of Optimal Control

J. M. Mendel and K. S. Fu. Adaptive, Learning, and Pattern Recognition Systems: Theory and Applications

G. Rosen. Formulations of Classical and Quantum Dynamical Theory

E. J. Beltrami. Methods of Nonlinear Analysis and Optimization

H. H. Happ. The Theory of Network Diakoptics